8.75

ELECTROMECHANICS

ELECTROMECHANICS

A First Course in Electromechanical Energy Conversion

HUGH HILDRETH SKILLING

Professor of Electrical Engineering

Stanford University

JOHN WILEY AND SONS, INC.

New York   London

Library of Congress Catalog Card Number: 62–10913

Printed in the United States of America

PREFACE

Let me say at once that this is a better book because of the kindness of the professors who used the preliminary edition. It was tried, across the country, under the temporary name of *A First Course in Electromechanics*, and the reports of this trial run have helped to crystallize our ideas of what the book should be.

It seemed clear from the beginning that the time had come for a fresh start. My colleagues and I knew that the old electrical machinery course was wrongly oriented. Why should we not adopt the plan that is used in other scientific fields but that has been so generally neglected in electromechanics? Surely, we thought, it should be recognized that a few principles are basic to the operation of many machines and devices.

We agreed that what we wanted was:

1. A course on principles, illustrated by important devices. There is no room in the modern curriculum for an encyclopedic treatment of machines one by one—the d-c generator, the d-c motor, the a-c generator, and so on. Let us rather seek out the most useful principles of electromechanical energy conversion. Let us apply them to generators and motors, of course, but also to transducers and rotating amplifiers, to sensing devices and indicating instruments, to microphones and speakers. Let us emphasize the *similarities* among electromechanical devices rather than their *differences*. A commutator motor is a commutator motor whether it maintains the level of an inertial guidance system or drives the propeller shaft of a submarine.

2. It should be a course for all students interested in electromechanical systems and devices rather than a course for training experts. All electrical engineers, no doubt, will use motors and

generators in their professional work, but few will be concerned
with the intimate details of their inner workings. Let this first
course, then, give the basic ideas of machines, and of other devices,
but without the detailed information required by a designer or a
specialist. Other authors can write longer books for those who
want them; our problem is to provide the elements of electromechanics that will be needed by all our students. And, indeed,
it seemed to us that what the electrical engineering student needs,
in general, the mechanical engineering student needs also.

3. Perhaps it is most important that the discussion extend to
the modern developments of recent years. Let us emphasize the
systems concept, stressing that a device is almost always part of
a system. The devices of control systems, the transducers of information systems, the motors and generators of electric power
systems have this in common. However (a point of vital importance) the utilization of power is mostly steady state; the operation of a control system is highly dynamic. It is no longer enough
to talk about machines running at constant speed, or devices at
a single frequency. We may begin with these, but dynamic operation, transient performance, time constants, response as a function
of frequency, and even the possibility of unstable behavior must
be brought into the modern picture.

Such a plan led to the following outline for a first course in electromechanics.

Chapters 1 through 5. Basic methods of electromechanical energy
conversion and their mathematical study. Magnetic methods are
given emphasis because of practical importance.

Chapters 6 through 9. Examples of electromechanical energy
conversion. These are mainly selected from the steady state to give
prominence to the energy conversion processes. Machines of general
use are taken as examples.

Chapters 10 through 13. Electromechanical devices as elements
in systems. Electromechanical principles are combined with the
laws of electricity and mechanics, and the resulting equations are
solved simultaneously.

Chapters 14 through 16. Examples of electromechanical devices
in dynamic systems. Devices of engineering importance are selected,
mainly in systems for control and for the transmission of information.

Chapters 17 and 18. Electromechanical systems. Feedback is
considered, and the instability that can result. Ideas and new de-

vices are suggested, beyond the scope of this book, that may lead the student on to further study.

For some, this book will be a stepping stone to more advanced courses in systems, in controls, in machinery, in design. It should therefore give as a minimum the background knowledge that is commonly presumed by authors of books on these subjects. For others it may be the only formal course in electrodynamics; for these it should prepare the student to read intelligently from advanced and specialized books as the need arises. At the same time it should give practical information about the real world of engineering. A student who is unacquainted with an induction motor, a microphone, or a strain gauge is to that extent illiterate.

Up to a certain point we all need to know the basic ideas of electromechanical systems. Although this idea does not appear in the book until Section 240, it has been my guide ever since the writing began. When Section 1 was written, on the ship *Albany* somewhere off the coast of Chile in the summer of 1957, it was already clear to me that the book must include what all our students would need to know, with examples drawn from the devices and machines that they would have to use. Since all engineers use electromechanical devices in their systems, though few will ever design the devices, the general outline of a book began to appear.

This principle seemed sound enough, but several years have gone into its interpretation. The table of contents that follows may give an idea of the subjects that I simply could not leave out.

The interest, patience, and cooperation of teachers and students alike I gratefully acknowledge. As it might be invidious to name one without naming all, I hope that the dozens of teachers and hundreds of students will forgive me. Please, each of you, say to yourself, "I helped."

For this book, more than for others I have written, Hazel, my wife, is truly the co-author. Only she could have made a book of it.

For the opportunity to prepare such a book I am indebted to the President, the Provost, and the Dean of Engineering at Stanford: J. E. Wallace Sterling, F. E. Terman, and J. M. Pettit. To Professors L. H. Brown, R. J. Smith, W. W. Harman, Bernard Widrow, and Rudolph Panholzer, at Stanford, go my special thanks for reasons that they will understand.

Electromechanics is planned for a course of about three semester hours. It is expected that general physics and the elements of calculus will come first, so that B and H will not be entirely unfamiliar

symbols, and the differentiation and integration of sine waves and
such will have meaning.   Also, there should have been something
about electric circuits, for it is supposed that the basic ideas of Ohm's
law and Kirchhoff's voltage law are known, and alternating currents
are not a complete mystery.

To those whose knowledge of magnetic circuits is rusty, Appendix
1 is offered.   Appendix 2 is for those who have not previously applied complex quantities to circuits.   Enough of the practical use of
Laplace transforms is in Appendix 3 to carry the reader through this
book, for there is a good chance that the Laplace method will be new.

The book in preliminary form has been used for electrical and
mechanical engineering students, and others, at various levels from
sophomore to senior.   I shall be most interested to know how it turns
out with you.

HUGH HILDRETH SKILLING

Stanford University
January, 1962

CONTENTS

ELECTROMECHANICAL PRINCIPLES

chapter 1

1. Uses of Electromechanics

It happens that I am writing this paragraph on a ship. A loud-speaker outside my room has just made an announcement; it does so by changing electrical energy to mechanical vibration of the speaker cone. A few minutes ago I spoke into a telephone and the mechanical energy of the sound of my voice controlled electrical energy that was transmitted to another part of the ship, and there it was returned to mechanical energy in the telephone receiver. A mimeographed sheet of news is issued daily; the news is received by radio, and electrical signals control an automatic typewriter that prints, of course, mechanically.

The drive for the propellers of this ship is not electrical, although on some ships it is, but auxiliaries for steering, for hoists, for pumping water or fuel, for fans and ventilators, for refrigeration, are run by electric motors.

All these things are electromechanical. On the other hand, electric lighting or heating, and battery charging or other chemical processes, are examples of electrical energy conversion that are not electro-mechanical.

The radar systems of the ship operate by letting electrical pulses deflect or accelerate a jet of electrons within an evacuated tube; this is electromechanical. The picture, as with television, is produced by altering the mechanical motion of electrons. The bearing repeater in the radar is an electromechanical servomechanism operated from the gyrocompass. A device in the navigator's office gives continuous indication of latitude and longitude, which it determines from our course and speed by an electromechanical computing system.

But in these exciting days we think beyond the ship. Navigation of the air, of space, is the newest of arts, and it requires electro-mechanical systems so effective as to seem fantastic. What automatic devices are now expected to do routinely (and often do) was not even in the realm of the fabulous until yesterday.

2. Energy and Information

As we see in the following pages, an electrical or electromechanical device is almost always part of a system. The output of one device is the input to the next: the output of an amplifier is the input to a loudspeaker; the output of a distribution transformer is the input to an induction motor.

A general term for a device that takes energy in one form and gives it out in another is a *transducer*. We find that we are most particularly interested in the ratio of what a transducer gives out to what it takes in; this is called a *transfer function*. The output voltage of a microphone divided by its input sound pressure is an example of a transfer function, and another is the relation between the speed of a motor and its excitation.

It is convenient to consider that there are two types of electro-mechanical systems. The commodity delivered by one is energy; by the other, information. This is the same distinction that runs through all electrical work and leads to such classifications of systems as power, on the one hand, and communication or control on the other.

A ship propulsion system, for example, delivers energy to turn the propellors and does not deliver information. A control system from the gyrocompass to the rudder, however, delivers information and not much energy. There must be enough power to turn the rudder, of course; an information system must be powerful enough to deliver its information in useful form.

The basic differences between the two types of systems are reflected in their design and in the kind of thoughts that engineers think about them. One of the chief requirements of a power system is to deliver as much of its power to the customer as can well be managed. That is, the efficiency must be high or the company loses money. Also, a power system should operate as steadily as possible, without fluctuations of speed or voltage.

A system for information, on the contrary, must necessarily fluctuate. Information is transmitted only when something changes. Steady-state operation delivers no information at all; this is one of the basic ideas of information theory. But in an information system, high efficiency is not often required. Enough energy must be delivered to give intelligible signals or to operate a control device. But only a little energy is required to vibrate a telephone receiver, and not really a great deal is needed even to move the rudder of a ship. The designer rarely worries about the power bill. He must ask himself, rather, does the information arrive? Is it intelligible? Does it give the result that it is supposed to give?

The power engineer never forgets efficiency. The communication engineer is more interested in maximum power transfer. These different points of view are reflected in the design of all electromechanical devices.

3. Principles

The possible variety of electromechanical devices is unlimited, and a survey of devices one by one would be endless. Instead of attempting so tedious a study, let us use the more scientific approach and seek for useful basic principles. We find that a very few principles will account for the behavior of nearly all the many devices.

First among principles is the *conservation of energy.* In studying the change of mechanical energy into electrical, and of electrical energy into mechanical, we always have in mind that the energy coming out of a device must be related to the energy going into the device. We cannot say that all the energy that goes in will come out immediately and in useful form; rather we say that it will be divided three ways:

1. Some will be delivered at once as useful output energy.
2. Some may be stored within the device, perhaps as kinetic energy of motion, or as energy of a magnetic field.
3. Some, being changed to heat, will be lost to further usefulness.

Thus we visualize the flow of energy through a device and the conversion of energy from one form to another within the device.

On one side of the electromechanical device the energy is electrical, and its behavior is described by Kirchhoff's laws, Ohm's law, and other familiar laws of circuits. This is suggested by Figure 3a. On the other side of the device the energy is mechanical, and the laws of Newton or d'Alembert and others are applied. In the device itself, in the region where energy conversion actually takes place, there is a law governing the conversion of electrical energy to mechanical and

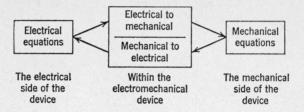

Figure 3a. An electromechanical problem involves, in general, the simultaneous solution of equations.

another related law governing the conversion of mechanical energy to electrical.

The ability to formulate the equations that describe an electro-mechanical system (to devise, that is, mathematical models of the elements), and to solve those equations simultaneously, is without doubt the most important matter to be learned from this book.

4. Electromechanical Relations

To study the process of energy conversion we need to relate what happens on the electrical side of a device to what happens on the mechanical side. The great majority of electromechanical devices are magnetic, so we have particular use for the following pair of principles, which tell how mechanical force and motion are related to electromotive force and current.

Induced electromotive force. Electromotive force is induced in a conductor if it moves in a magnetic field, or if the magnetic field about it is changing. The quantitative expression of this familiar relation, in one form or another, is known as Faraday's law. It is needed in electromechanics to tell how much electrical effect (electromotive force) may be expected from a given mechanical quantity (speed of motion).

Mechanical force on a conductor. Mechanical force is exerted on a conductor when it carries current in a magnetic field; also, there is mechanical force on iron (and certain other materials) in a magnetic field. This relation is in a sense the inverse of Faraday's law, for it tells how much mechanical effect (force) may be expected from a given electrical quantity (current).

These two are the essential electromechanical principles; they account for the action of electromechanical devices that operate magnetically. When we come to their quantitative expression we find that the electromotive force resulting from mechanical motion and the mechanical force resulting from motion of electric charge are not independent; either one may be deduced from the other with the aid of the principle of conservation of energy.

These electromechanical principles are based on experiment. Like all science, they are generalizations of many observations and measurements. It must never be forgotten that all scientific information comes from observation and measurement; principles and laws (even those as basic as conservation of energy) are but convenient generalizations of observations and measurements.

5. Electrical Relations

An electromechanical device serves as part of a system by connecting an electrical circuit or network on one side to a mechanical arrangement on the other. Behavior of the electrical part of the system is accounted for by various well-known principles. In particular, Kirchhoff's two laws tell how voltages and currents are interrelated in the electrical part of the system.

We most frequently use Kirchhoff's voltage law, which may be put as follows: *Electromotive force = sum of the opposing voltages,* including voltage across resistance, voltage across capacitance, and voltage across inductance. This law and Kirchhoff's current law describe what happens on the electrical side of our electromechanical system.

6. Mechanical Relations

On the mechanical side of the system the corresponding relation is given by Newton's second and third laws of motion. Thinkng of the force exerted on some device by a magnetic field, we may say: *Applied force = sum of the opposing forces,* including frictional force, spring force, and reactive inertial force. This statement of Newton's laws, in which his "reaction" is our reactive inertial force, is sometimes called d'Alembert's principle. The statement of Newton's law in this form is analogous to the statement of Kirchhoff's voltage law in the preceding paragraph.

Three sets of relations have now been mentioned. The relation embodied in Faraday's law and the force on a current-carrying conductor in a magnetic field are *electromechanical;* they explain how the electrical side of a system affects the mechanical side, and vice versa. Kirchhoff's laws apply on the *electrical* side of the system. Newton's laws apply on the *mechanical* side of the system. These three sets of relations are expressed as equations. The equations are then solved simultaneously (Figure 3*a*), for in general they depend on each other.

7. Definitions

It is assumed that the reader is acquainted with the basic laws of electric circuits.*

Electromotive force results when energy of another kind is converted into electrical energy, an example being the electromotive force induced in a conductor by mechanical motion through a magnetic field. Electromotive force in a circuit produces a potential difference or voltage between one part of the circuit and another.

The word *voltage* is used to indicate electric potential difference, as would be measured by a voltmeter between two terminals. The assumed reference direction is the direction that positive voltage would drive current through a voltmeter.

Magnetic field is a bothersome concept because most of us are accustomed to visualizing magnetic fields all too clearly. The usual concept of magnetic lines of force that act like mutually repulsive rubber bands, always trying to grow shorter and to spread apart sideways, certainly has its place in picturing field patterns. The pull attributed to the lines of force helps visualize the attraction of unlike magnetic poles, drawn together by the lines of force that run from one pole to the other. Their sideways repulsion suggests the magnetic pressure on a current-carrying conductor that tends to move it away from a denser field and toward a region of lesser flux density. But not all magnetic field situations are quite so simple as this, and there may be trouble if the rubber-band concept is too freely used.

What, after all, is a magnetic field? Perhaps the best we can say is that a magnetic field is a region of space in which force is exerted on a moving electric charge because of its motion. This may show itself as a mechanical force on a conductor carrying current, as in a motor, or as an electromotive force developed in a moving conductor, as in a generator. The idea to bear in mind is that a magnetic field is a *region of space* with certain interesting properties.

---

* See, for instance, the first five chapters of *Electrical Engineering Circuits* (Reference 7A of Appendix 5). Electromotive force is more fully discussed in pages 73 to 75 of *Fundamentals of Electric Waves* (Reference 7B).

How does a region of space become a magnetic field? Experiment shows that the space around a wire carrying electric current is a magnetic field. The magnetic field is particularly strong if the wire is wound into a coil. The presence of iron or steel is likely to strengthen a magnetic field, and sometimes the space around a piece of steel is a magnetic field even though there is no circuit carrying electric current. In the latter case we call the piece of steel a permanent magnet.

The terms magnetic intensity H, magnetic field strength or flux density B, permeability μ, magnetic flux Φ, magnetomotive force $\mathfrak{F}$, and magnetic reluctance $\mathfrak{R}$ are used in the following chapters with the expectation that they are not strange to the reader. Definitions can be found in any book on electrical physics, and some of these terms are defined as they are introduced. In Appendix 1 there is a summary of magnetic circuit ideas and terminology that may be of help to some readers.

The mks system of units is used. Anyone who works much with mechanical devices will unfortunately have to struggle, sooner or later, with "English" units, but later will be better than sooner. There is no use making an elementary book gratuitously complicated.

8. Other Electromechanical Principles

In the foregoing paragraphs we have given attention only to electromechanical devices that operate on magnetic principles. There are other principles that provide electromechanical coupling, but they are, on the whole, less important.

The *electric field* (rather than the magnetic) is used in electrostatic generators, such as the Van de Graaff generator, which convert mechanical energy to electrical by carrying electric charge in the direction it does not want to go. Another example, the capacitor microphone, is treated in some detail in Section 205. Such devices are generators, for they move a charge against the force exerted by an electric field. Thus they consume mechanical energy but increase the energy of the electric field.

As a familiar example of the inverse conversion, electrical energy is changed to mechanical through the agency of the electric field in a television or cathode-ray tube. The mechanical energy given to moving electrons is extremely minute, but the principle is that of the motor.

Ion propulsion for changing the speed or adjusting the attitude of a vehicle in space uses the electric field, too. Electrically charged ions of material, though having little mass, are gven tremendous speed by an electric field and are then cast off into empty space. The momentum of the vehicle is thus altered by the momentum that goes with the ions and changes its motion accordingly. The electric field acts as a motor on the discharged ions and on the vehicle.

Crystal microphones and devices for measuring force or pressure use the *piezoelectric effect* by which certain crystals produce an electric potential difference between crystal faces when they are stressed mechanically. By an inverse application of the same principle, alternating voltage applied between the crystal faces makes the crystal vibrate mechanically.

The *magnetostriction effect* in certain magnetic materials should be mentioned. There are also a few other minor means of electromechanical energy conversion.

Mechanical motion can affect the resistance of an electric circuit and can thus give electromechanical coupling. A signal is transmitted from such a device, not by energy conversion but by *modulating* the current supplied from a battery or other source. The common telephone transmitter is a good example of this; air pressure exerts force on a capsule of carbon particles and changes the electrical resistance of the capsule. Another example is the strain gauge in which electrical resistance of fine metal wires is changed when they are slightly stretched; such strain gauges are used to measure and record electrically the small distortions of beams and other mechanical members.

Some of these devices are described later, but magnetic devices are so much more important that they are given first attention.

PROBLEMS

(*Note.* Section numbers following problems show how far the text should have been studied before the problem is assigned.)

1-1. Name five electromechanical devices, giving a short description of each. **(Sec. 8)**

1-2. An electric motor is used to drive a hoist. Lifting a mass of 1,000 kg requires a force of F newtons. What is F? The hoist draws 10 amp from a 100-volt source. What is the minimum time necessary to lift the mass a distance of 10 m? Why might the actual time be somewhat longer than this? **(Sec. 3)**

1-3. Define an electric (or electrostatic) field. **(Sec. 7)**

1-4. Finding information elsewhere, write a paragraph on the piezoelectric effect, including various applications. Do the same for magnetostriction. **(Sec. 8)**

1-5. As shown in the figure, the starter of a certain type of automobile is operated by pushing a button (or turning a key), causing a magnetic contactor to close a switch in another circuit. This actu-

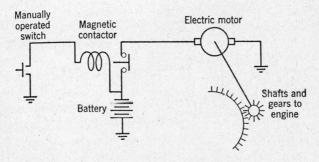

Problem 1-5

ates an electric motor, which, through appropriate shafts and gears, turns the automobile engine. Power comes from a storage battery. (*a*) List those elements of the system in which energy conversion takes place during normal operation of the starter from: (1) electrical to mechanical, (2) mechanical to electrical, (3) electrical to heat, (4) mechanical to heat, (5) other. (*b*) Indicate where there is storage of energy, during normal operation, in the following forms: (1) mechanical, kinetic, (2) magnetic, (3) chemical, (4) other. **(Sec. 3)**

MECHANICAL FORCE
chapter 2

9. Ampère's Law

We are familiar with electric forces, and with magnetic forces. When an electron or an electrically charged particle is near another there is a force on both. The force that exists when such particles are not moving is called an electric or electrostatic force. If the charged particles are moving there is an additional force owing to the motion, called a magnetic force. Both kinds of forces are useful, but magnetic forces are employed so much more commonly than electrical forces that we shall give them most of our attention.

Historically, André Ampère studied the force between two wires carrying electric currents (Paris, 1820).* The force Ampère studied was caused by electricity in motion, a magnetic force. Electrons within the conducting material of Ampère's wires were moving, and this motion constituted the electric current.

Ampère derived an expression for the observed force in terms of the currents and distances. Ampère's law is now commonly written in the following form: †

$$dF = \frac{ii'\,dl\,dl'}{r^2} \sin\theta \sin\theta'\, 10^{-7} \qquad (9\text{-}1)$$

where, as in Figure 9a,

dF is the force on a differential length of conductor dl (newtons)

i and i' are the two currents (amperes)

dl and dl' are the lengths (meters) of differential sections of conductors carrying these currents

r is their distance apart (meters)

---

* This and other stories are told in *Exploring Electricity*, Reference 9A.

† See any electrical physics book of intermediate level; for instance, Bleaney and Bleaney, Reference 9B.

(9)

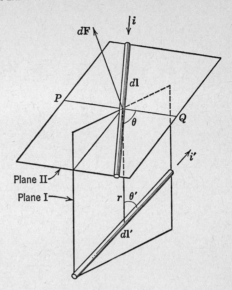

Figure 9a. Ampère's law of force between current-carrying conductors.

Plane I in the figure contains lines dl' and r; θ' is the angle between them. The line PQ is normal to Plane I.

Plane II contains lines dl and PQ; θ is the angle between them. The force dF is normal to Plane II.

Ampère visualized force exerted by one current on another as a kind of "action at a distance." This concept is often found helpful, though actual use of Ampère's law in computation is rather difficult and is therefore rare.

As an example, and perhaps the simplest possible example of Ampère's law, the force on a 1-meter length of a conductor carrying current i, parallel to another conductor that is long and straight, carrying current i', at a distance D meters from the first conductor, is

$$F = \frac{2ii'}{D} 10^{-7} \tag{9-2}$$

This is derived from equation 9-1 by integrating along the infinite length of the conductor carrying current i'.

For our later use it will be quite important to know the *direction* of force between currents. With two long, straight, parallel wires it was observed by Ampère (and it can easily be verified in any laboratory) that if the two wires are carrying current in the same direction the magnetic force draws them together; if they are carrying current in opposite directions the magnetic force drives them apart. This relation is conveniently though imprecisely phrased in the mnemonic *like currents attract; unlike currents repel.*

10. The Magnetic Field

Some twelve years later Michael Faraday (London, 1832) began a series of electrical experiments that resulted in our present concept of the magnetic field. Ampère considered that force was exerted on one current by another. Faraday, on the other hand, considered that an electric current produced a magnetic field in all surrounding space, and then conceived that there was a force on any conductor carrying current in that magnetic field. Thus Faraday thought in terms of an intermediate agent, the magnetic field. This concept has made both visualization and computation much easier.

Faraday's work led to an expression for the strength of the magnetic field circling about a long straight conductor carrying current i' (the Biot-Savart law):

$$B = \frac{\mu i'}{2\pi D} \qquad (10\text{-}1)$$

where μ is a constant, equal to $4\pi \cdot 10^{-7}$ for a field in air (henrys/meter)
  i' is current in the conductor (amperes)
  D is radial distance (meters) outward from the center of the conductor to the point at which B is measured
  B is the strength of Faraday's magnetic field at that radius, also called magnetic flux density (webers/meter^2)

B is the quantity from which force on another current-carrying conductor can be computed, as follows. On a straight conductor of length l carrying current i in a magnetic field B, the conductor being perpendicular to the magnetic field, the force is

$$F = Bli \qquad (10\text{-}2)$$

This is often called the *Bli* equation.

Equations 10-1 and 10-2 do in two steps what equation 9-2 does in one step. This can be seen by substituting B from equation 10-1 into 10-2.

The simple *Bli* expression applies, as stated, when the conductor on

(10)

which force is measured is perpendicular to the magnetic field. More generally,*

$$F = Bli \sin \beta \qquad (10\text{-}3)$$

where F is force (newtons)

B is magnetic flux density (webers/meter^2)

l is length of conductor (meters)

i is current (amperes) in the conductor

β is the angle from l to B.

If the magnetic field varies from place to place, or the wire is not straight, the total force is found by summation or integration. Equation 10-3 is used to find the differential force on each differential length, and the differential forces can then be added by integration to compute the total force. (Since force is a vector quantity, it may be necessary to find orthogonal components of each differential force in order to add or integrate.)

Equation 10-3 gives the *amount* of force on a current-carrying conductor. The *direction* of force is perpendicular to the conductor and also to the magnetic field. Figure 10a shows these directions and indicates the right-hand rule that tells which way along a perpendicular line the force is exerted. Note that the positive (or reference) direction for current is along the conductor in the way pointed by the length vector **l**. Then if the fingers of the right hand curl in the direction of the angle from **l** to **B** (the angle, less than 180 degrees, through which **l**

---

* In vector notation

$$\mathbf{F} = i(\mathbf{l} \times \mathbf{B}) \qquad (10\text{-}4)$$

By definition, when two vector quantities such as **l** and **B** of Figure 10a are written with a cross between them, (**l** × **B**), the indicated "cross product" or "vector product" is itself a vector. The magnitude of this new vector is $|lB| \sin \beta$, and its direction is normal to both **l** and **B**, headed as the thumb of the right hand points when the fingers are curved from **l** to **B** as shown in Figure 10a. This vector (**l** × **B**), when multiplied by the scalar quantity i (which changes only the magnitude), gives the vector of force **F**.

When two vector quantities are written with a dot between them, as **B**·**N** in equation 21-4, the indicated "dot product" or "scalar product" is by definition a scalar quantity equal to the product of the magnitudes of the vectors times the cosine of the angle between them (**B**·**N** = $|BN| \cos \psi$ in Figure 21a).

These "vector and scalar products" are part of a conventional notation adopted for convenience in vector analysis. See any book on vector analysis, or *Fundamentals of Electric Waves*, Reference 7B.

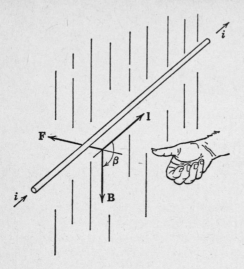

Figure 10a. Direction of force. The right thumb shows the direction of force when fingers, following the angle β, curl from 1 to **B**.

would have to be turned to make it coincide with **B**), the thumb points in the direction of positive **F**.

11. Force on Moving Charge

Electric current is electric charge in motion, and even more basic than the concept of force on a conductor carrying current is the idea that there is mechanical force on electric charge that is in motion in a magnetic field. This statement includes the force on a current-carrying conductor. It also includes the force on rapidly moving electrons of a cathode ray in an oscilloscope tube, or a television picture tube, when the electrons pass through a magnetic field. A stray magnetic field in such a tube distorts the pattern on the screen, for the electrons are deflected by the resulting mechanical force. Magnetic force is in all cases perpendicular to the motion of the electron and curves the electron's path.

To find how much force there is on a moving charge let us consider motion of charge when there is current in a wire. If current is i, the charge q passing a given cross section of the wire in time t is $q = it$. If the charge is moving with an average speed S during this time t, the distance that it travels is $l = St$. Dividing one of these relations by the other, we obtain

$$\frac{q}{l} = \frac{it}{St} = \frac{i}{S} \quad \text{or} \quad qS = li \qquad (11\text{-}1)$$

(11)

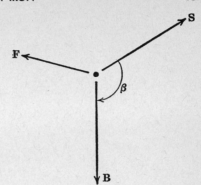

Figure 11a. The force on a positively charged particle moving in a magnetic field is normal to both **S** and **B**.

We know from equation 10-3 that force on a current-carrying conductor is proportional to li. To write this equation in terms of charge instead of current we substitute qS for li, obtaining

$$F = BqS \sin \beta \qquad (11\text{-}2)$$

where q is the amount of moving charge (coulombs)
          S is the speed at which it is moving (meters/second)
other symbols are as in equation 10-3

This equation * gives the force on a stream of electrons, or even a single electron, or a charged particle, moving in a magnetic field. For a single particle, as indicated in Figure 11a, β is the angle from its velocity vector **S** to the magnetic field-strength vector **B**. If the fingers of the right hand are curved through the angle from **S** to **B** the thumb points in the positive direction of the force **F**. (This is the direction in which force will be exerted if q is a positive charge; if q is negative, as is the charge on an electron, the force is negative, which means that it is in the opposite direction.)

12. Force on Iron

As stated in Section 7, a *magnetic field* is a region of space in which force is exerted on a moving electric charge. Experiment and observation from Ampère's time to the present have shown that every wire carrying an electric current is surrounded by a magnetic field, for force is observed on charges that move in the region about a current-carrying wire.

---

* In vector notation, $\mathbf{F} = q(\mathbf{S} \times \mathbf{B})$ $\qquad\qquad$ (11-3)

(12)

But it is also observed that a wire carrying current exerts a force on a piece of iron. Various materials, but notably iron and its alloys, are acted on by magnetic force when they are in a magnetic field. Moreover, if there are two pieces of iron in a magnetic field, each exerts force on the other.

Even at the time of his earliest observations, Ampère was not willing to believe that the magnetic force on iron was unrelated to the force on a wire carrying electric current. To explain the behavior of iron he postulated an electric current circulating perpetually within each atom of iron. In Ampère's century this seemed rather absurd, but now it seems entirely reasonable. Modern concepts of atomic structure suggest that electrons within the atom provide, by their motion, just such "Amperian currents." The greater part of the Amperian current effect comes from electrons spinning about their own axes; a small part is contributed by their motion in orbits about the atomic nucleus. Such subatomic Amperian currents cause the well-known magnetic action of iron and other ferromagnetic materials, and also the lesser effects seen in paramagnetic materials.

Each iron atom, because of the spin of electrons within the atom, has the equivalent of a circulating electric current. This circulating current makes each ferromagnetic atom (and to a lesser extent each paramagnetic atom) a small electromagnet. If many atoms of a piece of iron are oriented the same way, the net effect of all the microscopic circulating currents is as if there were a large electric current circulating at the surface of the piece of iron. See Figure 12a. Amperian current is not an ordinary conduction current; it is not a current of electrons passing among the atoms of the solid material. Hence it does not encounter the electrical resistance that must be overcome by a conduction current. Resistance of a conductor is due to energy loss resulting from random collisions of electrons with atoms; spinning electrons within atoms have no such energy loss. Amperian current therefore continues indefinitely, and iron continues to act as a magnet as long as the atoms are oriented in the same way.

Parallel orientation of the magnetic fields of atoms is induced when iron is placed in a magnetic field; the spinning electrons within the iron tend to orient themselves in line with the external field.* The

---

* Magnetic orientation acts within *domains* in the iron. Microscopic examination shows the domain boundaries or Bloch walls shifting, often discontinuously in the Barkhausen effect, as magnetization becomes more intense. It must not be conceived that the domains or even the atoms rotate when iron is magnetized; it is the axes of spin of the electrons that are reoriented.

(12)

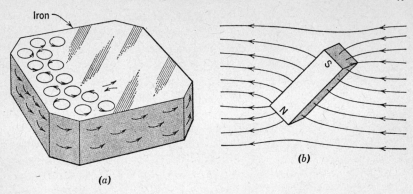

Figure 12. (*a*) Amperian current in a uniformly magnetized piece of iron. In every internal region the atomic circulating currents balance each other and effectively add to zero. At every point on the surface of the iron the Amperian current is equivalent to a sheet of current following the surface. (*b*) A bar of iron becomes a magnet when placed in a magnetic field.

magnetic field is strengthened by the magnetism of the iron atoms, so the total magnetic field is greater in the presence of iron than it would have been had the iron been absent.

Equivalent current at the surface of iron that results, as shown in Figure 12*a*, from Amperian electron spin may readily amount to hundreds or thousands of amperes. The evidence of its existence is the same as the evidence of existence of any other electric current: that is, it produces a magnetic field and has force exerted upon it by a magnetic field. The magnetic force on iron in a magnetic field is entirely due to its Amperian current.

As an aid to visualization, suppose the bar of iron of Figure 12*b* is placed in a magnetic field. The magnetic moments of electron spin become oriented, and the resulting Amperian current causes the piece of iron to be a magnet. The total magnetic field is the sum of the field produced by external causes and the field produced by Amperian current in the iron.

This magnet has a south pole where magnetic flux lines enter it (see the figure) and a north pole where magnetic flux lines leave it. Sometimes it is easier to think of these induced magnetic poles than to think directly in terms of Amperian currents. Thus on the bar shown in Figure 12*b* there is a clockwise torque; there is mechanical force on this bar as on any magnet in a magnetic field. Its

(12)

north pole is attracted by other south poles, and its south pole by other north poles.

It is found that steel and, more particularly, cobalt steel and certain alloys (such as Alnico) of iron, cobalt, nickel, aluminum, and copper that have been magnetized by the effect of an electric current retain part of their magnetization after the electric current ceases. It is of these materials that permanent magnets are made. In such materials the spinning electrons, once aligned, retain each other in alignment; each atom is held in the proper orientation by the magnetic field of all the atoms acting together.

Amperian current therefore continues, in a permanent magnet, after the external cause of magnetization has been removed. It is this continuing Amperian current that causes the material to be a magnet. Magnetism continues until the parallel orientation of electron spin is disturbed, as by a hammer blow or by the molecular agitation of a high temperature. Natural lodestones have retained magnetization for untold thousands of years.

13. A Dynamic Speaker

Let us consider a few examples of magnetic force in practical devices. A loudspeaker, used to change electrical energy to sound, is shown in Figure 13a.

This is a cross section, and there is symmetry about the axis shown; thus the field magnet has the general shape of a round box with a cylindrical stub in the middle. The field structure may be a permanent magnet, or it may be excited by a coil around the stub, inside the box, carrying constant field current. (Such a coil is not shown in the diagram.)

The moving cone that transmits sound vibrations to the air is firmly cemented to a small light cylindrical coil of a few turns, or a few dozen turns, of fine wire. This coil of wire is in the strong magnetic field between the north and south poles of the magnet. Current through the coil varies according to the speech, music, or other sound to be reproduced. This current in the magnetic field causes a force on the coil (the "voice coil"), and the coil and cone vibrate together, thus transmitting sound waves to the air.

We need to know the force on the voice coil when current passes and the motion of the cone that results. The force is easily found: with the simple geometry of the speaker, equation 10-2 applies, and

(13)

$$F = Bli \qquad (13\text{-}1)$$

where i is the current in the voice coil (amperes)

l is length of wire in the voice coil (meters)

B is magnetic field strength at the voice coil (webers/meter^2)

F is force (newtons)

Practically, l may be of the order of magnitude of 1, B rather less than 1, i perhaps 0.20. (One newton is the weight of 102.0 grams, or a little over $3\frac{1}{2}$ ounces, about a quarter of a pound.)

Equation 13-1 gives the amount of force on the voice coil. The direction of the force is found by the right-hand rule of Section 10: curl the right-hand fingers from l to B. In Figure 13a, suppose current is flowing toward the reader at the top of the voice coil and into the page at the bottom of the coil; that is, at the top the direction of positive l is out of the page, the direction of B is upward, the fingers pointing through the angle from l to B require the right thumb to point toward the left. This tells us that the force on the voice coil is toward the left at this moment. When current in the voice coil reverses, force will be toward the right.

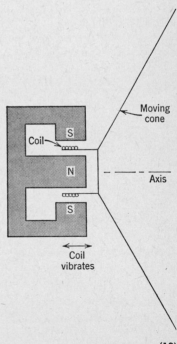

Figure 13a. A speaker.

(13)

14. The d'Arsonval Movement

The mechanism of the ordinary d-c ammeter, commonly known as the d'Arsonval movement, is essentially a spring balance to measure the force on a conductor carrying current in a magnetic field. Figure 14a shows an end view of a rectangular coil of wire that is pivoted to turn about the axis of a cylinder. This cylinder is a permanent magnet of steel alloy. It is magnetized along a diameter, vertically as shown in the diagram, so that it has magnetic poles in the regions marked N and S in the figure. An outer ring of iron completes the magnetic circuit.* Thus the coil of wire is free to move in the magnetic field in the air gap between the inner magnet and the outer iron ring.

Current to be measured is passed through the pivoted coil. Because of the magnetic field there is force on the sides of the coil. Current is in the direction that gives a clockwise torque, and the coil turns in that direction. As it turns it pushes against a spiral spring, similar to the hair spring of a watch.

Torque is proportional to the magnetic field strength B, the amount of current i, the length l of one side of each turn of the coil in the magnetic field, the number of turns of the coil N, and the radius of the coil ρ. The force on any one of the conductors of the coil is

$$F = Bli \qquad\qquad (14\text{-}1)$$

This is a tangential force, being normal to B, which is radial, and to l, which is parallel to the axis. The length l is somewhat less than the full axial length of the rectangular coil, for the coil extends a short distance beyond the magnetic field at each end.

Torque contributed by each side of each turn of the coil is the product of force and radius, $Bli\rho$. There are $2N$ sides, so the total torque is

$$T = 2NBli\rho \qquad\qquad (14\text{-}2)$$

With l and ρ measured in meters, i in amperes, and B in webers per square meter; T is in newton-meters.

The magnetic field B in which the coil moves is of uniform strength,

---

* d'Arsonval movements were formerly made with the outer structure a magnet and the inner cylinder of soft iron. Some are still made this way, but modern materials tend to make permanent magnets short and fat.

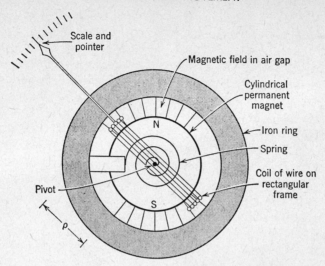

Figure 14a. A moving-coil ammeter movement.

so the magnetic torque, proportional to current, is independent of the coil position. The restraining torque of the spring is proportional to displacement of the coil from the zero position. Therefore when current flows steadily the displacement of the coil is proportional to the amount of current. A pointer attached to the coil moves over a scale that is uniformly calibrated in amperes.

It will be recognized that an ammeter is an electromechanical device although it provides only enough mechanical energy to twist the spring. No mechanical energy is delivered out of the instrument.

The same essential device can be made to serve as an element of a control system rather than an indicating instrument by providing some means for the rotation of the moving coil to affect another circuit. It may, for instance, serve as a sensitive relay by making an electrical contact when the coil has turned through a certain angle; when contact is made a circuit breaker is tripped, or some other action takes place. Another possibility is to have motion of the coil alter the amount of light falling on a photoelectric cell, and output of the cell can operate some control device. There are many possibilities.

(14)

15. A Motor

There is no great difference between this d'Arsonval movement and an electric motor. Motors, of course, are usually larger and more powerful than ammeter movements, but the principle is the same. A coil carrying current moves because it is in a magnetic field.

A motor, however, must turn continuously. The ammeter movement of Figure 14a can turn through nearly half a revolution with the coil sides in a magnetic field so directed that torque is clockwise. But if the coil turned more than half a revolution it would get into magnetic field that was oppositely directed and, if current remained the same as before, torque would then be in the other or counterclockwise direction. For a motor, this will not do. It is necessary to reverse the current in the coil as the coil passes from the field of a north pole to the field of a south pole, or vice versa. There are several practical ways to do this (see Chapters 6, 7, and 9). One common way is to use an automatic switch called a commutator which is operated by the turning of the motor itself.

A motor usually differs from a d'Arsonval movement in two other ways, also. The magnetic field to operate the motor is not provided by a permanent magnet (except in the smallest of motors) but by coils of wire on field poles as indicated in Figure 15a. These carry direct current to produce the necessary magnetic field.*

The inner cylinder of a motor turns with the rotating coil. It is mounted on bearings so that it is free to rotate, and the current-carrying coil is attached to it. In fact, the coil is commonly set into slots in the surface of the iron cylinder.† The iron cylinder, the *armature* of the motor, is made of soft iron with low residual magnetism (low tendency to be a permanent magnet) so it will have low hysteresis loss as its magnetization is reversed twice each revolution. It is laminated—that is, the cylinder is made of a stack of thin circular sheets, clamped together—to reduce eddy-current loss. (See Section 28.) There are many slots in the surface of the armature, and many coils of wire are set in them. These practical ar-

---

* In a cross section of a wire, a dot (the point of a head-on arrow) indicates current out of the page and a cross (the rear view of the arrow's feathered tail) shows current into the page.

† Motors in which the coil turns and the iron cylinder does not are sometimes used in control systems. They have low moment of inertia, and hence rapid acceleration, but small torque and poor mechanical strength.

(15)

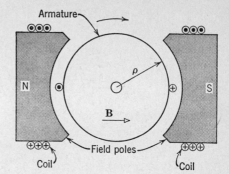

Figure 15a. Torque on a motor coil.

rangements are described in Chapters 6, 7, and 9; our immediate interest is in the principle by which a motor converts electrical to mechanical energy.

16. Concepts

In the simple device of Figure 15a, let current be into the page in the right-hand side of the rotating coil (the armature coil), and out on the left; the magnetic field will exert force on these coil sides. There will be a torque on the coil, and the cylindrical rotor (unless prevented) will turn.

Which way? There are several easy means of finding the direction of rotation. One is to consider the force of magnetic poles on each other. As in Figure 16a, consider that current in the armature coil, taken alone, will tend to produce a vertical magnetic field. Pointing the fingers of the right hand in the direction of current around the armature coil, the thumb shows that magnetic flux will be up through the central iron cylinder. Flux therefore leaves the iron of the cyl-

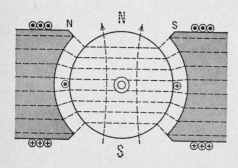

Figure 16a. Torque in a motor.

(16)

inder at the top, and reenters at the bottom; two dash lines indicate the paths of flux that would be due to armature-coil current alone. Considering the cylindrical armature as a magnet, the top of it is a north pole (as indicated by the dotted letter N) and the bottom a south pole. Consider the pole structure as one magnet and the cylindrical armature as another; since like poles *repel*, and unlike poles attract, the armature will turn clockwise.

Alternatively, consider the force of currents on each other. Refer again to Figure 16a and note that current in the field coils is out of the page at the top of each pole, and in at the bottom. Because like currents *attract*, the outward current at the left-hand side of the armature coil will be forced upward, and the inward current at the right will be forced down, by the effect of currents in the field windings. Again we find that a clockwise rotation is indicated.

Actually, the effect of current in the field winding on current in the armature coil is very slight. If the iron of the field structure and the iron of the armature were removed, the force of current in one winding on that in the other would be small. Force is increased some hundreds or thousands of times by the presence of the iron, and (from the point of view we are now using) that is because of Amperian currents. Amperian current circulates around each pole, at the surface of the iron, in the same direction as the current in the field winding itself, and around the armature iron in the same direction as current in the armature winding. These tremendous Amperian currents enhance the forces, and it is very largely the force of Amperian current that makes the motor turn.

Finally (and this is often the easiest rule to apply) the right-hand rule of Figure 10a tells us that force on the left-hand armature conductor of Figure 16a is upward. The l vector, direction of current, is out; the B vector is toward the right; curling the fingers through the angle from l to B, the thumb points up. Similarly, force on the right-hand conductor is downward; thus there is a clockwise torque on the rotor.

Torque has now been considered in three ways: as the force of pole on pole, the force of current on current, and the force of magnetic field on current. All three concepts are correct and all three should be known, for sometimes one is easier to apply and sometimes another.

17. Analysis

Only one of these concepts, however, is at all convenient for actual quantitative computation of the amount of torque in the motor.

(17)

The consideration of force between currents, particularly when Amperian currents are involved, requires taking into account current densities that vary from place to place in two or three dimensions, and this can lead to a sixfold integration. Moreover, the distribution of Amperian current has first to be established, which is at least equally difficult.*

Computation of torque from magnetic pole strength is as hard, and for the same reasons. First the distribution of magnetic pole strength is needed, and after that a difficult integration is required.

But it is easy to compute torque in the simple device of Figure 16a from the Bli equation. Current in the armature coil is i. The length of the armature conductor perpendicular to the page is l. (The armature coil ends, which run parallel to the page in Figure 16a, are not in a strong magnetic field and contribute nothing to torque.) The radius of the armature is ρ as in Figure 15a. Torque on *both* coil sides is then $T = 2Bli\rho$. If the coil has not one but N turns, each carrying current i, the total torque is

$$T = 2NBli\rho \quad \text{newton-meters} \tag{17-1}$$

To use this equation, we must find B. An approximation that is quite good as long as the iron is not becoming saturated magnetically is to assume that all the reluctance of the magnetic field circuit of the machine is in the air gaps, and that the permeability of the iron is so high it need not be considered.† Then B in the air gap is (see equation 5-2 in Appendix 1)

$$B = \frac{\mu_0 \mathfrak{F}}{2w} \tag{17-2}$$

where B is magnetic flux density (webers/meter^2)
μ_0 is permeability in the air gap ($= 4\pi \cdot 10^{-7}$)
$\mathfrak{F}$ is magnetomotive force of the field winding (ampere-turns)
w is the width of the air gap (meters); there are two gaps in series

Thus in two steps, first computing B, and then computing torque from B, we readily find a quantitative value of torque. One of the

---

* Amperian current density is proportional to the curl of **B** not accounted for by conduction current or displacement current, and occurs where there is a change of the magnetic properties of the medium.

† If there is considerable saturation of the iron it may be necessary to take the reluctance of the iron part of the magnetic circuit into account. Then the geometry of the iron and its magnetic properties must be known.

principal reasons that the concept of the magnetic field has remained in such general use since its introduction into electrical theory by Faraday, over a hundred years ago, is the beautiful simplicity that it gives to the solution of problems like this.

Equation 17-2 gives magnetic flux density B. Note that B is not a constant value, but varies from point to point in the air gap. The variation of B along a radius can be neglected; in fact, the derivation of equation 17-2 includes the assumption that such radial variation is negligible, and this is safe because the air gap of a machine is narrow.

B may also vary around the circumference of the machine. B is greater where the width of the air gap is least and smaller where the air gap is wider, as shown by w in the denominator of equation 17-2. If B varies around the circumference, torque varies correspondingly as the armature turns. If the detailed dimensions of the air gap are known, B can be found, and hence torque can be found, at every position of the armature.

However, for many practical purposes we are not much interested in the details of variation of torque as the machine turns, but rather we want to know the *average* torque. The average is easily found.

If the total magnetic flux entering the armature from the field structure of the motor is Φ (see Figure 16a), and the surface into which it enters is $\pi\rho l$ (this is the surface area of half a cylinder of radius ρ and length l), then the average B is $\Phi/\pi\rho l$, and the average torque is

$$\text{Average torque} = \frac{2N\Phi li\rho}{\pi\rho l} = \frac{2N\Phi i}{\pi} \qquad (17\text{-}3)$$

This is the average torque while the coil of Figure 16a, carrying current i, is making one complete passage under the poles of the machine.

If, by means of a commutator (or otherwise), current in the coil is reversed as the coil passes from the field of one pole to that of the next, torque continues to be applied in the same sense. Equation 17-3 then gives the average torque for continuous rotation. This is an important value in d-c motor design.

18. A Slotted Armature

Figure 18a shows a motor with a slotted armature, with coils in two pairs of slots. A practical motor would have coils in all the other

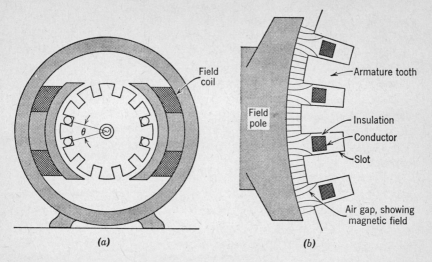

Field coil

Field pole

Armature tooth

Insulation

Conductor

Slot

Air gap, showing magnetic field

(a)   (b)

Figure 18. (a) Showing armature slots and field coils. (b) Little of the air-gap magnetic field enters the armature slots.

slots also. (More will be said about practical motor construction in Chapter 6.)

At first thought it seems that putting the armature conductors into slots would spoil the operation of the motor. Flux of the main magnetic field of the machine tends to follow paths of low reluctance and, as indicated in Figure 18b, most of the flux crosses the air gap from the field pole to the tips of the armature teeth (between slots). Within the slots, where the armature conductors are placed, there is very little magnetic field strength, and consequently there is very little force exerted on the armature conductors.

This seems bad, but in fact it is not, for though there is indeed little force on the conductors in slots, there is a strong and useful force exerted on the iron teeth of the armature. These teeth are magnetized by current in the armature conductors in the slots, with the result that the teeth themselves are strongly acted upon by the main field poles of the machine. Amperian currents are produced in the teeth, and these Amperian currents are strongly attracted or repelled by currents (conductive and Amperian) in the field structure.

There are decided advantages to the slotted type of armature. It is difficult to secure conductors on the smooth surface of an unslotted rotor; when the conductors are in slots, the problem of anchoring the conductors is solved. Moreover, conductors are surrounded by

(18)

insulation, and whatever force is exerted on the conductors has to be transmitted to the rotor through the insulation. Since most insulating materials are mechanically weak, this would not be easy if the force were great. But with conductors in slots, so that most of the magnetic force is actually exerted on the teeth, and little on the conductors, danger of crushing the insulation is avoided.

To decide whether slotted construction is justified by these advantages, we must know how much difference there is between the useful torque on a slotted rotor and that on a rotor without slots. We know the torque on the conductors of the unslotted rotor from equation 17-1. How can we compute torque on the slotted rotor?

Unfortunately, none of the methods considered so far seems to offer a practical means of computation. The Bli equation gives force on the conductors in the slots if we can compute B within the slots, but this is only a minor and perhaps negligible part of the total torque. As has been mentioned, computation from induced magnetic poles, or from Amperian currents, is almost prohibitively laborious. This leaves us without resources.

However, in Section 4 there was a suggestion that mechanical torque can be determined from induced electromotive force by applying the principle of conservation of energy. In Chapter 3 we shall study electromotive force, and in Chapter 4 this suggestion for computing torque from energy will be explored.

19. Summary

Mechanical force between currents was first studied by Ampère, giving Ampère's law. Faraday introduced the concept of force on current in a magnetic field, which is much more convenient.

There is force on any charged particle moving in a magnetic field. Electrons are charged particles. Electric current in a wire consists of electrons in motion. Hence there is force on a conductor carrying current in a magnetic field.

In iron and other ferromagnetic alloys the alignment of electron spin in a magnetic field is equivalent to current circulating at the surface of the iron. Because of this Amperian current there is force on iron in a magnetic field.

As examples of electromechanical devices employing magnetic force, a loudspeaker, an ammeter movement, and a motor are discussed. The Bli law is used, with the right-hand rule for direction.

(19)

In discussion of the motor, three useful concepts of magnetic action are given: the force of pole on pole, the force of current on current, and the force of magnetic field on current. Only the last is used for computation.

Average torque on a motor armature is computed, assuming armature conductors on the surface of the cylindrical rotor. Computation of torque on a slotted rotor is postponed to a later chapter.

P R O B L E M S

2-1. Two long, straight, parallel conductors are carrying currents i and i'. (See figure.) (a) Find dF, the force on dl, using Ampère's

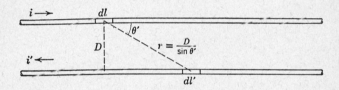

Problem 2-1

law. (b) Find the force per unit length (per meter) of the conductor. (c) Consider the units in your answers to parts (a) and (b), and explain. **(Sec. 9)**

2-2. Show that equation 10-3, together with the Biot-Savart law, may be used to derive equation 9-2. **(Sec. 10)**

2-3. A proposed pump for liquid metals is shown in the figure. The pump should raise the pressure of the liquid metal by 2.0 newtons/cm². Assume a uniform magnetic flux field of 0.5 webers/m². Assume a uniform distribution of current between electrodes. Calculate the current required. If the liquid metal is to be circulated inward, as shown by the arrow in the diagram, which way should the

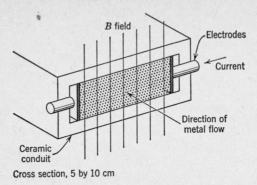

B field

Electrodes

Current

Direction of
metal flow

Ceramic
conduit

Cross section, 5 by 10 cm

Problem 2-3

magnetic field be directed? Discuss whether this would be a practical device for circulating mercury, or liquid sodium.   **(Sec. 10)**

2-4. Two heavy parallel conductors (bus bars) in a power station are spaced 50 cm between centers. During a short circuit in the power system these conductors each carry a sinusoidal current (in opposite directions) of 50,000 amp rms at 60 cycles/sec. (a) What is the maximum instantaneous force per meter of length acting to push apart the conductors? (Express in newtons and also in pounds.) (b) How does the force vary as a function of time?   **(Sec. 10)**

2-5. A small particle with charge q and mass m is moving in a direction perpendicular to a uniform magnetic field B. The magnetic force on the particle makes it travel in a circle of radius ρ. Find the speed of the particle in terms of q, m, B, and ρ, and show in a diagram the direction of curvature relative to B.   **(Sec. 11)**

2-6. The charge on an electron is $-1.59 \cdot 10^{-19}$ coulomb. The mass of an electron is $9 \cdot 10^{-31}$ kg. Force on a charged particle in an electric field is $F = qE$ newtons (in the same direction as E), where q = charge on the particle, coulombs, and E = electric field strength, volts/m. A magnetic field in which B is uniformly 0.01 weber/m² is entered by an electron with a speed of 10,000 m/sec perpendicular to B. By means of an electric field in the same region as the magnetic field, the electron is made to continue traveling in a straight line. How strong, and in what direction, is the electric field E? Show B, E, and S in a diagram.   **(Sec. 11)**

2-7. The dynamic speaker of Figure 13a has 12 turns in the voice coil. If $B = 0.30$ weber/m² in the region in which the voice coil moves, and the *rms* current in the voice coil is 0.10 ampere, find the *maximum* (not rms) force on the coil. Find force in newtons, and also in ounces. Figure 13a is a half-size drawing; there is cylindrical symmetry about the axis shown. **(Sec. 13)**

2-8. The speaker of problem 7 has its magnetic field provided by a field coil not shown in the diagram, wound around the central pole piece (not by a permanent magnet). How many ampere-turns are required to give the specified value of B? Assume the magnetic structure has an average relative permeability of 4,000. **(Sec. 13)**

2-9. What is the direction of current in Figure 14a? **(Sec. 14)**

2-10. Figure 14a shows an ammeter. The coil, which has 250 turns, moves in a magnetic field that is radial and uniform, in which $B = 0.20$ weber/m². This coil is rectangular with sides 2 cm long into the page, and 2 cm across the top and bottom. As the pivoted coil turns, it pushes against 2 spiral springs (only one is shown), one each at the top and bottom pivots. The spring constant of each is $K_r = 5 \cdot 10^{-6}$ newton meter/radian. (*a*) If 3 ma of current flow through the coil, find the force on each side of the coil. Sketch B, i, and l in a vector diagram. Which way will the coil turn? (*b*) How much current is required to turn the pointer through 1 radian, starting at the zero current position? **(Sec. 14)**

ELECTROMOTIVE FORCE
chapter 3

20. Magnetic Force on Electrons

Conducting materials, such as copper wire, contain great quantities of electrons that are free to move among the atoms of the material. It is the freedom of these electrons that makes the material electrically conducting. Free electrons are characteristic of metals; the best conductors are silver and copper, as is well known, but all metals conduct electricity.

Suppose that a straight piece of copper wire is moved through a magnetic field (Figure 20a). The wire is held at right angles to the magnetic field **B**, and the direction of motion **S** is perpendicular to both. As the wire moves it carries its electrons with it; each electron is therefore moving in a magnetic field and, as discussed in Section 11, each electron has therefore a force exerted upon it.

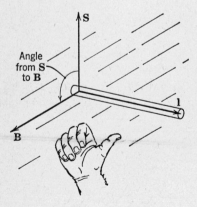

Figure 20a. The right thumb shows the direction of electromotive force when fingers curl from **S** to **B**.

(20)

This force exerted by the magnetic field upon the moving electrons tends to drive the electrons in a direction normal to both **S**, the motion, and **B**, the magnetic field, as in Figure 11a. Hence they are driven along the length of the wire in Figure 20a. Electrons, being negatively charged, are driven opposite to the direction marked 1; the *conventional current*, a hypothetical fluid of positive electricity, would be forced in the direction of the 1 vector.

Let us suppose that there is an external circuit to provide a return path from one end of the moving conductor to the other. This is not shown in Figure 20a, but a pair of flexible leads from the ends of the wire to a resistor or some other kind of load can be visualized. Electric charge forced along the moving conductor can then flow on around the circuit. As charge is driven from one end to the other of the moving wire there is work done on it by the magnetic force; the amount of the work is the product of the force and the distance:

$$\text{Work} = Fl \qquad (20\text{-}1)$$

Force is given by equation 11-2 to be BqS, so

$$\text{Work} = BqSl \qquad (20\text{-}2)$$

The magnetic field, in doing work on the moving charge, and driving the charge around the circuit, is said to produce *electromotive force*. (Some authors prefer the term *electromotance*.) By definition, electromotive force is equal to the work done on one unit of charge while moving along a specified path. It is, for instance, the energy given to one unit of charge by magnetic action in the moving wire. Dividing equation 20-2 by q, to get work per unit charge, gives electromotive force developed in the moving wire. The symbol e is used for electromotive force:

$$e = BlS \qquad (20\text{-}3)$$

The work done by magnetic action on electric charge in the moving wire can be expended by that charge as it passes around the circuit. It can be dissipated as heat in resistance, or it can be converted to chemical or mechanical uses. It can be stored, for a time, in inductance or capacitance. While stored in capacitance the charge produces an electric field. The line integral of that electric field is called *potential difference* or *voltage*, for which the symbol * is v.

---

* Although e and v may, under certain circumstances, be numerically equal, they must not be confused. Electromotive force appears where energy of another kind is being converted into electrical energy, as in a generator or battery. Electromotive force is the line integral of the component of electric field pro-

21. Electromotive Force in a Moving Conductor

Experiment, confirming the deductions of the foregoing section, shows that equation 20-3 is correct and the electromotive force induced in a moving conductor is indeed

$$e = BlS \qquad (21\text{-}1)$$

This may be called the *BlS* equation.* As in Figure 20*a*, the positive direction of the electromotive force is given by the right thumb when the fingers curl from **S** to **B**.†

The mutually perpendicular arrangement of **B**, **l**, and **S**, illustrated in Figure 20*a*, is the simplest possible geometry. In general the vectors of field strength, length, and speed may be at any angles to each other, and angular relations must then be taken into account in the equation for electromotive force. This is done by writing

$$e = BlS \sin \theta \cos \psi \qquad (21\text{-}2)$$

where θ is the angle from the **l** vector to the **S** vector (see Figure 21*a*) and ψ is the angle between the **B** vector and a line marked **N** that is normal to the plane containing the **l** and **S** vectors.‡

---

duced by such energy conversion. Voltage or potential difference is the line integral of the component of electric field that results from the presence of electric charge. (See Chapter 5 of *Electric Waves*, Reference 7B.)

As a hydraulic analog: if a pump circulates water through a system of pipes, e is the push given to the water by the pump, and v is the pressure in the pipes.

* It is more commonly called the *Blv* equation, using v for velocity, but we are reserving v for voltage and will use S for speed.

† Note the similarity to the rule that applies to Figure 10*a*. Electromotive force and mechanical force both result from motion of charge in a magnetic field. In both cases you curl the fingers *from* the direction of motion *to* the direction of **B**, and the thumb then points in the direction of the *resulting force*.

In Figure 10*a*, current is carrying charge in the direction l; you curl the fingers from l to B, and the mechanical force **F** is shown by the thumb.

In Figure 20*a*, the moving conductor is carrying charge in the direction S; you curl the fingers from S to B, and the force (electromotive force this time) is in the direction pointed by the thumb.

This rule is needed so frequently that it may as well be memorized.

‡ This equation is more conveniently written in vector notation as

$$e = \mathbf{B} \cdot (\mathbf{l} \times \mathbf{S}) \qquad (21\text{-}3)$$

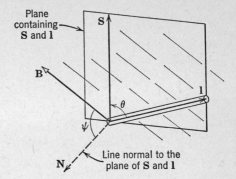

Figure 21a. Showing **B**, **1**, and **S** not perpendicular.

If a conductor is not straight, or the magnetic field varies from place to place, equations 21-1 and 21-2 cannot be applied directly. Electromotive force in the conductor is then found by integration. The differential electromotive force de, induced in differential length of conductor dl, is

$$de = BS \sin \theta \cos \psi \, dl \qquad (21\text{-}6)$$

Integration of this differential electromotive force along a finite length of conductor gives the electromotive force induced in that length of conductor, whatever its shape: [§]

$$e = \int BS \sin \theta \cos \psi \, dl \qquad (21\text{-}7)$$

The dot and cross products are defined in the footnote to section 10. Combined in equation 21-3, they make it mean the same as equation 21-2. The vector **N** in Figure 21a is equal to $(\mathbf{l} \times \mathbf{S})$; hence

$$e = \mathbf{B} \cdot \mathbf{N} \qquad (21\text{-}4)$$

It can be shown, as a purely mathematical transformation, that

$$e = \mathbf{B} \cdot (\mathbf{l} \times \mathbf{S}) = (\mathbf{S} \times \mathbf{B}) \cdot \mathbf{l} \qquad (21\text{-}5)$$

The latter form more obviously gives the same direction for e as that indicated by the right-hand rule in Figure 20a, for in equation 21-5 the vector that represents $(\mathbf{S} \times \mathbf{B})$ is normal to S and B, in the direction of the right thumb when the fingers curl from S to B.

[§] Or, in vector notation, from equation 21-5,

$$e = \int (\mathbf{S} \times \mathbf{B}) \cdot d\mathbf{l} \qquad (21\text{-}8)$$

(21)

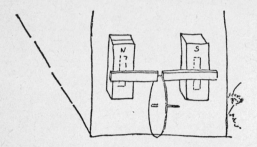

Figure 21b. Michael Faraday's sketch of his first electric generator, the original "Faraday disc." This drawing was made by Faraday in his diary on October 28, 1831: "Made many expts. with a copper revolving plate. . . ." (Courtesy, Managers of the Royal Institution, Publishers of Faraday's Diary.)

where e is the induced electromotive force (volts)

    l is the length (meters) of the conductor

    S is the speed (meters/second) at which it moves

    B is the magnetic field strength (webers/meter^2)

    θ is the angle from the dl vector to the S vector

    ψ is the angle between the magnetic field B and a line normal to the plane containing the dl and S vectors (as shown in Figure 21a)

As an example, certain d-c generators develop electromotive force in insulated copper conductors wrapped around a cylindrical iron armature that rotates in a strong magnetic field. Electromotive force in such a machine can be computed from the simple BlS equation.

The first rotating generator was "Faraday's disc" of copper turning between the poles of a magnet (Figure 21b). When the disk turns, electromotive force is generated between the axis of the disk and the edge, as Faraday detected by touching wires from a galvanometer to the shaft and the edge of the turning disk. This is another example of *motional* electromotive force. The homopolar generator is a more practical modern example of Faraday's disk.

22. Rate of Cutting Flux

Equation 21-7 is often interpreted as saying that the electromotive force induced in a length of conductor moving in an unchanging magnetic field is equal to the rate of cutting flux. The conductor is visualized as passing through the magnetic field and cutting flux lines as it goes.

To understand this interpretation, consider the piece of wire shown in Figure 22a. It may be bent into any shape and may or may not be a closed loop.

Consider the wire divided into a great many short sections, one of which is marked dl. This section of differential length, moving for differential time dt with speed S, travels a distance $S\,dt$, and sweeps across a surface of area $(S\,dt)(dl\sin\theta)$, as indicated, while the wire moves from the position shown by solid lines to that shown by dashed lines. The amount of magnetic flux through this surface is found by multiplying the area by the component of magnetic field normal to the surface, giving

$$(S\,dt)(dl\sin\theta)(B\cos\psi) \qquad\qquad (22\text{-}1)$$

where θ and ψ are the angles defined with equation 21-7.

Hence the section of wire of differential length dl cuts this amount of flux while traveling a distance $S\,dt$ in differential time dt. To find its *rate* of cutting flux, we divide by dt and (rearranging terms) obtain

$$\text{Rate of cutting flux} = BS\sin\theta\cos\psi\,dl \qquad\qquad (22\text{-}2)$$

Since this is the rate at which the differential section of length dl is cutting flux, the rate at which any finite length of wire is cutting flux can be found by integrating:

$$\text{Rate of cutting flux} = \int BS\sin\theta\cos\psi\,dl \qquad\qquad (22\text{-}3)$$

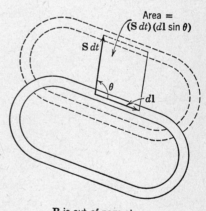

Area =
$(S\,dt)(dl\sin\theta)$

$S\,dt$

θ

dl

B is out of page at angle ψ to normal

Flux through area is
$(S\,dt)(dl\sin\theta)(B\cos\psi)$

Figure 22a. Conductor moving through a magnetic field.

(22)

Now, compare the rate of cutting flux, given by equation 22-3, with the electromotive force induced by motion, expressed as equation 21-7. They are identical. Hence we may say that electromotive force is equal to the rate of cutting flux. Notice that it is only shown to be valid in a magnetic field that is not changing with time. The field may, however, change from place to place, and the wire may change shape as it moves.

23. Faraday's Law

One of the earliest of Faraday's successful experiments on induction was to bring a coil of wire up to a magnetized bar of iron and slip the coil over the magnet. The ends of the coil of wire were connected to a galvanometer. As the coil approached the magnet, the galvanometer indicated that electromotive force was being induced.

Faraday also tried the converse of this experiment. Holding the coil still, he brought the magnet from a distance and slid it into the coil. The result on the galvanometer was exactly the same.

There is, in reality, no distinction between the two experiments. They are, in fact, merely two views of the same experiment.

Faraday formulated his experimental results in terms of flux linkages. When Faraday moved the coil toward the magnet he was moving it into a region of stronger magnetic field, and hence the number of flux linkages with the coil was increasing. When he moved the magnet toward the coil he increased flux linkages in exactly the same amount. The first experiment, moving the coil, could be accounted for in terms of a conductor moving through a magnetic field; but the second, in which the magnet was moved, could not. Faraday's law, to include both cases, says that the electromotive force induced in a coil or closed loop of wire is

$$e = -\frac{d\lambda}{dt} = -N\frac{d\Phi}{dt} \qquad (23\text{-}1)$$

where λ is the number of linkages of the magnetic flux with the loop of wire. That is, λ is the number of magnetic flux lines passing through a surface bounded by the loop.[*]

If a coil consists of more than one turn of wire, λ is conveniently

---

[*] See Reference 7B, or any book on electromagnetic theory, for a more precise statement.

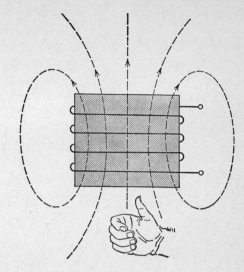

Figure 23a. Showing flux linkages: $\lambda = N\Phi = 20$.

visualized as the number of flux linkages with all the turns. The final form of equation 23-1 may then be used, in which Φ is the number of magnetic flux lines passing through a coil of N turns. As an example, Figure 23a shows a coil of wire of four turns, with five flux lines linking each turn. Thus N is 4, Φ is 5, and λ is 20.

Equation 23-1 is written with a negative sign. What is the meaning of this? The negative sign means that the electromotive force induced by an *increase* of magnetic flux linkages is *opposite* to the direction that would be given by the right-hand rule. That is, if the thumb of the right hand is pointed in the direction of positive rate of change of flux, the direction of induced electromotive force around the loop is *opposite* to the direction pointed by the fingers. And why is this negative? Merely because it is usual in science and mathematics to consider that the linear direction pointed by the right thumb and the direction-around-a-curve pointed by the fingers of the right hand are related by a positive sign; this is the accepted convention. The opposite relation, then, as met in Faraday's law of equation 23-1, requires a negative sign.†

---

† Lenz's well-known law is consistent with the negative sign in Faraday's law, as of course it would have to be. *Lenz's law* says, in effect, that if flux linkages with a coil are produced by current in the coil, and the flux linkages change because of a change in the amount of current, electromotive force induced by

(23)

As an illustration of the rule, if the flux in Figure 23a is increasing, and hence has a positive rate of change in an upward direction, the induced electromotive force is *opposite* to the direction pointed by the fingers sketched in the figure.

24. Comparison of Formulations

Faraday's law of induction, equation 23-1, is in agreement with the law that equates induced electromotive force to the rate of cutting flux. Consider again Figure 22a. The loop shown in that diagram is moving through a magnetic field and as a result of the motion there are more flux lines linking the loop after it has moved than there were before. Only a moment's consideration is needed to see that the net rate of cutting flux, when the whole periphery of the loop is considered, is identical with the rate of change of flux lines enclosed within the loop—the rate of change of flux linkages.

Thus we express electromotive force of motion in equation 21-7, and that caused by a changing field in equation 23-1. We show that these two equations give the same results in problems to which both are applicable.* We conclude that there is only one phenomenon of magnetic induction, though it may be formulated from different points of view.

In solving some problems, the concept of motional electromotive force is the more convenient, but for most the rate of change of flux linkages is the better method. It is possible to write a general expression for e, including both motion and change of field, but this becomes a bit unwieldy. For most problems the practical procedure is to compute e from the rate of change of flux linkages; or, if that method does not apply, to use the BlS equation.

25. A Warning

It is perhaps well to give explicit warning that the magnetic field, a condition of space, is not really as tangible as the usual concept of

---

the change of flux linkages is in a direction to oppose the change of current. Thus, if current increases, the induced electromotive force is *against* the current; if current decreases, the induced electromotive force *aids* the current.

* Though equation 23-1 is consistent with equation 21-7, it cannot be derived from that equation without either further experimental evidence, as given by Faraday, or the principle of restricted relativity. (See Art. 544 of Reference 24.)

flux lines seems to imply. In particular, it is dangerous to think of *moving* flux lines.

In a given region of space there is a certain magnetic field. Its strength or direction may change with time. The magnetic field can grow weaker in one place and stronger in another, but it is not advisable to think of magnetic flux lines as moving.

If a magnet is moved (relative to the observer), we should not think of flux lines that move with the magnet. Let us rather think of the field growing weaker in the region *from* which the magnet is moved, and stronger in the region *to* which the magnet is moved.*

It is true that many people like to think of flux lines moving. Men who work with rotating machinery often think in terms of flux lines that turn with the rotor of a machine. Men who work with plasmas of highly ionized gas speak of flux lines that are "frozen" into the moving plasma. Experience has shown these men that in many situations the concept of moving lines is safe and gives the right answers.

Other people, however, like to devise experimental situations in which this concept leads to wrong answers. The easiest way to evade such intellectual traps is to insist on thinking of electromotive force in terms of rate of change of flux linkages.

26. A Dynamic Phonograph Pickup

A type of pickup sometimes used on phonographs or record players to change mechanical motion into electromotive force is shown in Figure 26a. A permanent magnet has coaxial poles, shown shaded, to produce a magnetic field with radial lines of force in the annular

---

* This same warning is given by Page and Adams (page 330 of Reference 25A): "The concept of moving tubes of induction [lines of force] is one which should be avoided as it often leads to erroneous conclusions." A recent paper on the subject by D. L. Webster concludes even more firmly that "Altogether, relativity has no place for moving lines of force." (Reference 25B.)

The whole matter is involved in special relativity; measurements are to be made in the observer's frame of reference. Suppose there is an observer in a magnetic field. The field varies from place to place, but the observer has found by measurement that it is unchanging with time. He sees a loop of wire move past him through the field, and he attributes electromotive force induced in the loop to its motion through an unchanging field. Another observer is moving along with the loop (riding in the same car). For him the loop is stationary, but the magnetic field that this man observes is *changing* with time, so he attributes the same induction to a changing magnetic field linking a stationary loop.

space between the poles. We specify that the outer pole is north, the inner south, and hence the magnetic field is directed inward. A small, light coil of fine wire is held in this annular magnetic field; it is mounted on a light frame and is driven by a stylus to vibrate in a direction normal to the page. The stylus, in turn, is driven by the wavy groove in a phonograph record.

As the coil vibrates in the magnetic field, electromotive force is induced in the coil, and this appears as voltage at the terminals. This voltage is amplified and used to drive a speaker that reproduces the sound inscribed on the record.

Quantitatively, how much electromotive force is produced by a certain amplitude of vibration of the coil? The magnetic field strength (at the radius of the coil) is B. The total length of the fine wire that composes the coil is l (measured in meters), and the speed of motion of the coil (at any particular instant) is S (meters per second).

Since the coil moves perpendicularly to the magnetic field, and the wire is perpendicular to the field and to the motion, the simple BlS equation (equation 21-1) applies, and the electromotive force in volts is

$$e = BlS \tag{26-1}$$

Alternatively, equation 23-1 could be used to find the electromotive force in terms of the rate of change of flux linkages with the coil.

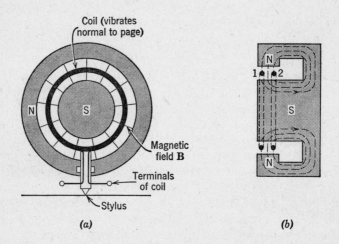

(a)   (b)

Figure 26. A "dynamic" phonograph pickup.

(26)

As the coil moves farther into the annular space, along the inner pole of the magnet (from position 1 to position 2 in Figure 26b), it surrounds more and more magnetic flux. The rate of increase of flux linkages is equal to the rate of cutting flux lines, which is BlS. Hence equation 26-1 can come from either equation 21-1 or equation 23-1.

Regarding direction of electromotive force, the convention given with equation 21-1 says that when the coil of Figure 26b is moving toward the *right*, and the field at the top of the coil is *down* (fingers curl from *right* to *down*), electromotive force is *in* at the top of the coil.

To use the convention of Section 24, note that when the coil of Figure 26b is moving toward the right, linkages with flux lines are increasing. Pointing the thumb toward the right (the direction of the increasing flux lines), the fingers of the right hand curl in a direction opposite to induced electromotive force. The fingers point out, and electromotive force is therefore *in* at the top of the coil. Thus it is seen that both conventions give the same result, as of course they must.

In this section the electromotive force induced in a "dynamic" phonograph pickup is computed. The result, equation 26-1, will be used in Section 149 in considering transfer functions of this device.

27. A Reluctance Phonograph Pickup

Another type of pickup device, called "reluctance" or "magnetic," is shown in Figure 27a. A small, light piece of soft iron is pivoted between the poles of a permanent magnet. In its neutral position, half way between poles, no magnetic flux traverses the soft iron vane from end to end, and hence no flux links the coil of the device. But as the vane is inclined to one side (or the other), so that the upper air gap on one side is shortened and the lower gap is lengthened (or vice versa), magnetic flux enters the vane at the top and travels downward (or upward). The vane is driven to vibrate about its pivot by the wavy grooves impressed in the phonograph record, and as it moves from side to side the magnetic flux in the vane changes in magnitude and direction in approximate proportion to the motion.

This change of magnetic flux linking the coil induces electromotive force in the coil, which is then amplified to operate a speaker. Note that the coil itself does *not* move, but the flux linkages with the coil are changing. Hence equation 23-1 is the appropriate equation to use.

(27)

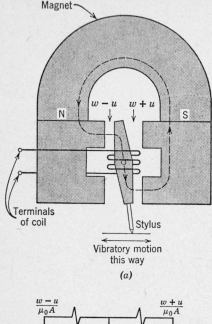

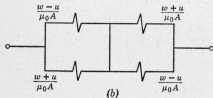

Figure 27. (*a*) A "magnetic" phonograph pickup. (*b*) The magnetic circuit of Figure 27*a*.

This is a problem for magnetic circuit methods (as reviewed in Appendix 1). The reluctance of the magnetic path is mainly in the air gaps. We shall consider that the iron part of the path has negligible reluctance, and that the magnetic potential across the air gaps, from pole face to pole face, has a value $\mathfrak{F}$ that is constant. Let us call the average length of each air gap w, and the displacement of the vane tip u; then as shown in the diagram the shorter gaps are $w - u$ and the longer gaps are $w + u$. The cross-sectional area of each gap is A; the permeability is $\mu_0 = 4\pi \cdot 10^{-7}$. Figure 27*b* shows the magnetic circuit diagrammatically, the reluctances being indicated.

Because of symmetry, magnetic potential difference across each half of the circuit is $\frac{1}{2}\mathfrak{F}$. Magnetic flux downward through the vane, the central member, is the difference between fluxes in the two unequal air gaps, and hence is

(27)

$$\Phi = \frac{\frac{1}{2}\mathfrak{F}}{(w-u)/\mu_0 A} - \frac{\frac{1}{2}\mathfrak{F}}{(w+u)/\mu_0 A} = \frac{\mu_0}{2}\mathfrak{F}A\left(\frac{1}{w-u} - \frac{1}{w+u}\right)$$

$$(27\text{-}1)$$

Assuming that u, the displacement, is small compared to w, the air-gap width (which may or may not be true), we may write as an approximation * of equation 27-1:

$$\Phi \approx \mu_0 \frac{\mathfrak{F}Au}{w^2}$$

$$(27\text{-}2)$$

We are interested in rate of change of flux linkages, so we differentiate equation 27-2 with respect to time. The only function of time in the right-hand member is u, so

$$\frac{d\lambda}{dt} = N\frac{d\Phi}{dt} = \mu_0 \frac{N\mathfrak{F}A}{w^2}\frac{du}{dt}$$

$$(27\text{-}3)$$

However, du/dt is the speed (meters/second) of an average point on the vane, and if this speed is called S we have

$$e = -\frac{d\lambda}{dt} = -\mu_0 \frac{N\mathfrak{F}AS}{w^2} \text{ volts}$$

$$(27\text{-}4)$$

This tells us that the electromotive force induced in the coil is (at least for small vibrations) proportional to the number of turns of the pickup coil N, the strength of the magnet, the area A of the pole faces, and inversely proportional to the square of the air-gap length w. These quantities are all constants determined by the design of the device. It is more interesting, however, in studying the operation of the pickup, to find that the induced electromotive force is proportional to S, the speed of motion of the vane.

Comparing equation 27-4 with 26-1, we find a similarity of form. Each is a constant times the speed of motion of the moving element. This means that the two pickup devices will respond in somewhat the same way over broad ranges of frequency, a similarity that is more apparent when transfer functions are discussed.†

---

* This approximation gives a linear relation between Φ and u, instead of the non-linear relation of equation 27-1. It is typical of the process that we later call "linearization."

† Ceramic and crystal pickups (piezoelectric) are used very commonly, for they give greater output voltage though perhaps less accurate reproduction than the magnetic types. The two magnetic types are analyzed in this chap-

28. A Rotating Generator

Electrical generators in which electromotive force is induced by mechanical motion in a magnetic field, or by a change of flux linkages with conductors or coils, can provide great amounts of eletrical energy. Most of the world's electrical power is produced in this way. Vibrating devices (as in the preceding paragraph) are useful for measurements and signals, but for handling large amounts of power rotating devices are used.

Figure 28a shows the basic principle of generators. The device is the same as the one used as a motor in Figure 16a; a cylindrical armature of iron rotates between stationary magnetic poles. A rectangular loop of copper wire is placed on this cylinder. The diagram shows one loop on the surface of the armature, but in practice there are many turns of wire and they are set into slots cut radially into the cylinder.*

Consider the loop of wire in Figure 28a. As the armature turns in the direction shown, the amount of magnetic flux that links through

---

ter because they are excellent examples of the two principles of magnetic induction.

* The armature is ordinarily not, in fact, a solid cylinder of iron, but a laminated cylinder of an appropriate iron alloy.

The iron alloy is chosen to give low magnetic reluctance. Also, in order to minimize hysteresis loss, it should have little tendency toward permanent magnetization. Each time the magnetization of iron is reversed, energy is lost in overcoming the residual magnetism left from its previous state. Hysteresis loss is important in d-c machines, for the magnetization of an armature is reversed twice in each rotation (of a two-pole machine), even though current in the external circuit is always in the same direction.

If an armature were of solid iron it would itself be a conductor, moving in a magnetic field. Electromotive force would be induced in it, and currents, called *eddy currents*, would flow, merely circulating in the iron, doing no good, wasting power, and heating the machine. Eddy currents are reduced to an economic minimum by making the armature of a stack of round sheets of iron alloy, clamped tightly together, instead of using a solid cylinder. There are thin layers of oxide or varnish between sheets. These insulating layers are perpendicular to the induced electromotive force, and hence prevent free circulation of eddy currents, but being parallel to the magnetic field they do not add appreciably to the magnetic reluctance of the machine.

Magnetic circuits in which flux is changing are nearly always made of thin sheets, or of powdered material pressed together. An alternative used at high radio frequency is an iron oxide that has high permeability and yet is a very poor conductor of electricity.

(28)

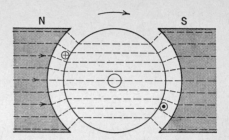

Figure 28a. Elements of a rotating generator.

the loop increases until the plane of the loop is normal to the direction of the flux lines. In this normal position (with the loop vertical) the flux linkages are maximum, and after this instant, as the cylinder continues to turn, the flux linkages decrease. Through half of each revolution of the cylinder the rate of change of flux linkages is positive, and through half of each revolution it is negative. As a result an alternating electromotive force is induced in the loop. This will not, in general, be a sinusoidal alternating electromotive force; a flattish wave like the one shown in Figure 28b is more usual.

Several important kinds of practical machines use the principle of Figure 28a. We should therefore consider how much electromotive force is induced in this device.

29. Average Electromotive Force

When the rotating loop is in the position that provides maximum flux linkages (that is, in the figure, when the plane of the rotating loop is vertical) the amount of magnetic flux linking with the loop may be called Φ. If there is a coil of N turns in which electromotive force is induced, and not just a single loop, the number of flux linkages is, at maximum, $N\Phi$. If the cylinder of the machine and the rotating coil (the rotor) turn at f revolutions per second, there is induced an alternating electromotive force with a frequency of f cycles per second. The flux linkages change from $N\Phi$ to zero in one-fourth of a cycle (while the machine turns through 90 degrees), so the *average* rate of change of flux linkages is $-4fN\Phi$. By Faraday's law of equation 23-1, the negative of this is the *average* electromotive force induced in the coil. During the quarter of a revolution

$$\text{Average } e = 4fN\Phi \qquad (29\text{-}1)$$

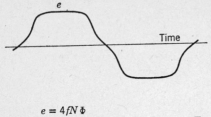

Figure 28b. The wave of electromotive force induced in one coil of an ordinary generator.

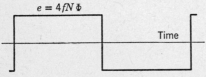

Figure 29a. An idealized rectangular form of generated wave.

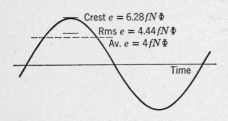

Figure 30a. An idealized sinusoidal form of generated wave.

If a machine were so designed that the wave of electromotive force was ideally rectangular, as indicated in Figure 29a, instead of the more realistic shape of Figure 28b, the electromotive force at each instant would have the average value given in equation 29-1, either positive or negative. Such a rectangular form cannot be achieved in fact, although it might be approximated by bringing the pole pieces of the generator quite close together, and having a small uniform air gap between the pole pieces and the rotating iron cylinder. However, the real value of equation 29-1 is its importance in connection with the design of d-c machines, as we see in Section 63.

30. Effective or Rms Electromotive Force

Some machines are designed to make the generated wave of electromotive force approximate a sine wave, more like the wave of Figure 30a than those of Figures 28b or 29a. This is done, as suggested in Figure 30b, by shaping the pole faces to provide a short air gap between pole and rotor at the middle of the pole face, thus giving maximum flux where the induced electromotive force is to be highest,

(30)

and increasing the air gap near the pole tips so that flux density and hence induced electromotive force diminish gradually toward zero.

Average induced electromotive force is dependent only on the maximum flux linked by the armature coil, and not on its distribution, as shown in deriving equation 29-1. The average of each half cycle of the induced wave is

$$\text{Average } e = 4fN\Phi \qquad (30\text{-}1)$$

and this formula applies to the sine wave of Figure 30a as well as to the waves of Figures 28b and 29a. It is well known from trigonometry or calculus that the maximum of a sine wave is greater than the average of the half cycle by a factor of $\pi/2$, so if the induced wave of electromotive force is sinusoidal its maximum value is

$$\text{Maximum } e = 2\pi fN\Phi = 6.28fN\Phi \qquad (30\text{-}2)$$

With most alternating voltages and currents, however, the most useful measure is neither the maximum nor the average, but the root-mean-square (rms) or effective value. The rms value of any sinusoidal wave is equal to the maximum divided by $\sqrt{2}$, so for the sine wave of induced electromotive force,

$$\text{Rms } e = \sqrt{2}\,\pi fN\Phi = 4.44fN\Phi \qquad (30\text{-}3)$$

This is an important equation for a-c machine design, as will be seen in Section 89.

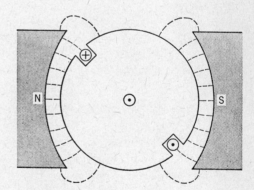

Figure 30b. Poles shaped to produce an approximately sinusoidal flux distribution.

(30)

31. Bilateral Operation

Since the motor of Figure 15a and the generator of Figure 28a are the same device, it is clear that the one machine can be either a motor or a generator. Indeed, it is both at the same time.

Consider the machine running as a motor for the purpose of driving a mechanical load of some kind. With the armature turning in the magnetic field of the machine, an electromotive force is being induced in the armature winding. Thus there is generator action in a motor. The electromotive force thus generated is in a direction to *oppose* the armature current that is causing the motor to turn; hence it is called the *counter electromotive force* of the motor. Voltage applied to the motor terminals, supplying electric power to the motor, must be great enough to overcome both the resistance of the armature winding and also the counter electromotive force induced within the motor. The amount of electric power converted by the motor to mechanical power is the product of the armature current and this induced counter electromotive force. It will be seen that behavior of a motor cannot be understood unless its simultaneous action as a generator is taken into account.

Similarly, when a machine is being used as a generator, supplying electricity to some circuit connected to its terminals, there is a magnetic torque developed within it. The load current flows in the armature winding of the machine, and this current, in the magnetic field of the machine, causes a torque to be exerted on the armature. This torque, although similar to motor torque, is in a direction to *oppose* the rotation of the machine. The prime mover that drives the generator must apply enough torque to the shaft to overcome friction and also this internal torque that is produced within the machine. The amount of mechanical power converted to electrical power by the generator is the product of the speed of rotation and the internal torque. Thus, analysis of generator operation requires simultaneous consideration of its action as a motor.

It is a general principle that a device that will convert electrical energy to mechanical (a transducer) will also convert mechanical energy to electrical. The motor and generator illustrate this principle. As another example, the speaker shown in Figure 13a and the phonograph pickup of Figures 26a and b are clearly similar. In each a coil vibrates in a magnetic field.

(31)

In the speaker, current in the voice coil provides energy to drive the cone. But if vibratory energy were supplied to the cone, forcing the coil to vibrate in the magnetic field, it would then have electromotive force induced in it and electrical energy could be delivered from the coil. (Instead of acting, in its normal manner, as a motor, it would then be acting as a generator.) As a matter of fact, a speaker can be used in just this way to serve as a microphone. One device can be made to serve as both microphone and speaker, and this is done in some telephone and "intercom" services, stenographic recording machines, and such.

This principle of reversibility will be given more careful attention in the next chapter. It is related to conservation of energy as energy is converted within the device.

32. Summary

There is force on the electrons in a metal conductor when the metal is moved in a magnetic field. This force tends to drive the electrons through the metal, and results in *electromotive force* (or electromotance).

With a mutually perpendicular geometry, electromotive force is given by the BlS law (the Blv law).

This motional electromotive force can also be equated to the *rate of cutting flux.*

For a closed circuit, electromotive force is given by *Faraday's law* in terms of the rate of change of flux linkages (equation 23-1). The two formulations are different expressions of the same phenomenon. Problems may be solved by using either formula. Faraday's law (equation 23-1) is recommended for practical use whenever it is applicable.

The *direction* of electromotive force is found from the right-hand rule (Section 21) or from a rule related to Lenz's law (Section 23).

Magnetic field is by definition related to the observer's frame of reference; other interpretations are dangerous.

Described as examples are a phonograph pickup device in which a coil moves in a magnetic field, a reluctance pickup device in which flux linkages with a stationary coil are made to change, and a rotating device that is the basic element of electric generators. Expressions are obtained for electromotive force developed in each of these devices.

(32)

An electromechanical energy converter is bilateral; it converts energy either way. This principle is given attention in the next chapter.

PROBLEMS

3-1. A wire 1 m long and 0.20 cm in diameter is moving at a speed of 15 m/sec normally through a magnetic field in which $B = 0.20$ weber/m^2. There are $5 \cdot 10^{22}$ free electrons per cubic centimeter of the material of the wire. The charge of an electron is $-1.59 \cdot 10^{-19}$ coulomb. (*a*) What electromotive force is induced in the wire? (*b*) What is the force on each electron in the wire? (*c*) How much energy is imparted to each electron while moving the length of the wire? (*d*) Ends of the wire are connected through an external circuit, and the total resistance of the circuit is 1.0 ohm. How much current flows? (*e*) What is the average speed of drift of electrons about the circuit? (*f*) How long does it take a coulomb to pass a point in the circuit?   **(Sec. 20)**

3-2. Michael Faraday tried to measure the average speed of flow of the Thames river at London by finding the electromotive force induced in the moving water by the earth's magnetic field. (Polarization of the electrodes probably caused his failure.) Derive a formula that he might have used. Put numerical values into your formula to find the number of millivolts he might have expected to measure if the average speed of flow was 1.0 m/sec and the distance between electrodes in the river was 100 m. (Any change in the earth's magnetic field in the last century or so may be neglected.)   **(Sec. 22)**

3-3. The figure shows a cross section of a duct that is electrically nonconducting. Water flows along the duct (perpendicular to the page). The duct is 5 by 10 cm. Magnetic field is produced across the duct, with $B = 0.6$ weber/m^2. (*a*) In terms of the speed of the water, how much voltage will appear between electrodes set into the duct? (*b*) How much magnetomotive force is required to produce B?

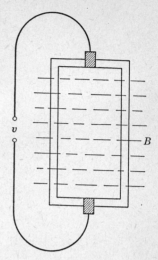

Problem 3-3

(c) Discuss whether this seems to be a practical means of measuring water flow.

(Sec. 22)

3-4. A Hibbert magnetic standard is a permanent magnet of the form shown in the figure. A circular coil is allowed to drop completely through a radial magnetic field. This produces an electro-

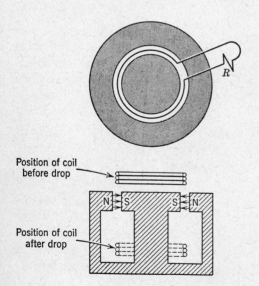

Position of coil before drop

Position of coil after drop

Problem 3-4

motive force that causes current in the coil and in the external circuit connected to the coil. If the coil of radius a has N turns, and the total flux crossing the air gap is Φ, and the resistance of the electric circuit including the coil is R, calculate the electric charge (that is, $\int i\, dt$) that passes through the external circuit when the coil is dropped. Show the direction of flow. (Any reasonable assumptions may be made if desired, but none are necessary. The result is independent of dimensions, speed, shape, or time.)   **(Sec. 23)**

3-5. Electromotive force is induced in a coil of 1,000 turns of fine copper wire. Sketch flux through the coil as a function of time to

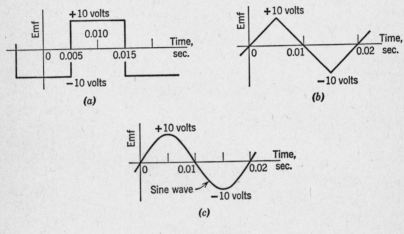

Problem 3-5

induce the three waves of electromotive force shown in the figure, and indicate numerical values.   **(Sec. 23)**

3-6. The movement of a d-c milliammeter is shown in Figure 14a. The effective axial length of the conductors of the coil is 2.5 cm, and the average diameter of the coil is 2.5 cm. The magnetic flux density in the air gap is radial and $B = 0.10$ weber/m^2 at the coil. The current is 10 ma. (a) Find the number of turns of wire required to produce a torque of $2\cdot10^{-5}$ newton-meter. (b) Which direction must current flow to move the pointer to the right? (c) In turning to a new position the coil moves upscale at the rate of 90 degrees in $\frac{1}{4}$ sec. How much electromotive force is being induced in each turn of the coil? How much in the entire coil? In which direction?   **(Sec. 23)**

3-7. An airplane with a wingspread of 125 ft flies north at 600 miles/hr. The magnetic field of the earth in the vicinity of the plane has a horizontal component of $0.25 \cdot 10^{-4}$ weber/m^2, and the field is inclined 60 degrees from the horizontal. What electromotive force is induced by magnetic field as measured by a passenger in the plane? As measured by an observer with a voltmeter on the ground, if this were possible?   **(Sec. 25)**

3-8. A phonograph pickup is as in Figure 26a. The amplitude of vibration is 0.01 cm (each way from neutral); the frequency is 256 cycles/sec. The coil has 10 turns, the length of each turn being 2.0 cm, and $B = 0.10$ weber/m^2. What is the maximum of the induced electromotive force wave? What is its rms value?   **(Sec. 26)**

3-9. A car with metal wheels and a metal axle travels at 50 meters/sec on a railroad track. The rails are 145 cm apart, and are insulated from each other and from ground. The magnetic field of the earth is $0.60 \cdot 10^{-4}$ weber/m^2 in a direction that is 30 degrees from vertical. The track is level and runs toward the magnetic east. (a) A rider connects a voltmeter in the car from one wheel to the other. Assuming no appreciable current is drawn by the voltmeter, what does it read? (b) A man standing on the ground connects a voltmeter from one track to the other. Assuming no appreciable current is drawn by the voltmeter, what does he read as the car passes?

(Sec. 26)

ENERGY RELATIONS
chapter 4

33. Energy Balance

It was easy, in Chapter 2, to find the force on a conductor carrying current in a uniform magnetic field provided the field was not distorted by the presence of ferromagnetic material such as iron. But when we tried finding force on a winding laid in slots in an iron armature the problem was too difficult; the Bli law became unworkable.

Then we turned, in Chapter 3, to the electromotive force generated in a moving conductor. The BlS law could be used in many cases, but when the mathematics became unmanageable there was available another relation, Faraday's law, that related the induced electromotive force to the rate of change of flux linkages.

Now we shall see that Faraday's law can be used in the former situation, too, to find mechanical force on a conductor carrying current, when the Bli law is intractable. To do this we need a new relationship between the mechanical quantities, such as force, and the electrical quantities, such as current and voltage. This new relationship, this bridge between the mechanical and electrical sides of a device, is furnished by the principle of conservation of energy.

The general idea is that we compute the mechanical output of a machine by knowing its electrical input. If every machine were ideal, so that the mechanical power output from it would be equal to its electrical power input, the torque of the machine could be found by merely equating output to input. In fact, however, some of the input energy may remain in the device, either in storage, or as irrecoverable heat. Let us be completely general and make a statement to take care of the possibility of energy remaining within the machine.

(33)

Energy may be stored as kinetic energy in the moving parts of the mechanical system, or as potential energy in stretched springs and such, or as energy stored in the magnetic and electric fields of the device. Also, some energy is lost as heat, in mechanical friction or in electrical resistance. To include all these possibilities we write an *energy-balance* equation:

$$\begin{bmatrix} \text{Energy put into an electro-} \\ \text{mechanical device on the} \\ \text{mechanical side} \end{bmatrix} + \begin{bmatrix} \text{Energy put in on} \\ \text{the electrical} \\ \text{side} \end{bmatrix}$$

$$= \begin{bmatrix} \text{Increase of stored} \\ \text{kinetic or poten-} \\ \text{tial mechanical en-} \\ \text{ergy in the device} \end{bmatrix} + \begin{bmatrix} \text{Increase of energy} \\ \text{stored in the elec-} \\ \text{tric and magnetic} \\ \text{fields of the device} \end{bmatrix} + \begin{bmatrix} \text{Energy} \\ \text{changed into} \\ \text{heat in the} \\ \text{device} \end{bmatrix}$$

$$(33\text{-}1)$$

The two left-hand terms relate to energy fed in from *outside the device*, to energy resulting from mechanical force applied by an *external* mechanical system, or voltage applied from an *external* circuit. The three right-hand terms refer to energy retained within the device.

This energy-balance equation is written to apply to either generators or motors. For a generator in ordinary use, the first term, energy put in mechanically, is a large quantity; the second term, energy put in electrically, is almost equally large, but negative, for electrical power is given *out* from a generator, not put *in*. Thus a large positive term, and a negative term that is nearly as large, usually appear on the left-hand side of the equation.

For a motor, consuming electrical energy and producing mechanical energy, the first term is negative. The second term, electrical energy input, is positive and somewhat larger. Again the left-hand side of the equation is usually small and positive.

The right-hand side has three terms that are ordinarily small and may be zero. The first, a change of stored mechanical energy, typically represents the change of kinetic energy that results from changing speed, for there is no potential mechanical energy in an ordinary generator or motor. In the second term, a change of current might affect the amount of energy stored in magnetic fields; there are no significant electric fields in the ordinary machine. Friction loss, friction with the air (called windage), hysteresis and eddy-current loss in the iron, and resistance loss in the armature winding comprise the third term.

(33)

For examples of the energy-balance method we can return to a computation of the torque on a conductor that is set in a slot in the armature of a generator.

34. The Slotted Armature

The problem of a conductor in a slot can now be approached with the aid of an energy balance. Consider an armature coil. The conductors may be *either* on the surface of the armature, as in Figure 28a, or in slots as in Figure 30b. The average induced electromotive force is given by equation 29-1 as

$$\text{Average } e = 4fN\Phi = \frac{2\Omega N\Phi}{\pi} \tag{34-1}$$

and this, derived from Faraday's law, is valid whether the coil is on the surface or in slots. In this equation, f is the number of revolutions per second, Ω the number of radians per second, N the number of turns of the armature coil, and Φ the maximum flux to link the armature coil.

To keep signs correct, we draw Figure 34a. Reference arrows are shown. The directions of the reference arrows are arbitrary, but arrows for v and i are so chosen that electric power at the terminals is *input* to the machine; this makes the diagram consistent with the energy balance equation. A reference arrow for direction of speed of rotation Ω and applied torque T is also shown. Since reference directions for Ω and T are in the same direction, *positive* mechanical power is power *input*.

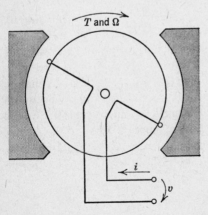

Figure 34a. Reference arrows for v and i, consistent with equation 34-2, show:

    Electrical power input = vi
    Mechanical power input = $T\Omega$

where T is torque exerted *on* rotor.

(34)

In this example, since the machine is being operated as a generator, mechanical power is in fact input, and is positive; thus T is in the same direction as Ω for they must have the same sign. Electrical power, however, is in fact output, so the mathematical expression for *electrical input* must be a negative quantity. Since this electrical input is vi, either v or i must be negative and hence against the arrow of Figure 34a. Actually, current reverses when the machine is running as a generator, so let us consider that i is a negative quantity in this example.

We now write the left-hand side of the energy-balance equation. Mechanical energy input in the short time dt is $T\Omega\,dt$. Electrical input in the same short time is $vi\,dt$. Then

$$\begin{bmatrix} \text{Mech.} \\ \text{input} \end{bmatrix} + \begin{bmatrix} \text{Elect.} \\ \text{input} \end{bmatrix} = \begin{bmatrix} \text{Mech.} \\ \text{storage} \end{bmatrix} + \begin{bmatrix} \text{Field} \\ \text{storage} \end{bmatrix} + \begin{bmatrix} \text{Heat} \end{bmatrix}$$

$$T\Omega\,dt \;+\; vi\,dt \;=\; 0 \;+\; 0 \;+\; 0 \qquad (34\text{-}2)$$

The machine in question is assumed to be running at steady speed so there is no increase in mechanical storage of energy. Voltage and current are not changing so there is no change of energy storage in the electric or magnetic fields. Assume in this example that the machine has negligible electrical resistance and negligible friction or windage of a mechanical nature, so heat is zero. With these assumptions the three terms on the right-hand side of the equation are all zero. (The next section considers the situation that actually exists, taking into account the fact that resistance and friction cannot really be zero.)

The torque required to turn this ideal generator is now found by solving the energy balance of equation 34-2:

$$T = -\frac{vi}{\Omega} \qquad (34\text{-}3)$$

Since, with generator action, the current is a negative quantity, torque is positive.

Now, since there is no resistance in the generator winding, and hence no voltage drop, the terminal voltage v is equal to the induced electromotive force e; that is, $v = e$. The equation for torque can therefore be written

$$T = -\frac{ei}{\Omega} \qquad (34\text{-}4)$$

(34)

Finally, equation 34-1 for average e is introduced into equation 34-4, and the result is average torque:

$$\text{Average } T = -\frac{2N\Phi i}{\pi} \tag{34-5}$$

We are now able to draw the conclusion toward which we have been working. Equation 34-5 applies to a coil either on the armature surface or in a slot. Since it applies to either, and gives the torque for either, the torque must be the same for both. Hence we come to the simple and possibly surprising conclusion that putting the armature coils into slots neither increases nor decreases the torque of the motor. If they are on the surface, torque is exerted on the conductors; if in slots, the torque is on the armature teeth. The amount of torque is the same in both cases.

This conclusion is confirmed by comparing equation 34-5 with 17-3, for (except for the reversal of sign that follows from considering electrical input instead of output) these are seen to be identical. It will be recalled that these two equations were derived by totally different arguments.

35. Losses

In this example, consideration of loss has been avoided. In equation 34-4 we let $v = e$, assuming no resistance in the generator winding. But v and e are different quantities: v is voltage at the machine terminals and e is the induced electromotive force. The difference between vi and ei is the power that goes into i^2R loss in the armature winding, part of the eddy-current and hysteresis loss in the armature, and a few other minor losses, in all of which electrical energy is changed into heat.

There are losses on the mechanical side of the device, too. Torque is required to overcome friction, as with the bearings, and windage, which is air friction, and other small losses. In these losses, also, energy is changed into heat, and because of these losses the torque developed magnetically by the machine is not quite the same as the torque at the machine's shaft.

These electrical and mechanical losses comprise the last item, "heat," in the energy balance. To provide this heat it is evident that a quantity of energy exactly equal to these losses appears on the left-hand or input side of the energy-balance equation, for either the electrical input or the mechanical input must be increased by the amount of the losses to provide for the energy they turn to heat.

In the complete energy balance, therefore, one side has a term for the "energy changed into heat," and on the other side there are the true electrical input and the true mechanical input energies. Formulation of this complete energy balance requires writing an item for losses on one side and writing on the other side the total energy input at the terminals and at the shaft.

But if we are willing to simplify the energy balance (and we usually are), equal quantities may be omitted from both sides. Then the term for "heat" is set equal to zero, and on the other side of the equation the electrical losses are subtracted from electrical energy input, and the mechanical losses are subtracted from mechanical energy input, before the equation is written. In this way losses are omitted from the equation, and the resulting energy balance, without losses, is easier to write and easier to solve. This is an alternative means of solution, and of course neither method will give the final answer to a practical problem until the actual losses are either known, or estimated, or neglected.

36. Energy Storage

Any magnetic device has more or less energy stored in the magnetic field. If the amount of stored energy is not changing it probably need not be considered. In the determination of armature torque with constant current there was no necessity to consider the stored energy of the machine's magnetic field. Similarly, with constant speed there was no need to take into account the kinetic energy of rotation of the armature. These merely remain constant. In some devices, however, the change of stored energy is not only significant—it may constitute the whole problem.

There are many formulas for stored energy, all no doubt familiar to the reader. A number of them are listed for convenience in Table 36-I. The formulas of this table assume linearity of the systems involved: that is, for the magnetic formulas permeability and inductance must be constant; for the mechanical energy of a spring, the strain must be proportional to stress, and so on. At first thought this seems a serious limitation on the computation of magnetic energy, but in fact it is only a minor inconvenience. Since the magnetic circuits of electromechanical devices have air gaps (to permit mechanical motion) and since the energy density in air is hundreds

(36)

Table 36-I. Energy in Linear Systems

(Energy is in joules = watt-seconds = newton-meters = $\mathrm{kg \cdot m^2/sec^2}$)

Energy in the magnetic field [a]

$$\text{Energy} = \tfrac{1}{2}i\lambda = \tfrac{1}{2}Li^2$$

i is current (amp)
λ is flux linkages (webers)
L is inductance (henrys) (not a function of i)

$$= \tfrac{1}{2}\mathcal{F}\Phi = \tfrac{1}{2}\mathcal{R}\Phi^2$$

$\mathcal{F}$ is magnetomotive force (ampere-turns)
Φ is flux in a magnetic circuit (webers)
$\mathcal{R}$ is reluctance (amp/weber)

Magnetic energy density (joules/m³)

$$\text{Density} = \tfrac{1}{2}BH = \tfrac{1}{2}\mu H^2$$

B is magnetic flux density (webers/m²)
H is magnetic intensity (amp/m)

$$= \tfrac{1}{2}B^2/\mu$$

μ is permeability (henrys/m)
(not a function of B)
For air, $\mu = \mu_0 = 4\pi \cdot 10^{-7}$

Energy in the electric field

$$\text{Energy} = \tfrac{1}{2}Cv^2$$

C is capacitance (farads)
v is voltage (volts)

Electric energy density (joules/m³)

$$\text{Density} = \tfrac{1}{2}DE = \tfrac{1}{2}\varepsilon E^2$$

D is electric flux density (cmb/m²)
E is electric intensity (volt/m)

$$= \tfrac{1}{2}D^2/\varepsilon$$

ε is dielectric constant (farad/m)

Mechanical kinetic energy

$$\text{Energy} = \tfrac{1}{2}mS^2$$

m is mass (kg)
S is speed (m/sec)

$$= \tfrac{1}{2}J\Omega^2$$

J is moment of inertia (kg·m²)
Ω is angular velocity (radians/sec)

Mechanical potential energy

With constant force (e.g., gravitation):

$$\text{Energy} = wF$$

F is force (newtons)
w is distance of motion (m)

With force proportional to displacement (e.g., elastic deformation of a spring):

$$\text{Energy} = \tfrac{1}{2}wF = \tfrac{1}{2}cF^2$$

c is elastic compliance (m/newton)

---

[a] Appendix 1 gives a short discussion of magnetic circuits. Appendix 4 gives units and dimensions.

or thousands of times that in iron with the same flux density, most of the energy storage of the system is ordinarily in the air gap even though the iron may occupy much more volume. Hence it is often possible to neglect energy storage in the iron, giving attention to that in the air gap where all relations are strictly linear and the formulas of the table apply.

The possibility of neglecting energy storage in the iron is illustrated in the following example.

37. Virtual Displacement

A magnetic device often used as a switch-operating mechanism (known as a *contactor*) and typical of devices used for many control operations is shown in Figure 37a. The pivoted armature is normally in the "open" position shown, and there is no current in the coil. To operate, current is passed through the coil and the armature is magnetically drawn inward to close the air gap. How much force is exerted by the armature?

We wish to find the force when the armature is at the indicated position, and our problem does not require that we consider an actual motion of the contactor. The method, however, requires a balance of energies, and energy results only from some amount of motion, however small. Therefore we suppose that our armature moves, but only through a differentially short distance dw. It is not necessary that the armature actually move, for the force is the same, but the supposition gives a means of finding an energy balance. It is called the method of *virtual displacement*.

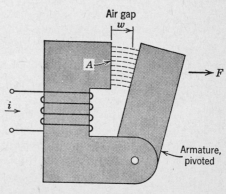

Figure 37a. An electromagnet.

(37)

38. An Electromagnet

We assume that flux in the magnetic circuit is held unchanged during motion of the armature by adjusting the coil current. This assumption makes the problem easier for it means that there is no induced electromotive force, $N \, d\Phi/dt$ being zero as the magnet moves. Also, let us suppose that motion takes place slowly, the armature being restrained from rapid motion by a string tied to it, or in some other manner. The force exerted on the armature by this string we shall call F; the string is relaxed to permit the armature to move through the distance dw.

We now begin to write an energy balance. The first term is mechanical energy input, which is the product of force and distance, $F \, dw$. Motion is in fact from right to left, and force is exerted by the string from left to right, so the energy input $F \, dw$ is a negative quantity.* This means that there is actually energy output; work is done *by* the armature *on* the string. When we write $F \, dw$ for the first term of the energy-balance equation, we recognize that this represents a negative number.

$$\begin{bmatrix} \text{Mech.} \\ \text{input} \end{bmatrix} + \begin{bmatrix} \text{Elect.} \\ \text{input} \end{bmatrix} = \begin{bmatrix} \text{Mech.} \\ \text{storage} \end{bmatrix} + \begin{bmatrix} \text{Field} \\ \text{storage} \end{bmatrix} + \begin{bmatrix} \text{Heat} \end{bmatrix}$$

$$F \, dw \quad + \quad ri^2 \, dt \quad = \quad 0 \quad + \frac{B^2}{2\mu_0} A \, dw \; + \; ri^2 \, dt \qquad (38\text{-}1)$$

Electrical power input to the device is vi, the product of terminal voltage and current in the coil. In this example let us *not* neglect resistance, or avoid its consideration. Since flux in the magnetic circuit is unchanging, there is no electromotive force induced in the coil, and terminal voltage is equal to the resistance drop; that is, $v = ri$. Input power is therefore $vi = ri^2$, and if dt is the time required

---

* To keep signs correct: draw an arbitrary reference arrow (drawn from left to right in Figure 37a). If force F is *applied to* a body in the direction of this arrow, F is a positive number; if in the opposite direction, negative. If motion is in the arrow direction, distance (w or dw) is a positive number; if in the opposite direction, negative. The algebraic product (as $F \, dw$) is energy *input* to the body; if the product is a negative number, the body is in fact giving out energy. In the present example F is a positive quantity, dw is a negative quantity, and $F \, dw$ is therefore a negative quantity.

for the motion dw to take place, input energy is $ri^2\,dt$. This is the second term of the energy-balance equation.

All this input energy, being lost in resistance, is transformed into heat in the device. Hence the last term on the right-hand side is also $ri^2\,dt$. These two equal quantities are entered in the energy balance of equation 38-1 as term 2 on the left and term 3 on the right. They cancel and, as explained in Section 35, both could have been left out without invalidating the balance.

The first term of the right-hand member has to do with mechanical stored energy. Since speed of motion is held to be very small, kinetic energy of motion is negligible; and since there are no springs or elastic members and no motion against gravity, there is no potential energy change. Hence this term is zero.

The second term on the right-hand side then remains. Clearly energy stored in the magnetic field of the device is going to change. We assume that permeability of the iron is so high that practically all the stored energy is in the air gap. Also, we neglect fringing of flux and accept the simple pattern of Figure 37a, with uniform magnetic energy density. Then from Table 36-I the energy density in the air gap before motion of the armature is uniformly $B^2/2\mu_0$. Volume of the air gap is Aw, A being area of the pole face and w width of air gap. The total amount of energy stored in the air gap is therefore $B^2AW/2\mu_0$.

When the armature has moved from width w to its new width $w + dw$, the volume is changed to $A\,(w + dw)$. The change of energy stored in the magnetic field as the armature moves through the distance dw is the difference, the new energy minus the former.

$$\text{Field storage} = \frac{B^2A}{2\mu_0}\,(w + dw) - \frac{B^2A}{2\mu_0}\,w = \frac{B^2A}{2\mu_0}\,dw \quad (38\text{-}2)$$

We insert this expression in the energy balance as the increase of stored energy. Since dw is a negative number (in a direction opposite to the reference arrow of Figure 37a) the change of volume in the air gap is negative, and this expression for the change of energy stored in the air gap is negative also. It represents a *decrease* of energy in the magnetic field, as we know it should.

The energy balance of equation 38-1 is now complete. It tells us that

$$F\,dw = \frac{B^2}{2\mu_0}\,A\,dw \quad (38\text{-}3)$$

(38)

whence
$$F = \frac{AB^2}{2\mu_0} \tag{38-4}$$

where F is force (newtons) exerted on the armature by the string

A is area of the pole face (meters^2)

B is magnetic flux density in the air gap (webers/meter^2)

μ_0 is the air-gap permeability, $4\pi \cdot 10^{-7}$

This is an expression for force in terms of B, but we want force in terms of current. Assuming that permeability of the iron is so high that practically all the magnetomotive force Ni is used in producing magnetic potential difference across the air gap, we equate Ni to Hw, H being magnetic intensity and w the width of the gap. In the air gap, $B = \mu_0 H$, so

$$Ni = Hw = \frac{Bw}{\mu_0} \tag{38-5}$$

whence
$$B = \frac{\mu_0 Ni}{w} \tag{38-6}$$

Introducing this into equation 38-4 gives

$$F = \frac{\mu_0}{2} \frac{AN^2 i^2}{w^2} \tag{38-7}$$

in which the new symbols are

N = number of turns in the operating coil

i = current in the operating coil (amperes)

w = width of the air gap (meters)

To see how this works out with numerical values, let us consider a design for such a contactor. An operating current of 10 amperes in a coil of 300 turns on an iron core of 4 square centimeters cross-sectional area (something less than an inch square) would be reasonable for a device of medium size. Let the armature be 1 centimeter from the pole face. If we consider the pivoted construction, this can only be an average value, but it will serve for this computation. Putting these numbers into equation 38-7 the force turns out to be 22.6 newtons, which is something like 5 pounds. The purpose for which the device is to be used must determine whether this amount of force is suitable. This is the force with which the device starts to operate; as the armature closes the air gap the flux density will in fact increase (contrary to our assumption) and the force will become much greater.

(38)

Before accepting this design it is necessary to find whether the value of B that results from these dimensions is safely below the saturation value for iron or steel of an appropriate quality. Computed from equation 38-6, B is 0.377 weber/meter². The magnetic circuit of this device will be made of steel laminations from steel sheets or plates. The maximum permeability of sheet steel (transformer steel) and of many other magnetic alloys is reached at a flux density between one-half and one weber per square meter, so the value of 0.377 is certainly not too high. Indeed it is rather low, and this suggests that the device might be designed more economically. (See Figures 5a, b, and c in Appendix 1.)

39. Pressure at a Boundary

The work in the preceding section can be generalized. If each side of equation 38-4 is divided by A, the area, we have

$$\frac{F}{A} = \frac{B^2}{2\mu_0} \tag{39-1}$$

and this equates force per unit area, which may be called **pressure**, to the magnetic energy density in the air gap:

$$\text{Magnetic pressure} = \text{Energy density} \tag{39-2}$$

This is a general relation which suggests the following concept.

There is pressure on a surface between two regions of different permeability in a magnetic field. The simple statement of equation 39-2 assumes that there is infinite permeability in one region (hence no energy density in that region) and that B in the other region is normal to the surface (which it will be at a boundary between finite and infinite permeability).

Picture a piece of iron of any shape in a magnetic field. The field pattern is affected by the presence of the iron, and where flux lines enter the iron they are practically normal to the surface. Figure 12b is one possible example; Figure 27a is another; so, of course, is Figure 37a. All over its surface the iron is being sucked into the air space by a magnetic pressure. The amount of this pressure on any part of the iron surface is equal to the energy density in the air at that part of the surface, and hence is proportional to the square of the magnetic flux density.

For actual iron these statements are not exact, although if the permeability is high they are excellent approximations, and in any

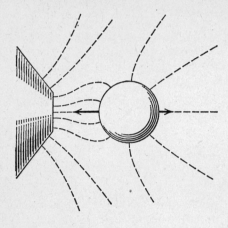

Figure 39a. Pressure at iron-air boundary moves a ball of iron toward a magnet pole.

case they lead to a useful mental picture of mechanical force on iron in a magnetic field. In Figure 12b, for instance, the left end of the bar is sucked up while the right end is sucked down, so there is a torque tending to turn the bar into a position parallel with the magnetic field. Also, the bar is stretched lengthwise, but there is no net translational force.

If this magnetic field were of such a pattern that it was stronger at one end of the bar than at the other, the bar would be sucked more strongly into the region of greater energy density, and hence there would be a net translational force and the bar would tend to move sideways as well as turning.

As another example, the ball of iron near the pole of a magnet in Figure 39a is drawn toward that pole, into the region of greatest energy density at the pole face, because the suction is greater on that side of the ball than on the other. If the same ball were placed in a field that was uniform before the ball was placed in it, giving a symmetrical pattern with the ball in place, the pressures would be symmetrical and the ball would not tend to move (although it might be imperceptibly stretched).

Another helpful concept, obviously related to this idea of energy density, is that the force on a small particle of iron in a magnetic field is proportional to the product of the magnetic intensity and the rate of change of the magnetic intensity (in space). Hence a field must not only be strong to exert a large force, but it must also be rapidly diverging.

Mathematical formulation of the general principle of pressure at a boundary is not attempted here. But the simple relation of equa-

(39)

tion 39-2 is surely plausible when it is considered that the motion of iron into a magnetic field in air results in wiping out the magnetic energy stored in the field in air. Where does this energy go? It reappears as mechanical energy of the iron, accounting for the tendency of the iron to move. If, on the other hand, the iron is forcibly moved in the direction in which it does not want to go, the opposite energy conversion takes place.

40. Soft-Iron Instruments

A practical example of magnetic force on a soft-iron boundary is found in the movement of an ordinary a-c ammeter or voltmeter. Such instruments are designed and produced in a number of quite different styles, but in all of them the current to be measured passes through a coil and a soft-iron element moves in the magnetic field produced by the current.*

One type of iron vane movement is shown diagrammatically in Figure 40a. Two thin strips of soft iron within a coil are magnetized by the current, and a force results that tends to drive these vanes apart. One vane is fastened rigidly; the other is on a pivoted arm, free to turn, but restrained by a spiral spring. A pointer attached to the pivoted arm shows, by its position on a scale, the amount of current in the coil.

It is easy to see that the ends of both vanes of iron will be magnetized alike. Both upper ends will be north poles when current is in one direction, and both become south poles when current has reversed. With current in either direction the vanes repel each other. But how much?

Figure 40b is a view looking down on the tops of the vanes. The magnetic field is shown as seen from above looking down. Only the horizontal component shows in this view, but that is enough, for only the horizontal component is effective in producing the force in which we are interested. Note that there is practically no magnetic field between the vanes if they are close together. The movable vane on the left has a magnetic field at its left-hand surface. Hence there is a force pulling it in this direction, whereas on its right-hand surface there is little force to pull in the opposite direction. The amount of force can be found from equation 39-1 if the magnetic flux density and the dimensions of the vane are known.

---

* See, for instance, Chapter 10 of Harris (Reference 40).

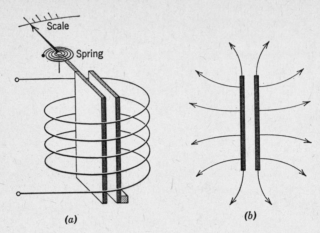

Figure 40. (*a*) A soft-iron vane ammeter. When current flows the vanes repel each other. (*b*) Flux lines radiating from vanes, as seen looking down on the top of Figure 40*a*.

It is not easy to compute magnetic flux density at the surface of the vane, but an approximate solution (perhaps graphical) is quite possible. In this discussion we do not attempt such a solution, but we can nevertheless deduce some interesting and important relations.

1. Force on the vane is in the same direction regardless of the direction of current; hence the instrument is deflected by either direct or alternating current.

2. Force is proportional to B^2. Since B is proportional to current, the deflection of the instrument is determined by the square of the current. With alternating current, average torque is determined by the average of the instantaneous current squared, and the instrument is inherently an rms ammeter.

3. Since the magnetic force is proportional to the square of current, and the restoring force of the spiral spring is proportional to displacement, the scale of the ammeter will be compressed at the lower end and will spread out for higher values of current (approximately a "square scale").

4. However, as the vanes move apart there will be more magnetic field in the space between vanes, reducing the torque at large spacings, for there will be magnetic pressure on both sides of the vane. The instrument scale will, for this reason, be more nearly uniform than the square-law relation would predict.

(40)

41. Reluctance Torque

The contactor of Sections 37 and 38 illustrated the computation of force from energy balance by the method of virtual displacement. Another example, in which rotational motion is obtained, is shown in Figure 41a. This device is similar to the motors and generators of previous chapters except that the rotor is not cylindrical but is roughly dumbbell shaped. This shape is, in fact, typical of many machines. Large synchronous motors with salient-pole rotors are similar to this diagram, and the tiny motors in electric clocks operate on the principle now to be explained.

Magnetic field between stator and rotor is shown in the diagram, and it is clear, however magnetic force is visualized, that the rotor can exert a clockwise torque. This torque exists because motion of the device results in a change of reluctance, and the torque is therefore called *reluctance torque*. We can write an energy balance for this device.

As shown in Figure 41a, the rotor pole face overlaps the stator pole face through the angle θ. It is only in this overlapping region that magnetic field in air is significant, so it is in this region that most of the magnetic energy is stored. The volume of this region, considering both poles, is $2\rho\theta wl$, ρ being radius to the air gap, w width of the air gap, and l axial length of the air gap (normal to the page in Figure 41a). Flux density in this air-gap region we call B, and since energy density is $B^2/2\mu_0$, the energy stored in the air gaps is

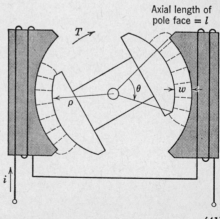

Figure 41a. A salient-pole rotor has reluctance torque.

$$\text{Stored magnetic energy} = \frac{\rho\theta wlB^2}{\mu_0} \qquad (41\text{-}1)$$

Total flux passing through the device is B times the effective pole-face area, or

$$\Phi = \rho\theta lB \qquad (41\text{-}2)$$

We now use the method of virtual displacement, assuming a very small rotation of the rotor, $d\theta$. But to know what is going on in the device as the rotor turns we must know which quantities are constant and which variable.

First we consider operation with direct current in the coil. There are two obvious possibilities. It can be assumed that Φ, the total flux, stays constant; or it can be assumed that i, current in the magnetizing circuit, stays constant. In actual operation of the device, both Φ and i would vary more or less; if motion of the rotor were slow and resistance of the electric circuit were high, i would be very nearly constant, whereas a rapid rotation and a very low-resistance magnetizing circuit would result in nearly constant Φ. For simplicity, we can assume one extreme or the other—but which is best? To find out, we shall try both, and see what is to be learned by comparing them.

42. Assuming Constant Flux

If flux is assumed to be constant there will be no induced electromotive force in the coil of the device. We start, therefore, with this assumption. As the first step, we compute the change of energy stored in the magnetic field as the armature rotates.

Total energy stored in the magnetic field when the rotor is at angle θ is given by equation 41-1. Using equation 41-2 to express energy in terms of Φ (instead of B), we have

$$\text{Stored magnetic energy} = \frac{w\Phi^2}{\mu_0\rho\theta l} \qquad (42\text{-}1)$$

The *increase* of stored energy could be found as in the previous example, but it is more expeditious to note that it is the rate of change of stored energy times the angle through which that change takes place. That is, the change of stored energy as the rotor moves through the angle $d\theta$ is

$$\frac{d}{d\theta}\left(\frac{w\Phi^2}{\mu_0\rho\theta l}\right) d\theta = -\frac{w\Phi^2}{\mu_0\rho\theta^2 l} d\theta \qquad (42\text{-}2)$$

(42)

The negative sign indicates that stored energy is decreased when θ increases, flux being held constant (and since stored energy varies as B^2 this is a reasonable conclusion).

There is no significant electric field in the device, so equation 42-2 gives the field-storage term of an energy balance:

$$\begin{bmatrix} \text{Mech.} \\ \text{input} \end{bmatrix} + \begin{bmatrix} \text{Elect.} \\ \text{input} \end{bmatrix} = \begin{bmatrix} \text{Mech.} \\ \text{storage} \end{bmatrix} + \begin{bmatrix} \text{Field} \\ \text{storage} \end{bmatrix} + \begin{bmatrix} \text{Heat} \end{bmatrix}$$

$$T\,d\theta \quad + \quad 0 \quad = \quad 0 \quad - \quad \frac{w\Phi^2\,d\theta}{\mu_0\rho l\theta^2} \quad + \quad 0 \qquad (42\text{-}3)$$

As to the other right-hand terms, there is no increase or decrease of mechanical energy storage if rotation of the device is so restrained that the speed is negligible (or if speed is held to a constant value). This makes the first term zero. If we now agree to leave friction and resistance loss out of account on both sides of the equation, the third term is zero also.

Finally, electrical input must be considered. Induced electromotive force is zero because magnetic flux is unchanging; this we assumed. Electric power is vi, and since e is zero, v is zero, and power is zero. It makes no difference what the current i may be; since we are not considering resistance, the current flows steadily without voltage. Hence the electrical energy input term is zero. All terms of the energy balance have now been evaluated and are entered in equation 42-3.

To find torque, equation 42-3 is divided by $d\theta$. This gives T, which is the torque that must be exerted on the rotor, by some external force, to make it turn. But equation 42-3 shows that T is a negative quantity, thereby proving (what we already knew) that torque is not exerted *upon* the rotor but *by* the rotor and our device is therefore a motor. Consequently, instead of solving for T we solve for $-T$, which is the torque that the rotor is capable of exerting upon a load. This, the *output* torque, is

$$-T = \frac{w\Phi^2}{\mu_0\rho l\theta^2} \qquad (42\text{-}4)$$

Here we have torque when the rotor is at the angle θ, in terms of the constant total flux Φ. It is perhaps more convenient to express it in terms of flux density, for it happens that this eliminates both Φ and θ. Substituting equation 41-2, we get, as output torque:

(42)

$$-T = \frac{w\rho l}{\mu_0} B^2 \tag{42-5}$$

where $-T$ is output torque (newton-meters)
   w is length of flux path in air gap (meters)
   ρ is radius to the air gap (meters)
   l is axial length of the pole face (meters)
   B is flux density in the air gap (webers/meter^2)
   $\mu_0 = 4\pi \cdot 10^{-7}$ (henrys/meter)

Torque can also be expressed in terms of magnetizing ampere-turns. Since $B = \mu_0 H$ and, for the two air gaps in series, $2wH = Ni$, we have

$$B = \frac{\mu_0 Ni}{2w} \tag{42-6}$$

and substitution into equation 42-5 gives as the output torque:

$$-T = \frac{\rho l \mu_0}{4w} N^2 i^2 \tag{42-7}$$

43. Assuming Constant Current

If, on the other hand, the current i is assumed to be constant, it follows that the flux Φ will vary as the rotor turns. However, constant current gives constant magnetomotive force, which provides constant magnetic potential difference across the air gap and therefore constant H and constant B in the magnetic field of the air gap. This is seen in equation 42-6, in which B is constant when i is constant.

The change of *energy stored* in the magnetic field may be computed as the first step toward an energy balance. Again, equation 41-1 gives the total stored energy. This time, however, we express energy in terms of i by means of equation 42-6 and write

$$\text{Stored magnetic energy} = \frac{\mu_0 \rho l}{4w} N^2 i^2 \theta \tag{43-1}$$

Current being constant, θ is the only variable, so the *change* of stored energy as the rotor moves through the angle $d\theta$ is

$$\text{Field storage} = \frac{\mu_0 \rho l}{4w} N^2 i^2 \, d\theta \tag{43-2}$$

Notice that with constant magnetizing current, stored energy increases as the rotor turns.

As flux changes it induces electromotive force in the magnetizing winding. Since flux is increasing with θ the induced electromotive force e is in a direction opposite to current i, and to maintain constant current the external circuit must supply energy. The *input electrical energy* is $vi\,dt$, v being input voltage, i the current, and dt the time in which the rotor turns through the differential angle $d\theta$. Since we are disregarding the resistance of the winding (and, correspondingly, the resistive heating) $v = d\lambda/dt = N\,d\Phi/dt$. Then

$$\text{Electrical input} = vi\,dt = N\frac{d\Phi}{dt}i\,dt = Ni\,d\Phi \qquad (43\text{-}3)$$

This gives electrical input in terms of the flux Φ, but we want it in terms of the angle θ. We therefore combine equations 41-2 and 42-6 to express Φ in terms of θ, getting

$$\Phi = \rho l B\theta = \frac{\mu_0\rho l}{2w}Ni\theta \qquad (43\text{-}4)$$

and when the differential of this is used in equation 43-3,

$$\text{Electrical input} = \frac{\mu_0\rho l}{2w}N^2 i^2\,d\theta \qquad (43\text{-}5)$$

We are now prepared to write the energy balance:

$$\begin{bmatrix}\text{Mech.}\\\text{input}\end{bmatrix} + \begin{bmatrix}\text{Elect.}\\\text{input}\end{bmatrix} = \begin{bmatrix}\text{Mech.}\\\text{storage}\end{bmatrix} + \begin{bmatrix}\text{Field}\\\text{storage}\end{bmatrix} + \begin{bmatrix}\text{Heat}\end{bmatrix}$$

$$T\,d\theta \quad + \quad \frac{\mu_0\rho l}{2w}N^2 i^2\,d\theta = \quad 0 \quad + \quad \frac{\mu_0\rho l}{4w}N^2 i^2\,d\theta + \quad 0 \quad (43\text{-}6)$$

This time there are three terms in the energy balance. Remembering that input torque is expected to be negative, we solve for $-T$, the output torque, and obtain

$$-T = \frac{\mu_0\rho l}{2w}N^2 i^2(1 - \tfrac{1}{2}) \qquad (43\text{-}7)$$

$$= \frac{\mu_0\rho l}{4w}N^2 i^2 \qquad (43\text{-}8)$$

But this expression for torque with constant i is identical with equation 42-7, our expression for torque with constant Φ. Thus the question at the end of Section 41 is answered. It makes no difference

(43)

whether constant current or constant flux is assumed; the same result is obtained from either.

44. Division of Electrical Energy

An important principle is illustrated by the solution in which constant current is assumed. In equation 43-7, the 1 in the parentheses comes from the term for electrical input, and the ½ in the parentheses comes from the term for *field storage* energy increase. This means that when current in the magnetizing circuit is held constant, exactly *twice as much energy is received from the external electric circuit as is converted into mechanical energy; the other half of the electrical input energy goes into increasing the stored magnetic energy.*

This general principle applies to any linear magnetic system with constant magnetizing current. It can be proved in general (see Section 55). Its usefulness is obvious. If electrical input energy is known, *or* if mechanical output energy is known, *or* if the increase of energy storage in the magnetic field is known, the other two are at once evident without any need for computation *provided* the magnetic system is linear, magnetizing current is being held constant, and losses are not taken into account.

45. A Reluctance Motor

Several of the preceding sections have had to do with torque on a device shown in Figure 41a, and in the description of this device it was compared to certain types of practical motors. But clearly the device we have described, with direct current in the coil, is no motor. It would turn from the position shown in the diagram until the axis of the rotor came in line with the horizontal axis of the field structure. If it coasted on beyond that central position, as no doubt it would, there would then be torque exerted on it the other way, to return it toward the horizontal axis, and the rotor would oscillate until friction brought it to rest on the horizontal axis.

Suppose, however, that current in the stator winding is turned off just as the rotor reaches the horizontal position (at time t_1 in Figure 45a). Suppose the poles are then left demagnetized while the rotor coasts on, in a clockwise direction, through another 90 degrees; while the current is off there is no magnetic torque to retard the rotor. Then (at time t_2) when the rotor has passed the vertical position, let the current be turned on again, and there is again a clockwise

(45)

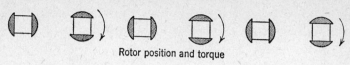

Rotor position and torque

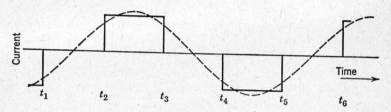

Figure 45a. An alternating-current wave of sinusoidal form approximates the rectangular wave that would be ideal for a reluctance motor.

magnetic torque driving it on. The rotor is then driven in the same clockwise direction until it has again reached the horizontal axis (at time t_3) when the current is again switched off. Thus, by switching the current on and off at the right instants, it can be contrived to have magnetic torque always in a clockwise direction. The device will turn continuously. Notice that the direction of current makes no difference. If current is reversed during the interval from t_4 to t_5, as shown in Figure 45a, torque is nevertheless directed clockwise, as it was during the interval from t_2 to t_3.

It would be possible with a little ingenuity to devise a rotary switch, driven by our motor, that would automatically switch current off as the rotor passed the horizontal axis, and on again as it passed the vertical. There is, however, an even easier way, and this is the practical way of operating such a device. Alternating current is supplied to the winding. Alternating current goes on and off each half cycle. If our motor is turning at the right speed, synchronous speed, the rotor will be approaching the horizontal axis each time the alternating current is at its maximum, and the driving torque is strong in the positive direction. Consider the dashed line, representing alternating current, in Figure 45a. When the rotor is passing away from the horizontal position, the torque on the rotor is backward, but the current and torque are small, and the rotor continues to turn in the forward direction. Thus a reluctance motor can turn steadily, and can drive a mechanical load, provided it is turning exactly at synchronous speed and has the right phase relation to the current.

(45)

It is this synchronous operation that makes a reluctance motor suitable for driving an electric clock. With the a-c line frequency held exactly right, all clock motors run at precisely the correct speed.

Reluctance motors, being cheap and simple, are suitable not only for clocks but also for other light loads. They are sometimes used to turn barbecue spits, for instance—a job that was sometimes done, a few centuries ago, by a dog in a treadmill.

46. Reluctance Torque in Large Machines

Most motors that operate entirely on reluctance torque are small, but the principle is not limited to motors with a fraction of a dog-power. It applies equally to machines of thousands of horsepower. An important part of the mechanical torque of large generators and synchronous motors is reluctance torque if the machines are designed with salient poles. The rotor of Figure 41a is said to have salient poles; the rotor of Figure 18a does not. Rotors with salient poles and rotors with non-salient poles are both used in practice, although nearly all synchronous machines have some saliency of poles, and hence have some reluctance torque. Perhaps 10 to 30 per cent of the total power of even very large machines is due to reluctance torque. Thus the reluctance power of a large machine may be in the tens of thousands of horsepower.

47. Equality of Transfer Functions

There is another general energy relationship that will keep reappearing in various forms in future discussion. It relates to energy transfer in an electromechanical device, and it says that under certain circumstances the transfer function in one direction is *equal* to the transfer function in the other direction.

The transfer function, for purposes of this section, may be considered as being the ratio of output to input. Thus if a wire of length l is at right angles to a magnetic field B, and carries current i, the force F is (by equation 10-2) equal to Bli; then the transfer function between output force and input current is

$$\frac{F}{i} = Bl \qquad (47\text{-}1)$$

(47)

On the other hand we know from equation 21-1 that if the same wire moves at speed S through the magnetic field, the electromotive force induced in the wire is $e = BlS$, and the transfer function between output electromotive force and input speed is

$$\frac{e}{S} = Bl \tag{47-2}$$

These two transfer functions are, as we see, the same.

We can show that this equality illustrates a basic principle, and is not just a happy coincidence, by looking at the energy balance—which is to say, by considering it from the point of view of conservation of energy. Think of energy *at the air gap* of a device; that is, think of the mechanical energy that is actually converted to electrical energy, and of the electrical energy that is actually converted to mechanical energy. This means that we consider only energy that is converted; energy that is stored within a device or energy that is lost as heat is not part of our present problem. This energy *at the air gap*, then, includes no storage or losses, and all there is left of the energy-balance equation is

$$\begin{bmatrix} \text{Mech.} \\ \text{input} \end{bmatrix} + \begin{bmatrix} \text{Elect.} \\ \text{input} \end{bmatrix} = 0 \tag{47-3}$$

Now if the mechanical input, whatever the device may be, is $FS\,dt$, F being force and S speed (in the same direction), and the electrical input is $vi\,dt$, v being applied voltage and i the entering current driven by that voltage, we have

$$FS\,dt + vi\,dt = 0 \tag{47-4}$$

If electromotive force is measured in the same direction as current (see Figure 49a) a negative e produces a positive v and

$$FS\,dt - ei\,dt = 0 \quad \text{or} \quad FS\,dt = ei\,dt \tag{47-5}$$

Then $FS = ei$, or

$$\frac{F}{i} = \frac{e}{S} \tag{47-6}$$

Thus the transfer function between force and current is equal to the transfer function between electromotive force and speed, and with recourse to no law except the principle of conservation of energy this relationship is shown to be true *at the air gap* of any energy conversion device of any shape or kind. It is illustrated for the simple

(47)

wire in a magnetic field by equations 47-1 and 47-2. It is worth noticing that when the Bli law has been found experimentally the BlS law follows from the principle of conservation of energy and may be so derived without further experimental evidence, although historically the BlS law was deduced from a separate and additional set of experiments.

The numerical equality that is here shown between transfer functions, though it applies with great generality, is of course dependent on the use of a consistent system of units. The mksc system that we have used is such a system, and all is well. On the other hand, if the force were measured in ounces, or the speed in inches per second, the relation would be obscured. Still it would not be lost, and it might be usefully recovered by appropriate juggling.

48. Summary

This chapter begins by considering that in a device that converts electrical energy to mechanical, or vice versa, the energy input and the energy output are equal except for energy that is stored within the device, or lost within the device as heat. An energy-balance equation is written.

This gives a means of computing mechanical power, or force, or torque, from the electrical power. The method is often applicable when Faraday's law for computing electromotive force is easier to use than the Bli equation for force. For instance, an energy balance is used to compute torque on a slotted armature.

Even if a device is not free to move, force can be found by the method of virtual displacement. The method is applied to an electromagnet.

The energy-balance method is used again, with two different assumptions, to find torque in a reluctance motor. There follows a consideration of practical applications of reluctance torque.

Three important generalizations are introduced. One is the concept of magnetic pressure at an iron-air boundary. A discussion of the iron-vane ammeter movement illustrates this principle.

Another generalization is the equal division of input electrical energy between mechanical output and field storage if magnetizing current is held constant.

The third generalization is the equality of transfer functions in either direction at the air gap of a device.

(48)

The next chapter continues the discussion of energy balance, with particular attention to the evaluation of energy in terms of inductance.

P R O B L E M S

4-1. (*a*) Consider the operation of some rotating electromechanical device. Write in words the five energy components of this operation as analyzed in equation 33-1. (*b*) Repeat for some non-rotating device. **(Sec. 33)**

4-2. A bar rests on rails 80 cm apart, between which is a uniform magnetic field of 0.5 weber/m² directed out of the paper. (See figure.) To the rails a 6-volt battery is attached, through a 50-ohm

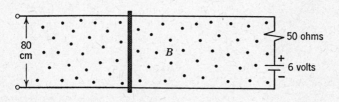

Problem 4-2

resistor; bar and rails have good conductivity. Neglect any change in the magnetic field caused by the flow of electric current. First, the bar is pinned at both ends so that it cannot move. (*a*) What force does it exert on the restraining pins? (*b*) In what direction is the force? (*c*) List all the significant items of energy exchange in a time Δt. (*d*) Show by a diagram how energy flows, and how the items balance to conform with the conservation law.

Then the pins are removed and the bar is pushed with whatever force F is necessary to cause it to move to the right at constant speed S. (*a*) Derive a formula for F as a function of S. (*b*) List all the significant items of energy exchange in a time Δt. (*c*) Show by a diagram how energy flows, and how the items balance to conform with the conservation law. **(Sec. 33)**

4-3. A copper disk (Faraday disk, Figure 21b) of radius r meters is mounted on an axle that is parallel to a uniform magnetic field of flux density B webers/m². (a) Current i flows into the disk at a contact on the edge, and out along the axle. Find the magnitude and direction of torque. (b) The disk turns with angular velocity Ω radians/sec. Find the electromotive force induced between the axle and the contact at the edge. (c) Compare electrical power ei with mechanical power $T\Omega$. Exactly what powers are these? **(Sec. 35)**

4-4. Verify all units for energy and energy density in Table 36-I. **(Sec. 36)**

4-5. In a sketch of the magnet discussed in Section 37, show Amperian currents. **(Sec. 37)**

4-6. Discuss what happens to the force developed by an electromagnet (equation 38-7) when the air-gap width becomes zero. (This may require a careful re-examination of the derivation.) Using the numerical values given in Section 38 for the contactor of Figure 37a, which is made of transformer sheet steel, find the force required to pull it open when it is closed. Is this a valid answer for a practical device? **(Sec. 38)**

4-7. The last paragraph of Section 38 suggests that the electromagnet could be more economically designed, though giving the same mechanical force with the same magnetomotive force. Design a more economical device of the same general form but different dimensions. The opening that contains the coil must be no smaller. Use Armco iron (Section 5 of Appendix 1). **(Sec. 38)**

4-8. Find the actual shape of soft iron vanes in an ammeter, either from the ammeter itself or from a detailed description. Give the manufacturer's name, and tell how the device works. **(Sec. 40)**

4-9. The device shown in the figure is a practical form of magnet. It is cylindrical about a vertical axis. When the coil current is zero the plunger drops until the gap $g = 1.5$ cm. When the coil is energized by 3.0 amp direct current the plunger rises, hitting a stop when $g = 0.5$ cm. The air gap between the shell and the plunger is uniformly 0.02 cm. The coil has 1,000 turns. Assume infinite permeability of the iron, and make other suitable assumptions. When the coil is energized, compute (a) the flux density between the flat

faces of the center core and the plunger when the gap is $g = 1.5$ cm;
(b) the magnetic pressure, and the force on the plunger (compute

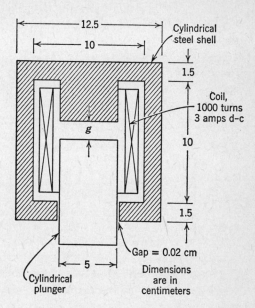

Problem 4-9

force in newtons and convert to pounds, 1 newton = 0.225 lb); (c)
repeat, computing flux density, magnetic pressure, and force when
$g = 0.5$ cm.   **(Sec. 39)**

4-10. Write an energy-balance equation (following the form of
equation 33-1) for the device of problem 4-9. Let the plunger move
through an extremely short distance starting at $g = 1.5$ cm. (a)
The plunger is constrained to move slowly. (b) The plunger is not
constrained to move slowly, but can accelerate as a free body.

(Sec. 39)

4-11. Equation 39-2 says: Magnetic pressure = Energy density.
Can the units of this equation be justified? If it can be done, do so.

(Sec. 39)

4-12. A magnetic core has the dimensions shown. (Assume reasonable dimensions for any needed and not given.) Neglect leakage of
magnetic field and fringing at the air gaps. (a) Find the ampere-turns
required in the coil to produce a flux density of $B = 1.2$ weber/m²
in the central leg about which the coil is wound. In working this
problem, assume infinite permeability in the iron. (b) Find the

mechanical force of attraction, assuming infinite permeability of the iron. (c) Solve the problem again, assuming average permeability

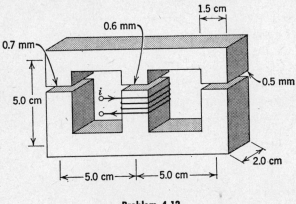

Problem 4-12

of 3,000 times the permeability of air for all iron. (d) Find the mechanical force of attraction with relative permeability of the iron equal to 3,000 as in Part c. **(Sec. 39)**

4-13. Use the method of virtual displacement to calculate the force of an electric field between parallel plates. Energy stored in the field $= Cv^2/2$ and capacitance is $C = q/v = \varepsilon A/w$, where v is potential difference, q is charge on one plate, A is area of one side of one plate, and ε is dielectric constant, which, for air, is $8.855 \cdot 10^{-12}$. (a) Assume constant charge q on the plates. (b) Assume constant voltage v between the plates. (c) Show that force is equal in (a) and (b). **(Sec. 44)**

4-14. In Sections 42 and 43 torque is found, assuming first constant flux and then constant current. Now find torque with the assumption that both flux and current are variables. Write the energy-balance equation with the assumption that both flux and current vary, and solve for torque. Show that equations 42-3 and 43-6 are special cases of your energy balance. **(Sec. 43)**

4-15. In problem 4-13 compute force with the assumption that *both* q and v may change. **(Sec. 44)**

4-16. Refer to the electromagnet of Sections 37 and 38. With dimensions given, 10 amp of direct current gives $F = 22.6$ newtons. (a) Will it operate on alternating current? If so, what rms current will give the same average force? Why? Neglecting resistance, what rms voltage will be required at the terminals (sinusoidal, 60 cycles/ sec)? The armature is now allowed to move until the average distance from the pole face is reduced from 1.0 cm to 0.5 cm. (*b*) What is now the force, if the same direct voltage and current are used as with the larger gap? (Motion of the armature is slow.) (*c*) What is now the force if alternating current is used, and the terminal *voltage* is kept the same? (*d*) Returning to Part *b*, what will be the effect on the flux and the force while the armature is closing if the armature is allowed to close quite rapidly? Explain in terms of the energy-balance equation, but qualitatively; numbers are not required.   **(Sec. 38)**

ENERGY AND INDUCTANCE

chapter 5

49. Inductance

In Chapter 4 a problem is solved with two different assumptions, one of constant flux and the other of constant current. This solution is not entirely satisfactory, although the answers are the same. Fortunately there are more general ways, and one of them is to write force or torque in terms of inductance.

Inductance can be defined as the ratio of flux linkages to current:

$$L = \frac{\lambda}{i} \qquad (49\text{-}1)$$

Faraday's law says that $d\lambda/dt = -e$ (equation 23-1) so a positive rate of change of flux linkages gives an e that is opposite to the arrow direc-

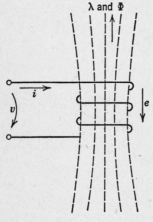

Figure 49a. Reference directions for v, i, λ, Φ, and e, shown by the arrows, are as used in equations 23-1 and 49-2.

(49)

tion in Figure 49a. The terminal voltage v is therefore in the arrow direction (that is, the upper conductor is at the higher potential), and

$$v = \frac{d\lambda}{dt} = \frac{d(Li)}{dt} \tag{49-2}$$

where i is current in a circuit with inductance L and v is the terminal voltage across that inductive circuit.* Because L is a circuit quantity, some of the energy relations are most simply expressed in terms of inductance, and as we go on to consider multiply excited devices we shall value anything that makes for simplicity.

50. Energy in Terms of Inductance

We shall do well to avoid limiting our analysis in this chapter to a particular device, for if the treatment is thoroughly general the results will apply to all devices. Think, therefore, of any kind of a device with one coil and some provision for mechanical motion. Figure 50a suggests such a device. One restriction, however, is practically necessary to avoid interminable complications: *the device is assumed to be linear.* This means that if there is iron in the magnetic circuit its magnetic saturation is negligible. This is often a safe assumption in practice because most of the reluctance of the magnetic circuit of an electromechanical device is in the air gap or air gaps, and even though the iron may become somewhat saturated magnetically its share of the reluctance may still remain quite small.

With only this much information about the device, a good deal can be deduced from an energy balance. Using equation 33-1, we can write, as we have done before,

$$\begin{bmatrix} \text{Mech.} \\ \text{input} \end{bmatrix} + \begin{bmatrix} \text{Elect.} \\ \text{input} \end{bmatrix} = \begin{bmatrix} \text{Mech.} \\ \text{storage} \end{bmatrix} + \begin{bmatrix} \text{Field} \\ \text{storage} \end{bmatrix} + \begin{bmatrix} \text{Heat} \end{bmatrix} \tag{50-1}$$

Let us put the electrical quantities in terms of inductance and see what can be learned from this energy balance.

The *electrical input* term (Figure 50a) is $vi\,dt$. The terminal voltage

---

* Equation 49-2 reduces to the more familiar form of $v = L\,di/dt$ if inductance L is constant. We are now considering devices in which L is not constant but varies as the electromechanical device moves.

It is expected that the concept of inductance is familiar to the reader. It is found in any good book on electrical physics or electrical engineering circuits. Reference 7A gives a brief treatment in Sections 1-4 through 1-7.

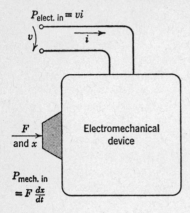

$P_{\text{elect. in}} = vi$

v

i

F
and x

Electromechanical
device

$P_{\text{mech. in}}$
$= F \frac{dx}{dt}$

Figure 50a. Reference arrows for electrical and mechanical power input.

v is composed partly of the resistance drop, which is Ri, and partly of the voltage to overcome the electromotive force induced by changing flux linkages, which is $d(Li)/dt$. Hence

$$\text{Electrical input} = vi\,dt = \left[Ri + \frac{d(Li)}{dt} \right] i\,dt$$

$$= Ri^2\,dt + Li\,di + i^2\,dL \qquad (50\text{-}2)$$

In performing this latter differentiation, we must remember that both L and i may be variables.

Next, *field storage* is expressed in terms of current and inductance. The stored energy in the magnetic field is $\tfrac{1}{2}Li^2$. Energy stored in the electric field is $\tfrac{1}{2}Cv^2$, and this term can be included in the equation if needed; but in many devices the electric field energy is negligibly small and therefore we neglect it here. The term that we require is the *increase* in stored energy during the short time dt, and this is

$$\frac{d}{dt}\left(\tfrac{1}{2}Li^2\right)dt = Li\,di + \tfrac{1}{2}i^2\,dL \qquad (50\text{-}3)$$

By substituting these expressions for input and stored energy increase into the energy balance of equation 50-1, we obtain

$$\begin{bmatrix}\text{Mech.}\\ \text{input}\end{bmatrix} + Ri^2\,dt + Li\,di + i^2\,dL$$

$$= \begin{bmatrix}\text{Mech.}\\ \text{storage}\end{bmatrix} + Li\,di + \tfrac{1}{2}i^2\,dL + \begin{bmatrix}\text{Heat}\end{bmatrix} \qquad (50\text{-}4)$$

Subtraction of similar terms, and rearrangement, gives

(50)

$$- \begin{bmatrix} \text{Mech.} \\ \text{input} \end{bmatrix} + \begin{bmatrix} \text{Mech.} \\ \text{storage} \end{bmatrix} + \begin{bmatrix} \text{Heat} \end{bmatrix} - Ri^2 \, dt = \tfrac{1}{2} i^2 \, dL \quad (50\text{-}5)$$

A few more changes are now made in this energy balance for convenience. First, the mechanical output is the negative of the mechanical input, and is substituted for it. Also, it will be noted that when $Ri^2 \, dt$, which is energy lost as heat in the electrical resistance of the system of Figure 50a, is subtracted from the total energy converted to heat in the system, the remainder is largely mechanical heat loss such as that resulting from friction with the bearings and with the air. Although some hysteresis loss, and other small losses, may also be included in this remainder, it is nevertheless called *mechanical loss*. Then

$$\begin{bmatrix} \text{Mech.} \\ \text{output} \end{bmatrix} + \begin{bmatrix} \text{Mech.} \\ \text{storage} \end{bmatrix} + \begin{bmatrix} \text{Mech.} \\ \text{loss} \end{bmatrix} = \tfrac{1}{2} i^2 \, dL \quad (50\text{-}6)$$

Finally, the mechanical output, which is useful energy that appears at the shaft, plus the increase in mechanical storage, which includes kinetic energy due to change of speed and also potential energy if any, plus the mechanical loss, which is mostly friction, are all lumped together as the mechanical energy delivered to the moving part of our device by the magnetic field that operates it. They are lumped together under the name of *mechanical energy developed*, and with this understanding equation 50-6 becomes simply

$$\text{Mechanical energy developed} = \tfrac{1}{2} i^2 \, dL \quad (50\text{-}7)$$

This equation looks as if it might turn out to be quite useful.

51. Force or Torque in Terms of Inductance

We must now decide whether our device has translational motion, or rotational. If it is translational, the mechanical energy developed is equal to the mechanical force developed times the distance moved. Distance is measured in the same direction as force (see Figure 50a). The distance dx is moved in the short time dt, and the force developed within the device is

$$F_{\text{developed}} = \tfrac{1}{2} i^2 \frac{dL}{dx} \quad (51\text{-}1)$$

Thus the force developed is found in terms of the current and the rate of change of inductance—and nothing else.

If the device rotates, the mechanical power input is $T\, d\theta/dt$, and the developed torque is

$$T_{\text{developed}} = \tfrac{1}{2}i^2 \frac{dL}{d\theta} \tag{51-2}$$

An interesting and important conclusion from either of the above equations tells the direction of magnetic force. A force (or torque) is developed by the device to make dL/dx (or $dL/d\theta$) positive. Since i^2 is always positive, the sign of the developed force (or torque) must depend on whether there is an increase or a decrease of inductance within the device as x (or θ) increases. In other words, *the operating force on a device is in the direction that increases its inductance.*

In the previous chapter a number of singly excited devices were considered. The above formulas for force or torque can now be applied to each of them.

52. The Electromagnet

Consider the electromagnet of Figure 37a, applying to it equation 51-1. L is inductance of the coil, and x is the width of air gap, which we call w. By definition (equation 49-1), $L = \lambda/i$, with $\lambda = N\Phi$ being the flux linkages. Flux density $B = \mu_0 H$ in the air gap, and, if reluctance of the iron is considered negligible relative to that of the air gap, $B = \mu_0 Ni/w$ (see equation 38-6). Since $\Phi = BA$, A being cross-sectional area of the air gap, $\lambda = N\Phi = NBA = \mu_0 N^2 iA/w$, and

$$L = \frac{\mu_0 N^2 A}{w} \tag{52-1}$$

Differentiating with respect to w, the only variable, we obtain

$$\frac{dL}{dw} = -\frac{\mu_0 N^2 A}{w^2} \tag{52-2}$$

When this is substituted into equation 51-1 we find

$$F_{\text{developed}} = -\frac{i^2 \mu_0 N^2 A}{2w^2} \tag{52-3}$$

The negative sign indicates that this developed force is from right to left, opposite to the arrow in Figure 37a, and hence the armature of the contacter is pulled in to close the air gap. Except that the sign is different, because here we compute the magnetic force on the armature

(52)

whereas in Chapter 4 we computed the opposing force exerted by a restraining string, this result is the same that was obtained in equation 38-7. Of course, it would be rather surprising and disturbing if it were not.

53. Reluctance Torque

Next consider the motor of Figure 41a, and find the reluctance torque by using equation 51-2. The rate of change of inductance, $dL/d\theta$, is needed.

Again, by definition, $L = \lambda/i$, and when this is worked out as in the preceding section we find, as in equation 52-1, that

$$L = \frac{\mu_0 N^2 A}{2w} \tag{53-1}$$

This time it is A, the cross-sectional area, that is variable as the rotor turns, while the width of the air gap w remains constant. The area is $\theta \rho l$, θ being the angle of overlap of stator and rotor pole faces, ρ the radius, as shown in Figure 41a, and l the axial length of the pole faces. Hence

$$L = \frac{\mu_0 N^2 l \rho \theta}{2w} \tag{53-2}$$

and

$$\frac{dL}{d\theta} = \frac{\mu_0 N^2 l \rho}{2w} \tag{53-3}$$

Inserting this value in equation 51-2, we obtain

$$T_{\text{developed}} = \tfrac{1}{2} i^2 \frac{\mu_0 N^2 l \rho}{2w} = \frac{\mu_0 \rho l}{4w} N^2 i^2 \tag{53-4}$$

Thus easily we have reached the same result obtained in equation 42-7, and this time with no restrictions regarding constancy of either current or flux.

54. The Soft-Iron Ammeter Movement

An important type of instrument movement was described in Section 40. In actual construction it may take many forms, but in all there is a magnetic force on a soft-iron element, and the resulting torque moves a pointer against the restoring force of a spring.

(54)

According to equation 51-2, the torque that moves the pointer against the spring is proportional to the rate of change of inductance. Whatever the design of the instrument, it will surely move, when current flows, in a direction to increase its inductance. Thus the iron vanes of Figure 40a move apart and increase the inductance of the coil in that figure. There are many styles of soft-iron instruments produced by various manufacturers, but they all have this in common: motion of the pointer upscale corresponds to an increase of inductance of the instrument.

If inductance is known, or can be measured, as a function of position of the pointer, the torque of the instrument can easily be computed. Thus we have a quantitative means of finding the deflection of the ammeter movement.

55. Energy Balance with Multiple Excitation

In previous examples, energy-balance methods are illustrated by singly excited devices. There is only one coil in the electromagnet, the iron-vane ammeter, or the reluctance motor. But the most common types of motors and generators, as well as control devices, have two or more coils and are said to be doubly or multiply excited. A d-c generator with field and armature windings is an obvious example, and an induction motor with rotor and stator windings is another.

Energy balances can be written for multiply excited devices as well as for those that are singly excited. Let us give particular attention to double excitation. A singly excited device can then be considered as a special case in which only one of the currents exists. And if it becomes necessary to study multiply excited devices with more than two coils, the same methods applied to double excitation can be extended merely at the cost of additional complication.

The same energy balance will be used:

$$\begin{bmatrix} \text{Mech.} \\ \text{input} \end{bmatrix} + \begin{bmatrix} \text{Elect.} \\ \text{input} \end{bmatrix} = \begin{bmatrix} \text{Mech.} \\ \text{storage} \end{bmatrix} + \begin{bmatrix} \text{Field} \\ \text{storage} \end{bmatrix} + \begin{bmatrix} \text{Heat} \end{bmatrix} \quad (55\text{-}1)$$

The procedure will be the same as in Section 50, though the terms will be less simple.

Now that there are two electrical circuits connected to the device (Figure 55a) the *electrical input* energy in the short time dt is

$$\text{Electrical input} = (v_1 i_1 + v_2 i_2)\, dt \quad (55\text{-}2)$$

(55)

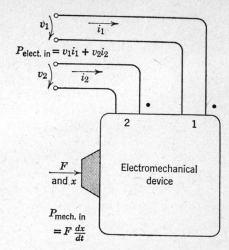

$P_{\text{elect. in}} = v_1 i_1 + v_2 i_2$

$P_{\text{mech. in}}$
$= F \frac{dx}{dt}$

Figure 55a. Reference arrows for a doubly excited device.

The terminal voltage of circuit 1, v_1, is equal to $R_1 i_1$ plus the result of changing magnetic flux in the device. Changing flux can result from a change of either current i_1 or i_2, and in general

$$v_1 = R_1 i_1 + \frac{d}{dt}(L_{11} i_1) + \frac{d}{dt}(M i_2) \qquad (55\text{-}3)$$

where L_{11} is the self-inductance of circuit 1 and M is the mutual inductance between the two circuits (both in henrys),* and R_1 is the resistance of the circuit (in ohms). There is a similar expression for v_2, with subscripts 1 and 2 interchanged.

We now use these expressions for voltage in equation 55-2 to obtain

$$\text{Electrical input} = \left[R_1 i_1 + \frac{d}{dt}(L_{11} i_1) + \frac{d}{dt}(M i_2) \right] i_1 \, dt$$

$$+ \left[R_2 i_2 + \frac{d}{dt}(L_{22} i_2) + \frac{d}{dt}(M i_1) \right] i_2 \, dt \quad (55\text{-}4)$$

We can expand these derivatives, remembering that inductance and current are both variable, to obtain

---

* Equation 55-3 is written with a plus sign before the mutual term, and M may be either a positive or a negative quantity depending on the geometry of the circuits. If corresponding ends of coils are dotted, M is positive. (See Chapter 12 of *Electrical Engineering Circuits* Reference 7A.)

(55)

Electrical input $= (R_1 i_1{}^2 + R_2 i_2{}^2)\, dt + i_1{}^2\, dL_{11} + i_2{}^2\, dL_{22} + 2i_1 i_2\, dM$

$$+ (L_{11} i_1 + M i_2)\, di_1 + (L_{22} i_2 + M i_1)\, di_2 \quad (55\text{-}5)$$

This is the form we use for electrical input.

Next we find the increase of *field storage* energy. When there are two circuits with mutual inductance, energy stored in the magnetic field is

$$\tfrac{1}{2} L_{11} i_1{}^2 + \tfrac{1}{2} L_{22} i_2{}^2 + M i_1 i_2 \qquad (55\text{-}6)$$

(This expression is restricted to linear systems.†) To find the *increase* of energy during any short time dt, we differentiate and multiply by dt. We thereby obtain the term called *field storage* (the electrostatic field being neglected):

Field storage $= \tfrac{1}{2} i_1{}^2\, dL_{11} + \tfrac{1}{2} i_2{}^2\, dL_{22} + i_1 i_2\, dM$

$$+ (L_{11} i_1 + M i_2)\, di_1 + (L_{22} i_2 + M i_1)\, di_2 \quad (55\text{-}7)$$

Returning now to the energy balance, we introduce equations 55-5 and 55-7, subtract similar terms, and rearrange other terms to obtain

$$-\begin{bmatrix}\text{Mech.} \\ \text{input}\end{bmatrix} + \begin{bmatrix}\text{Mech.} \\ \text{storage}\end{bmatrix} + \begin{bmatrix}\text{Heat}\end{bmatrix} - (R_1 i_1{}^2 + R_2 i_2{}^2)\, dt$$

$$= \tfrac{1}{2} i_1{}^2\, dL_{11} + \tfrac{1}{2} i_2{}^2\, dL_{22} + i_1 i_2\, dM \quad (55\text{-}8)$$

Then, since the mechanical output is the negative of the mechanical input, and since the total heat minus the energy changed to heat in the resistance of the windings may be called the mechanical loss (as in equation 50-6), we write

$$\begin{bmatrix}\text{Mech.} \\ \text{output}\end{bmatrix} + \begin{bmatrix}\text{Mech.} \\ \text{storage}\end{bmatrix} + \begin{bmatrix}\text{Mech.} \\ \text{loss}\end{bmatrix}$$

$$= \tfrac{1}{2} i_1{}^2\, dL_{11} + \tfrac{1}{2} i_2{}^2\, dL_{22} + i_1 i_2\, dM \quad (55\text{-}9)$$

Finally, we consider that these three terms comprise the *mechanical energy developed* in the device (as in Section 50), and we write

---

† The expression for energy of a singly excited field, $\tfrac{1}{2} L i^2$, is no doubt familiar. Equation 55-6 is an extension of this to the doubly excited field, and if it is not familiar it may be derived by integrating equation 55-4, assuming field storage only, with 0 as the lower limit for currents. In this integration the inductances, although they may be variable with time, must not be functions of current, and hence the result is restricted to linear systems.

(55)

Mechanical energy developed $= \frac{1}{2}i_1{}^2\,dL_{11} + \frac{1}{2}i_2{}^2\,dL_{22} + i_1i_2\,dM$

$$(55\text{-}10)$$

and here we have an expression for energy converted from electrical to mechanical form by the device, in terms of current and inductance. Note that there is no requirement of constant current or constant flux; the only requirements are linearity of the system and negligible energy in an electric field.

[Incidental to the main line of discussion we may note that equations 55-5 and 55-7 provide proof of the statement that was made in Section 44. If, in a doubly excited device, both i_1 and i_2 are held constant, so that di_1 and di_2 are zero, and if R_1 and R_2 are zero, the electrical input will be just twice the field storage. That is, if *currents are constant,* and there is no resistance loss, half the input energy goes to storage in the field and (from the energy balance) the other half is converted to mechanical energy. Thus we have obtained the desired proof for any linear, conservative, doubly excited system with magnetic field storage. It can be applied to a singly excited system by letting $i_2 = 0$, or to a multiply excited system by an extension of the same development.]

56. Force or Torque with Multiple Excitation

Now that we have found mechanical energy developed, it is a simple step to find force or torque. If the device is translational, the mechanical force developed is the mechanical energy developed divided by dx, where dx is the distance moved in the direction of the force in the short time dt. Then the mechanical force developed is

$$F_{\text{developed}} = \frac{1}{2}i_1{}^2\frac{dL_{11}}{dx} + \frac{1}{2}i_2{}^2\frac{dL_{22}}{dx} + i_1i_2\frac{dM}{dx} \qquad (56\text{-}1)$$

Should the device rotate about a fixed axis, torque rather than force will be wanted. Torque developed is the mechanical energy developed divided by $d\theta$, so the torque developed by the device is

$$T_{\text{developed}} = \frac{1}{2}i_1{}^2\frac{dL_{11}}{d\theta} + \frac{1}{2}i_2{}^2\frac{dL_{22}}{d\theta} + i_1i_2\frac{dM}{d\theta} \qquad (56\text{-}2)$$

These two equations are, in a sense, the end products of this chapter. It is evident that they can be reduced to equations 51-1 and 51-2 for a singly excited device by letting i_2 equal zero. Also, they can be extended to a multiply excited device with any number of electric circuits,

(56)

if that should ever be necessary, by an exactly similar development. In these two equations:

F is force (newtons)
T is torque (newton-meters)
i is current (amperes)
L and M are inductance (henrys)
x is distance (meters)
θ is angle (radians)

57. The Electrodynamometer Movement

There are three important kinds of instrument movements. Almost all ammeters, voltmeters, wattmeters, and other electrical indicating instruments use one of these three movements.* The d'Arsonval instrument was described in Section 14, and the soft-iron instrument in Section 40. The third type is the electrodynamometer instrument.

The electrodynamometer movement is doubly excited. As shown in Figure 57a, it has two coils; one is rigidly attached to the frame and the other is pivoted and free to turn about a vertical axis except for the restoring force of the spring.

To consider the torque of this doubly excited device, we refer to equation 56-2. Rotation of the inner coil on its pivots does not change either the self-inductance of the inner coil or the self-inductance of the outer coil. Only the mutual inductance is changed, and hence only the third term of equation 56-2 is needed to find the torque:

$$T_{\text{developed}} = i_1 i_2 \frac{dM}{d\theta} \qquad (57\text{-}1)$$

When the planes of the two coils are perpendicular, as shown in the figure, there is no mutual inductance between the coils; $M = 0$. If the inner coil rotates one way from this perpendicular position, M becomes positive; rotation in the other sense causes M to become negative. The maximum value of M, either positive or negative, is reached when the two coils lie in the same plane.

---

* Thermocouple meters, rectifier meters, vacuum-tube voltmeters, and others, take their names from associated circuitry, but the actual instrument is almost always one of the three basic types, and usually d'Arsonval. See Chapter 4 of Reference 7A, or a book on electrical measurements, such as Harris, Reference 40.

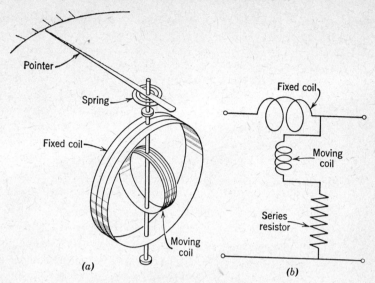

Figure 57. (a) Dynamometer movement. (b) Connection of a dynamometer instrument as a wattmeter.

It will be recalled that M is equal to the number of linkages of one coil with the magnetic flux produced by unit current in the other coil. When the coils are perpendicular, the flux produced by one coil does not link the other coil at all and M is zero; when the coils are parallel there is maximum linkage and hence maximum M. (It is an important but by no means obvious fact that unit current in coil 1 always produces the same number of linkages with coil 2 that unit current in coil 2 would produce with coil 1; hence there is only one value of M for a pair of coils.)

The derivative $dM/d\theta$ is maximum when the coils are perpendicular and zero when the coils are in the same plane. Thus two coils in the same plane exert no torque on each other. The derivative has a fairly large value through a range of 45 degrees to each side of the perpendicular position, and this is about the practical range of operation of an electrodynamometer instrument.

The electrodynamometer instrument can be used as an ammeter. For this purpose the fixed and moving coils are connected in series and so carry the same current. Then $i_1 = i_2$, and equation 57-1 becomes

$$T_{\text{developed}} = i^2 \frac{dM}{d\theta} \qquad (57\text{-}2)$$

(57)

Thus we see that the electrodynamometer ammeter, like the soft-iron instrument, is inherently an rms meter, and also we know that its scale will be cramped at the lower end. Electrodynamometer ammeters are not common, for they are more expensive and more delicate than soft-iron instruments. On the other hand, they can be made more accurate, particularly for measuring alternating current at frequencies of several hundred or even a few thousand cycles per second.

Wattmeters almost always have electrodynamometer movements. If, in equation 57-1, i_1 is the current in a circuit and i_2 is proportional to the voltage between the terminals of that circuit, the product i_1i_2 is proportional to the power entering that circuit. Thus the instrument can be used as a wattmeter by passing line current through the fixed coil (see Figure 57b), which usually has a relatively small number of turns of large wire, and connecting the moving coil, with many turns of fine wire, in series with a high resistance, to the input terminals.

Torque on the moving coil of the dynamometer instrument connected as a wattmeter is thus proportional to power. The torque at every instant is proportional to power at that instant, and average torque is proportional to average power. Hence the electrodynamometer instrument is an accurate wattmeter with alternating current of any wave shape, as well as with direct current.

58. Summary

The energy balance is perhaps more easily understood when written in terms of magnetic flux, as in Chapter 4, but it is often more convenient to use when written in terms of *inductance*. In this chapter, therefore, the energies involved and the force or torque developed in a device are expressed in terms of inductance.

Energy is first expressed in terms of inductance for *singly excited* devices, and the examples of the preceding chapter are repeated.

Energy is then so expressed for *doubly excited* devices. The case of double excitation serves as a general development, for single excitation is a special case of double excitation, and multiple excitation is an extension of double excitation.

Proof is given in Section 55 of a statement made in the previous chapter regarding division of energy.

The *electrodynamometer* instrument is an example of a doubly excited device. This instrument can be used as an ammeter or voltmeter, but is most commonly used as a wattmeter.

Many electric motors and generators, having two windings, are doubly excited devices. The commutator motor, for instance, has field and armature windings. The Amplidyne is one of many examples of multiply excited devices, having more than two windings. The following chapters treat several types of motors and generators, considering that they are all various illustrations of a *generalized* rotating machine, subject to the developments of this chapter.

PROBLEMS

5-1. A relay of electrical sheet steel requires $5 \cdot 10^{-5}$ weber of flux for operation; 670 ampere-turns of magnetomotive force are needed to produce this flux, and the coil has 10,000 turns of wire. (*a*) Compute the approximate inductance of the coil. (*b*) What is the force, at an air gap with cross-sectional area $A = 1.0$ cm², to operate this relay?
(Sec. 49)

5-2. Derive equation 49-2 from 49-1.
(Sec. 49)

5-3. Section 51 states that the magnetic force on any singly excited device is so directed that it tends to increase the inductance. Explain how this statement applies to the electromagnet of Figure 37*a*, the iron ball of Figure 39*a*, and the reluctance motor of Figure 41*a*. Mention several other singly excited devices by which the rule can be illustrated.
(Sec. 51)

5-4. Section 50 leads to a formula for mechanical energy developed if force is produced and energy is stored in a magnetic field. Find equations similar to 50-2, 50-3, 50-4, and 50-7 if force is produced and energy is stored in an electric field, there being no appreciable magnetic field. In Figure 50*a*, think of the electromechanical device as a capacitor with an electric field, in parallel with a resistor.
(Sec. 50)

5-5. Equation 52-3 is valid for any variation of i, but the similar equation 38-7 assumed that i varied in a certain manner. Explain why there is this difference.
(Sec. 52)

5-6. Why is inductance of the coil of Figure 40*a* increased as the vanes spread apart?
(Sec. 54)

5-7. Coil 1 of the figure is driven by a constant-current source: $i_s = \cos 10t$. The coil inductances are fixed at 10 henrys. The coils have a mutual inductance of 5 henrys with a rate of change of dM/dx

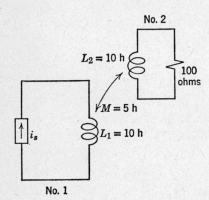

No. 2

$L_2 = 10 \text{ h}$

100 ohms

$M = 5 \text{ h}$

i_s

$L_1 = 10 \text{ h}$

No. 1   **Problem 5-7**

$= 10$ henrys/m. Find the mechanical force between coils in this position, averaged over one cycle of current. **(Sec. 56)**

5-8. Can a statement similar to the italicized statement in the paragraph following equation 51-2 be made about a doubly excited device? Your statement may be restricted, but let it be general enough to apply to the dynamometer movement of Figure 57a.

(Sec. 56)

5-9. Verify the units of equations 56-1 and 56-2. See Appendix 4.

(Sec. 56)

5-10. If there are three electric circuits leading to a device, and one mechanical port (a shaft perhaps): (a) Draw a diagram with reference arrows and dots. (b) Write electrical input. (c) Write field storage (magnetic). (d) Write mechanical energy developed.

(Sec. 56)

5-11. Plot the torque on the moving coil of a dynamometer instrument as a function of its angle, currents in the coils being constant. Show the practical range of operation of such an instrument. Compare this, if an instrument is available, with the range actually used, and compare the scale with your plot. **(Sec. 57)**

5-12. A dynamometer instrument, as in Figure 57a, has the two coils connected in series. The moving coil can be turned to any angle.

When it is turned to make the terminal inductance of the two coils in series a maximum, the value is 0.20 henry. When it is turned to make the terminal inductance minimum, the value is 0.10 henry. What is the magnetic torque produced by 0.050 amp in the two coils when one coil is in a plane normal to the other? (You can assume that flux linkages are a sinusoidal function of angle.)   **(Sec. 57)**

5-13. It is stated, relative to the dynamometer movement, that "two coils in the same plane exert no torque on each other." Describe the forces that are exerted by each of the two coplanar concentric coils on the other, and explain why there is no torque.   **(Sec. 57)**

5-14. Consider the possibility that error in a dynamometer watt-meter might result from mutual inductance between the two coils. Can current in either of the coils be appreciably altered by induction from current in the other coil? Can you devise any means of eliminating such error?   **(Sec. 57)**

EXAMPLES OF ENERGY CONVERSION: THE COMMUTATOR MACHINE

chapter 6

59. The Rotating Machine

Torque developed within a rotating machine is given by equation 56-2:

$$T_{\text{developed}} = \tfrac{1}{2}i_1{}^2 \frac{dL_{11}}{d\theta} + \tfrac{1}{2}i_2{}^2 \frac{dL_{22}}{d\theta} + i_1 i_2 \frac{dM}{d\theta} \qquad (59\text{-}1)$$

Figure 15a is reproduced here as Figure 59a, to be interpreted in terms of this equation. We shall show that the last term of the equation accounts for most of the torque of an ordinary motor, and that it is a good approximation to write

$$T_{\text{developed}} = i_1 i_2 \frac{dM}{d\theta} \qquad (59\text{-}2)$$

Let i_1 be current in the field circuit and L_{11} be inductance of the field circuit. L_{11} remains constant as the armature turns; hence L_{11} does not vary with θ and $dL_{11}/d\theta = 0$. Hence the first term in the expression for torque is practically zero.

Does L_{22}, the armature inductance, remain constant with rotation, also? We say yes, noticing that this is an approximation although a rather slight one. Since magnetic flux produced by armature current must cross the air gap twice regardless of the angular position of the armature, L_{22} is at least relatively constant. Letting the derivatives of L_{11} and L_{22} be zero in equation 59-1, we have a good approximation of torque in equation 59-2. This tells us that torque is very nearly proportional to current in the field circuit, and to current in the armature circuit, and to the rate of change of the inductance between the two circuits.

Current in the field circuit, i_1, is constant. Current in the armature

(59)

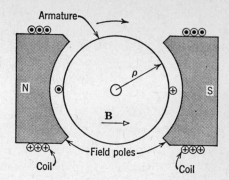

Figure 59a. Torque on a motor coil.

coil is constant until commutation. In this section we shall consider torque on a coil at a moment when it is not undergoing commutation, so within this limit the current i_2 is constant also.

Mutual inductance, however, is not constant; $dM/d\theta$ is a variable. Take the dots and crosses in Figure 59a as indicating the reference directions of currents, and suppose that field current is always in the reference direction. Armature current is in the reference direction also (and will remain so until commutation takes place). The mutual inductance M is zero in the position shown. It will be maximum positive 90 degrees later when the armature coil is parallel to the field coil with the magnetic fields reinforcing each other, and it was maximum negative 90 degrees earlier when the coils were parallel but with the magnetic fields opposed.

To a first approximation the mutual inductance can be related to the sine of the angle of the armature coil. If the position shown in Figure 59a is arbitrarily called $\theta = 0$, then approximately

$$M \approx M_{\max} \sin \theta \tag{59-3}$$

and

$$\frac{dM}{d\theta} \approx M_{\max} \cos \theta \tag{59-4}$$

The conclusion is that torque on the coil is large at the instant shown in the figure when $dM/d\theta$ is maximum. Since, from equation 59-2, torque is in the direction that increases $dM/d\theta$, the torque is clockwise, i_1 and i_2 being as shown. (The same conclusion regarding direction of torque was reached in Section 16, but the present conclusion, based on increasing M, is obviously the simplest.) Because there is torque on the coil, the device is a motor that runs in a clockwise direction.

In view of what we have said, the device would turn through 90 degrees. Torque on the coil would then become zero as $dM/d\theta$ became zero (equation 59-4), and, if rotation were continued, torque would become negative. To prevent this from happening, current in the coil is reversed at the proper instant. Then i_2 becomes negative at the same instant as $dM/d\theta$ becomes negative, and thus torque (equation 59-2) remains positive. Current is reversed by a commutator, as described in the following sections.

60. The Direct-Current Motor or Generator

Figure 59a shows an elementary motor or generator. Figure 18a comes closer to resembling a practical machine but is still incomplete.

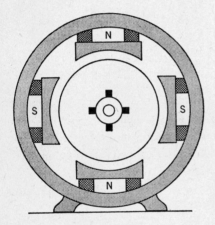

Figure 60a. A four-pole machine.

Coils must be placed in the other armature slots, and commonly two coil sides are placed in each slot. Also, there are usually more than 12 slots; the number of slots is often in the range between 24 and 72. In Figure 18a the field structure is shown with two poles, but there may be any even number of poles. Two-, four-, or six-pole machines are the most common.

Figure 60a shows a machine with four salient (i.e., projecting) poles. The field windings are indicated by cross-hatched areas. The poles alternate in polarity, north and south, around the field structure.*

---

* As a matter of conventional usage, it is customary to divide the angle between a north pole and the next south pole into 180 *electrical* degrees. In a

The commutator is an automatic switch that reverses the connections of each armature coil as it passes between poles of the field structure. Current in an external circuit is steadily in the same direction, but the commutator reverses current in each coil periodically.

61. The Commutator

The commutator is a cylinder of copper segments, insulated from each other and from the shaft of the rotor with which they turn. The ends of the armature coils are connected to these bars, and the ter-

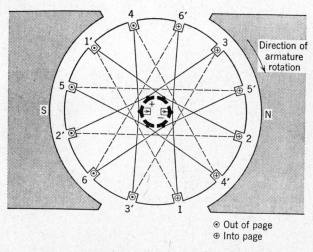

Figure 61a. Armature winding and commutator. Dashed lines show coil ends at far end of armature. Dots and crosses show direction of induced electromotive force.

minals of the machine are connected to a pair of brushes (carbon blocks), held stationary by the frame of the machine, that rub on the copper bars as the commutator turns beneath the brushes. Figure 61a shows a commutator of six segments. Brushes are represented by rectangles in the diagram, and for convenience these are shown within the commutator; but they actually rub on the *outer* surface of the commutator segments. In practice, there are usually many

four-pole machine this angle from pole to pole occupies only 90 actual *mechanical* degrees, in a six-pole machine it is 60 mechanical degrees, and so on.

(61)

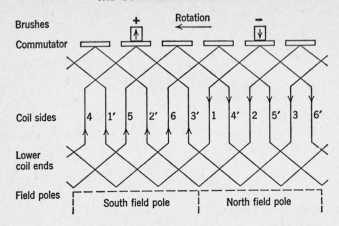

Figure 61b. A developed diagram of the machine of Figure 61a.

more than six segments in a commutator. Sixty would be a more reasonable number of segments on a machine with a rating of several kilowatts.

There are a number of schemes for winding armatures, and a great deal of ingenuity is used in design, but only a single simple example will be given here. Figure 61a shows an armature with twelve slots (as in Figure 18a). In each slot there is one side of an armature coil. The other side of the same coil is not diametrically opposite; for instance, 1 and 1′ are opposite sides of the same coil and they are 5 (not 6) slots apart. This is called a fractional pole-pitch winding, and it is used here to make possible a symmetrical winding pattern. (To see why, try designing a full pole-pitch winding.)

Connections from this coil 1 (coil sides 1 and 1′) to the commutator are shown in Figure 61a. The winding scheme is simple. The side marked 1′ of coil 1 is connected to the same commutator bar as is the side marked 2 of coil 2; then 2′ is connected to the same bar as 3, 3′ to the same bar as 4, and so on.

Figure 61b shows a "developed" diagram of the same winding. Such developed diagrams are conventionally and conveniently used to display armature windings. Commutator bars are indicated at the top, field-pole regions at the bottom.

(61)

62. Commutation

Consider coil 1. In Figure 61a magnetic flux is passing through it from right to left, from the north pole of the field to the south pole (point your right thumb across Figure 61a in this direction). Because of the clockwise rotation of the armature (see arrow), flux linkages with coil 1 are at this instant increasing. Electromotive force, therefore, is being induced *against* the direction of your fingers; that is, electromotive force is directed out of the page in 1′ and into the page in 1. The directions of induced electromotive force are indicated in Figure 61a, and also in Figure 61b.

The direction of electromotive force in each coil side can thus be determined. All coil sides (inductors) moving upward in the magnetic field have electromotive force out of the page; all those moving downward have electromotive force into the page, as indicated in the diagram.

Now we inspect the connections from coil to coil. Start at the brush that has an arrow pointing toward the commutator bar. Pass along a connecting wire to coil side 1; go down in coil side 1, follow around coil 1, and come out in coil side 1′. From coil side 1′ we go to a commutator segment on which there is no brush, and on to coil side 2. Go down in coil side 2, up in 2′, down in 3, and up in 3′, thereby arriving at the commutator bar on which the other brush is rubbing. Thus we have completed a circuit from brush to brush, and (as shown by the arrows) electromotive force in each of the six coil sides through which we have passed is directed along the circuit in the way we have traveled. Thus the left-hand brush, at which we have come out, is at the higher electric potential and is called *positive*.

Total voltage between the brushes is the sum of the electromotive forces induced in coil sides 1 and 1′, 2 and 2′, 3 and 3′, or, alternatively, the equal electromotive force induced in the parallel circuit consisting of coil sides 6′ and 6, 5′ and 5, 4′ and 4 in series. Note that there are these two parallel circuits through the armature from brush to brush. When current is allowed to flow, each carries half the current.

The machine may, of course, run as either a generator or a motor. If it is generating, current is in the same direction as induced electromotive force, and therefore in the directions shown by dots and crosses in Figure 61a or by arrows in Figure 61b. If the device is running as a motor, an external source of energy forces current to be opposite to the induced electromotive force, and current is then opposite to the directions indicated in the diagrams.

(62)

We have already seen that when the machine runs as a motor, with current opposite to electromotive force, the rotation (in order to increase mutual inductance) is in the direction shown. To see the action of the commutator when the machine is running as a generator, consider that the armature turns in the same direction, as indicated. Soon the brushes will make contact with a different pair of commutator bars. The voltage between brushes, however, will still be the same, though the rotor has turned, for though individual coils have moved on, the pattern of induced electromotive forces and connections that is shown in Figure 61a or b remains the same. Only the identifying numbers need be changed to make the same diagram apply at a later instant.

Of course there are minor variations of voltage as the commutator segments slide under brushes. This "commutator ripple" is minimized by having a large number of armature slots and a large number of commutator segments, but even so some ripple remains in the output voltage. In practice, the irregularity of the voltage is likely to be further increased by sparking at the brushes as armature coil current is interrupted and reversed by the commutator motion.

63. Generated Electromotive Force, Direct-Current Machine

In Section 29 we saw that the average electromotive force induced in a single armature coil of N turns is $4fN\Phi$. The electromotive force of a d-c generator is found from this value. Actually we want the average electromotive force in a large number of coils that occupy various positions under the field poles, rather than the average in a single coil as it moves through all these positions successively; but the result is essentially the same. Hence, with minor modifications of symbols, the formula can be written in terms of speed or angular velocity as

$$e_{av} = 4n(p/2)N_s\Phi = 2npN_s\Phi = \frac{pN_s\Phi}{\pi}\Omega \qquad (63\text{-}1)$$

where Φ is flux entering the armature from each field pole, webers

N_s is the number of armature-coil turns in series between a positive and a negative brush

p is the number of field poles of the machine; hence $p/2$ is number of pairs of poles

n is speed of the machine, revolutions per second; hence $n(p/2)$ is the frequency in the individual armature coil

(63)

Ω is speed in radians per second; hence $\Omega = 2\pi n$

e_{av} is the electromotive force generated in the N_s conductors, and hence is the no-load terminal voltage of the machine, provided the brushes are located in the so-called neutral axis

There must be a few words about brush position. Normally a commutator segment connected to a particular armature coil passes under a brush, thereby reversing the direction of current in the coil, just as the generated electromotive force in the coil becoms zero and is reversed. This is the position shown in Figures 61a and b, and brushes in this position are said to be in the neutral axis.* This brush setting provides maximum terminal voltage. Modern machines usually have the brushes fixed firmly in this neutral-axis position; older machines were sometimes built with the brush position adjustable.

64. Excitation

A magnetic field must be provided to produce electromotive force in the armature winding. For this purpose a coil is placed on each of the field poles, as indicated in Figures 18a and 60a, and direct current in these coils produces the magnetic field. In some small devices a permanent magnet can be used. It is convenient but not economic except for the smallest machines, such as tachometer generators in control systems and "magnetos" in light gasoline engines.

To excite a d-c generator, an obvious possibility is to use part of the output of the generator in its own field winding. This is called *self-excitation*, to distinguish it from the *separate excitation* provided from some other source. Self-excitation is further classified as *shunt* or *compound*. Figures 64a, b, and c show the three types of excitation.

Figure 64a shows a separately excited generator; its field current is supplied from some independent source, such as another generator. A rheostat (variable resistance) is shown, to be used for adjusting

* As will be seen in Figures 61a or b, they are physically located (in a machine of ordinary design) opposite the centers of the field poles, although diagrammatically, as in Figures 64a, b, and c, they are customarily shown at right angles to this position. (The reason for this conventional position seems to be an unhappy anachronism coming from the obsolete Gramme ring winding.)

(64)

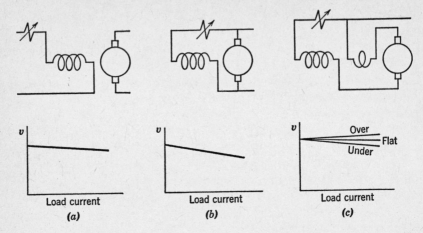

Figure 64. (*a*) Separately excited generator. (*b*) Self-excited generator. (*c*) Self-excited compound-wound generator.

field current and hence generator voltage, but for any given setting of the rheostat the field current is constant.

65. Voltage Regulation

A graph in the same figure shows that terminal voltage of the generator becomes slightly less when the generator is loaded, and current flows in the armature winding. The principal reason for this voltage drop is the resistance of the armature winding, which causes terminal voltage to be less than generated electromotive force when there is current to a load. The amount of this voltage drop is commonly expressed as the *voltage regulation* of the machine, which is, by definition, the following ratio:

$$\text{Voltage regulation} = \frac{\text{No-load voltage} - \text{Full-load voltage}}{\text{Full-load voltage}}$$

A self-excited generator supplies its own field current as in Figure 64*b*. The terminal voltage of a self-excited machine droops more than that of a separately excited generator because the field current does not stay constant. When load is increased the terminal voltage of the generator drops, and since field current is supplied from the machine terminals the field current is thereby reduced. But when the field current is reduced the generated voltage is reduced also, and

(65)

so the field current is reduced still more, and so on. The result, as shown in Figure 64b, is that voltage regulation of a self-excited generator is markedly greater than that of a separately excited machine.

The relation shown in Figure 64a can be more fully expressed mathematically. As in equation 63-1, the average electromotive force generated is

$$e = kn\Phi \tag{65-1}$$

where k is a design constant involving the number of poles and number of turns, and n is speed in revolutions per second. If the main flux Φ is proportional to the field current i_f (that is, if the relation is linear), we can write

$$e = k_1 n i_f \tag{65-2}$$

This is an electromechanical equation relating electromotive force and speed.

On the electrical side of the generator we know that the terminal voltage is equal to the generated electromotive force less the voltage drop in armature resistance:

$$v = e - R_a i_a \tag{65-3}$$

This is an electrical equation. Simultaneous solution of equations 65-2 and 65-3 gives

$$v = k_1 n i_f - R_a i_a \tag{65-4}$$

This is a system equation relating output voltage and armature current to input speed and field current.

It is clear that terminal voltage is not constant even if speed and field current are constant because of armature current. In fact, Figure 64a is an example of the drop in terminal voltage as armature current is increased. The equation shows what happens when other quantities are changed also. For instance, it can be seen that voltage regulation is greater if speed is less.

It is interesting to see what happens mathematically when the machine is self-excited. Then, as in Figure 64b, the field current comes from the generated voltage:

$$i_f = \frac{v}{R_f} \tag{65-5}$$

where R_f is the total resistance of the field circuit. The armature current is the sum of the load current and the field current (the former being probably much the larger):

$$i_a = i_l + i_f = \frac{v}{R_l} + \frac{v}{R_f} \qquad (65\text{-}6)$$

Substitution into equation 65-4 then gives

$$v = k_1 n \frac{v}{R_f} - R_a\left(\frac{v}{R_l} + \frac{v}{R_f}\right) \qquad (65\text{-}7)$$

Now the only solution to this equation is $v = 0$ unless

$$\frac{k_1 n}{R_f} - \frac{R_a}{R_l} - \frac{R_a}{R_f} = 1 \qquad (65\text{-}8)$$

and in that case v can have any value. The interpretation of this mathematical result is that such a generator is impossible except for one particular adjustment, and then it is unstable. And this would be perfectly true if the relationship between field current and flux were linear, as it is assumed to be in equation 65-2. A self-excited generator is stable and hence practical only because there is magnetic saturation of the iron, as is discussed in more detail in Section 68.

66. A Direct-Axis Series Winding

The compound generator of Figure 64c provides a means of avoiding this undesired drop of terminal voltage under load. A few extra turns of wire are wound on the field poles and are connected in series with the armature winding of the machine. When there is load, armature current passes through this *series* coil and increases the magnetomotive force of the field as load on the generator is increased. The effect is to increase flux, and hence to increase electromotive force in the armature, and thus to maintain terminal voltage. Depending on the number of turns in the series winding the generator can be *overcompounded* (with terminal voltage actually increasing as load increases), *flat-compounded* (with terminal voltage the same at full load as at no load), or *undercompounded* (with terminal voltage drooping, but less than it would if there were no series winding). Typical curves are shown in Figure 64c.

The amount of compounding of a machine can be reduced by shunting the series winding with a low-resistance *diverter* to carry part of the armature current. It is not usually possible to change the number of turns of the series winding of a given machine, but a diverter is a practical means of adjusting the amount of compounding.

Compounding that strengthens the magnetic field of a generator when there is armature current is called *cumulative* compounding. If connections between the armature winding and the series coil were reversed, armature current would act to weaken rather than to strengthen the field. This is called *differential* compounding. It has little practical value.

A series winding used for compounding, being wound on the main field poles and producing magnetomotive force in the same axis as the main field, is called a *direct-axis* winding.

The mathematics of the previous section is easily extended to include the compound machine. Its main flux is now no longer produced by field current alone; armature current is also a factor, though with a different constant because the number of turns of the series winding is much smaller than that of the main field winding. Equation 65-2 becomes, for the compound machine,

$$e = k_1 n i_f + k_2 n i_a \tag{66-1}$$

Substitution into the electrical equation 65-3 gives

$$v = k_1 n i_f + (k_2 n - R_a) i_a \tag{66-2}$$

If the generator is separately excited, so that i_f is constant, the last term accounts for the compounding. When $k_2 n$ is equal to R_a the generator is flat-compounded; if less, the machine is under-compounded; if more, overcompounded. Should n be negative, the generator is differentially compounded.

However, if the generator is self-excited (and this is usual) equations 65-5 and 65-6 are used in equation 66-2. The result is then rather complicated, and since the practical behavior is entirely dependent on saturation of the iron, the mathematics will not be pursued. See Section 68.

67. A Quadrature-Axis Series Winding

Another series winding is commonly used in d-c generators and motors to prevent destructive sparking between commutator segments and the carbon brushes. The compounding winding of the previous section is a direct-axis winding, producing magnetomotive force in the same axis as the main field winding. The winding designed to improve commutation, on the other hand, is a *quadrature-*

(67)

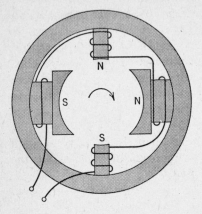

Figure 67a. Field structure of a 2-pole commutating machine showing commutating poles or interpoles and series winding, for use as a generator.

axis winding, producing magnetomotive force at right angles to the direct axis (at 90 electrical degrees). It is not wound on the main field poles (these are in the direct axis) but on additional small iron poles projecting from the field structure of the machine between the main field poles. See Figure 67a. These are called commutating poles or interpoles. They can be small for they do not have to carry much flux.

The purpose of the interpole is to reverse current in the armature coil as the commutator segments to which it is attached pass under a carbon brush. As the commutator turns, one segment follows another beneath the brush. For a moment, as a brush touches two segments, an armature coil is short-circuited. (In Figure 61a, when the armature has turned a few more degrees the negative brush short-circuits coil 1 and the positive brush short-circuits coil 4.) Unless current in the coil can be reversed by magnetic means during this brief time of short circuit, there is a spark as the commutator segment leaves the brush.

If the armature coil current is properly reversed during the interval of short circuit, there is no current between the commutator segment and the brush as the segment slides out from under the brush, and there is no spark. If there is current at the instant contact is lost, a spark follows the segment.

The reason for the spark is that the armature coil is inductive, and its current cannot be reversed abruptly. An electrokinetic impulse ($vt = Li$) is necessary to stop the current, and as much again to start it in the other direction. This electrokinetic impulse can be provided by having one or both sides of the armature coil pass through the flux of an interpole during the brief time of short circuit, thereby generating an electromotive force sufficient to stop the current going one way and start it going the other. To give the electromotive force at the right time, when the coil is being commutated, the interpoles are located in the quadrature axis of the machine, as in Figure 67a.

The impulse necessary for good commutation is $2Li$. Hence the strength of the interpole field should be such that $N\Phi = 2Li$. The flux Φ of the interpole should therefore be proportional to armature current, and this is automatically achieved by connecting the interpole winding in series with the armature circuit.

68. Saturation

At first thought it would seem that a self-excited generator would be unstable. Any slight rise in field current would increase the magnetic flux, terminal voltage would rise, field current would increase further, and so on, the voltage becoming greater without limit. This would, indeed, be true except for saturation of the magnetic field.

By equation 63-1, generated electromotive force is proportional to flux, speed being constant. If the magnetic circuit of the machine did not saturate, flux would be proportional to field current. But, in fact, as field current is increased to higher values, the flux, and hence the generated electromotive force, and therefore the terminal voltage, fail to increase in proportion. Figure 68a shows the magnetization curve (or saturation curve) of a typical generator. The effect of magnetic saturation is seen in the bending of the curve with increased excitation. If the iron did not saturate, the magnetization curve would continue straight as shown by the dash line in the figure.

When field current is well below its rated value the curve is nearly straight; in this region the permeability of the iron part of the machine's magnetic circuit is so high that the magnetomotive force of the field current is almost entirely used in overcoming the reluctance of the air gap. The dashed line is therefore called the air-gap line.

In its upper, curved region the no-load saturation curve lies to the right of the air-gap line by a distance that represents the magnetomotive force required to overcome reluctance of the iron. Note that a horizontal distance on Figure 68a corresponds to a certain magnetomotive force, and a vertical distance represents a certain amount of flux.

(68)

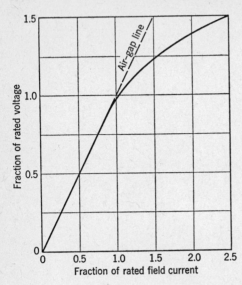

Figure 68a.   Magnetization curve for a generator, showing no-load voltage.

Figure 68*b* shows a magnetization curve with two superimposed field-circuit resistance lines. Any point on one of the sloping dashed lines shows the voltage required to produce the indicated amount of field current through the resistance of the field circuit (the field winding plus the rheostat). The two lines correspond to two different field-circuit resistances, to two different settings of the field rheostat. The slope of each line is equal to the corresponding circuit resistance.

With the field rheostat set at the lower value of resistance, the generator will operate stably at the point i_{f1}, v_1. Since this point is on both the solid line and the dashed line, the machine generates just enough voltage to produce the needed field current.*

With this particular value of resistance, no other amount of field current is stable. Suppose field current is i_{f2}, instead of i_{f1}. Then the voltage generated is v_2. But the voltage required by the field-circuit resistance is only v_{r2}, which is less, and the difference, $v_2 - v_{r2}$, acts to increase the field current. It produces a positive rate of change of current through the inductance of the field circuit. As field current increases, voltage increases, following the solid curve of Figure 68*b*, while the voltage required to maintain field current follows the dash line. As long as the solid line is above the dash

---

* It is assumed that field current in the armature winding is too small to reduce terminal voltage appreciably.

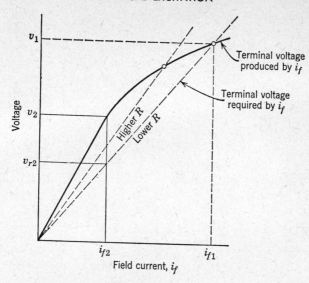

Figure 68b. Operating points of a self-excited generator.

line, current continues to rise. The point of intersection, at which current is i_{f1} and voltage is v_1, is reached in due time and becomes the stable operating point.

If the resistance of the field rheostat were now increased to correspond to the upper field-circuit resistance line instead of the lower, the new stable operating point would be the new point of intersection, and terminal voltage would be correspondingly less. Thus by operating the rheostat the terminal voltage of the generator can be adjusted.

69. Critical Excitation

However, if the field resistance is increased too much the dash line becomes so steep that it intersects the magnetization curve only at the origin. Terminal voltage then becomes and remains zero, except for a small voltage caused by the residual permanent magnetism of the field iron of the machine. (It is, indeed, this residual magnetism that initiates build up of voltage in a machine that has been stopped and restarted, or one in which the field circuit has been opened and then reconnected.) When the field resistance exceeds this critical value the machine fails to "build up voltage."

(69)

A certain type of electromechanical amplifier (Regulex) makes use of the almost-unstable operation that results when the field resistance is adjusted to have very nearly its critical value. The field-resistance line (the dashed line of Figure 68b) then lies upon, and almost coincides with, the lower section of the magnetization curve. This section of the magnetization curve is nearly straight, and the point of intersection of the two lines, the operating point of the generator, is highly sensitive to small changes of excitation. There is an additional winding on the field poles of the machine, a "control field," and when a small current flows in this control winding it moves the field-resistance line slightly to one side or the other, very greatly altering the terminal voltage of the generator. Thus a small current in the control field causes a large change in the output voltage of the generator, and a great amount of amplification is obtained. See Section 82.

70. Armature Reaction, Commutating Machines

When considering the coils that produce magnetic field within a machine, it must not be forgotten that the armature winding itself is such a coil. When there is armature current (that is, when there is load) the magnetic intensity of the armature winding combines with that of the other windings in producing the total field. The magnetic effect of armature current is called armature reaction.

We see in Figure 61a that armature current is so distributed in the conductors that it produces (if acting alone) a magnetic field in the quadrature axis of the machine. This is determined by the position of the brushes on the commutator. Armature reaction is therefore in the same axis as the field produced by the commutating poles; unfortunately, however, it is not helpful in improving commutation for it is in the wrong direction. It makes commutation worse rather than better, and in fact the magnetic field of the commutating poles must be great enough to oppose armature reaction as well as to provide the necessary impulse to reverse current in the armature coils.

Figure 70a shows in solid lines the magnetic field that would be produced by current in the field winding alone. The magnetic field that would be produced by armature current alone is shown in dash lines. (Both of these are diagrammatic, rather than realistic, and many details are omitted for simplicity.) The essential fact is that the axes of the fields are perpendicular. Armature reaction is

(70)

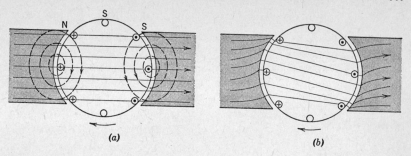

Figure 70. (*a*) Superimposed fields, showing armature reaction. (*b*) Combined fields, including armature reaction.

cross magnetizing and neither strengthens nor weakens the main field.

Figure 70*b* shows the effect of adding the two fields. (Again it is diagrammatic rather than realistic.) This total magnetic field is distorted. However, if the total field is merely the result of superimposing the component fields, the average flux density is not changed; the number of flux lines entering the armature is the same with as without armature reaction. Hence the average electromotive force generated in armature conductors remains unchanged.

In fact, however, simple superposition, which assumes linear relations between H and B of the magnetic field, is not justified. Because of saturation, the increase of flux density is less where the fields add than the decrease where they subtract. Total flux *is* therefore reduced. Hence average electromotive force is somewhat diminished by armature reaction in an actual machine.

One practical solution is to compensate for the drop of voltage that results from armature reaction by a small increase of the compounding of the excitation (see Section 66). Another means, which can almost entirely eliminate armature reaction, is to use a *compensating winding*. This is a winding similar to the armature winding, but stationary, being placed in slots in the field pole faces. The compensating winding is connected in series with the armature winding and carries the same current as the armature winding. The compensating winding and the armature winding are thus arranged to face each other across the air gap, with equal but opposite ampere-turns, so that the compensating winding cancels out the magnetic field of the armature winding and hence eliminates armature reaction. This is better than merely correcting for armature reaction by strengthening the series winding and commutating poles, for it prevents the

(70)

magnetic field of the machine from being distorted under load. However, it is more expensive, and is used only for critical applications. Compensating windings are used in such control devices as the Amplidyne (see Section 83), and for propulsion motors in submarine ships where good performance is more important than economy.

The field of armature reaction is not always undesirable, however. It generates an electromotive force in the armature that can be collected at the commutator, and this electromotive force has various useful applications.

A pair of brushes rubbing on the commutator in the position shown in Figure 61a collects a voltage dependent almost entirely on the direct-axis flux. In a similar manner a pair of brushes located half way between these (spaced on the commutator at 90 electrical degrees from the main brushes) will collect a voltage produced by the quadrature-axis flux only. When current flows from the armature through the regular pair of brushes of the generator, armature reaction produces a quadrature-axis field, electromotive force is generated in the armature coils by their motion through this quadrature field, and hence a voltage is produced between the second pair of brushes. Current from this second pair of brushes can be used to influence excitation of the machine, to operate control circuits, or to supply a load.*

Generators on automobiles and trains use armature-reaction voltage to adjust their field current so that they can supply approximately constant output while running at variable speed. One or two additional brushes are used on the commutators to collect the voltage caused by the quadrature-axis field.

An important control device, an electromechanical amplifier called

---

* The idea of electromotive force being generated in a coil by its motion through a field that it itself produces suggests bootstraps, and rightly so, but in a commutating machine the armature-reaction field is held fixed by the action of the commutator while the armature coils move through it. From a less convenient point of view the electromotive force is induced through mutual inductance by the reversal of current in the coils being commutated.

The author was told by the late Harris J. Ryan, inventor of the compensating winding, that the Patent Office hesitated to admit its practicability. The argument was used that motor torque arises from interaction of the main field and the armature-winding field, and if a compensating winding cancels out the armature-winding field it plainly eliminates the torque and the motor will not run. Professor Ryan was able to give assurance that he had operated a motor with a compensating winding, that in fact it did run, and ran very well. The patent was issued. The theoretical point remains interesting, however, and warns us against too ready acceptance of simple ideas.

the Amplidyne, actually has a short circuit between what would normally be the main brushes, and its output from a second pair of brushes is generated by the armature-reaction field. This design gives high amplification of an input signal. See Section 83.

71. The Machine as a Shunt Motor

A machine connected to an electric supply line may be either a motor or a generator depending on whether it drives or is driven. Figure 71a shows a machine with reference arrows directed for motor operation; that is, the arrows are so directed that power *from* the electric supply line *to* the machine is positive. The line voltage is sufficient to overcome the electromotive force induced in the machine and also provide for the drop caused by resistance of the armature:

$$v = e + Ri \qquad (71\text{-}1)$$

(Equation 65-3 is essentially the same except that it assumes the machine to be a generator and the reference arrow for current is taken in the opposite direction, causing a reversal of sign.) Writing equation 71-1 explicitly for current, we have

$$i = \frac{v - e}{R} \qquad (71\text{-}2)$$

Now if the machine is turning at such a speed that e is equal to the line voltage v, there is no armature current. If a mechanical load is put on the shaft of the machine so that it slows a little, e becomes less than v. The armature current i is then positive, power from the line is positive, and the machine runs as a motor.

On the other hand, if the machine is not mechanically loaded but is driven through its shaft it increases slightly in speed; e becomes greater than v. Then the armature current is negative (meaning

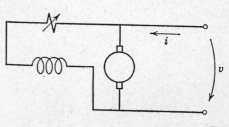

Figure 71a. A shunt motor.

(71)

opposite to the arrow of Figure 71a) and power is delivered to the electric line from the machine, which has become a generator.

Note that the direction of armature current is reversed when the machine changes from motor operation to generator operation, but there is no change of line voltage or of directon of rotation of the machine. Note also that the direction of shunt field current does not change although the direction of armature current is reversed. This fact is essential in the behavior of compound windings, for a compound winding that strengthens the flux of a generator weakens the flux when the machine is motoring.

Direct-current commutator motors are classified as shunt motors, compound motors, or series motors. In shunt motors the field circuit is connected to the electric line, which also supplies armature current. Field current is maintained constant by the constant voltage of the supply line. There is no distinction between self-excitation and separate excitation.

Compound windings are not used as commonly on motors as on generators. Field current remains constant without the use of compounding, being normally supplied at constant voltage. Also, the effect of compounding a motor is not always desirable. It will be remembered that armature current reverses when a machine changes from generator to motor operation; so also, therefore, does current in a series winding (relative to current in the shunt winding). Hence a compound winding that increases the main field flux of a machine running as a generator decreases the main field flux when the machine is a motor. With this connection, armature current in the compounding winding acts to reduce the main flux, causing the motor to increase its speed under load and to draw more armature current. The increased armature current further weakens the field, and excessive speeding, usually developing into surges of speed, can result, particularly when the motor is being started.

If, on the other hand, the series winding is oppositely connected and acts to increase the flux in the main field when the machine is motoring, the motor is called cumulatively compounded. The main flux is then greater when the machine is slowed by heavy load, or at starting, and torque is correspondingly increased. Such a motor loses the constant-speed characteristic that is sometimes useful, but it gains a higher starting torque, and finds practical application in crane hoists, elevators, and similar loads.

The speed characteristics of a cumulatively compound motor are something between those of a shunt motor and those of a series motor, which is next considered. We may, indeed, think of a com-

pound motor as a shunt motor with a series winding to increase starting torque, or as a series motor with a shunt winding to limit the
no-load speed.

72. The Series-Excited Machine

A series motor has an armature and commutator not unlike those
of a shunt motor or a d-c generator. Its field structure is similar,
also, but its entire field winding consists of a few turns of heavy
wire connected in series with the armature (Figure 72a).

When it is connected to a supply line, current passes through the
armature winding and the field winding in series. The armature coils

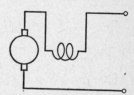

Figure 72a. A series motor.

are carrying current in a magnetic field, and motor torque is developed. The torque is very great at low speed, when both armature and field currents are heavy, and diminishes rapidly as speed
increases.

A series-excited machine operates as a generator as well as a
motor. It is not useful for ordinary power generation, for both its
voltage and its current change radically with changes of load resistance. (It is, of course, the extreme example of an overcompounded generator.) Indeed, it can supply only heavy loads; if
the load on its terminals is light (high resistance), voltage drops to
zero. However, it is useful as an element in an electromechanical
amplifying system in which it supplies a load of constant resistance.
An example is the Rototrol (Section 83) in which a series generator
feeds into the control circuit of the next stage of amplification.

73. Motor Speed

A shunt motor is used for tasks requiring constant speed; a series
motor for work that needs large starting torque. The speed characteristics of shunt and series motors are entirely different. Never-

theless, the controlling principle is the same. All kinds of motors turn at such a speed that *the electromotive force* generated in the armature winding *balances the applied voltage.*

This is not to say that they are equal. If applied voltage were opposed by an equal electromotive force, no current could enter the armature. For a machine to run as a motor, its generated electromotive force must be less than the voltage applied to its terminals so that the necessary armature current can flow. If current is too little to develop the torque needed to keep the motor running (the torque required by the mechanical load), the motor slows down, less electromotive force is generated, current increases, and torque increases correspondingly until it becomes sufficient to drive the mechanical load.

These relations are expressed by equation 71-1:

$$v = Ri + e \qquad (73\text{-}1)$$

where v is voltage between the machine terminals
$\quad R$ is resistance of the armature circuit, including series field coils
$\quad i$ is armature current
$\quad e$ is electromotive force generated in the armature

This equation applies to either motor or generator action, with the reference directions of Figure 71a; and when it is applied to a shunt motor it says that the motor must run slightly slower under load, as is shown graphically in Figure 73a.

Equation 65-1 says that the average electromotive force is

$$e = kn\Phi \qquad (73\text{-}2)$$

where k is a design constant involving number of poles and numbers of turns
$\quad n$ is speed of the machine, revolutions per second
$\quad \Phi$ is flux entering the armature from each field pole, webers

We have torque from equation 17-3. For a two-pole machine with the same current and flux it is $T = 2N\Phi i/\pi$. When this is generalized to a machine with p poles, and N_s armature-coil turns in series between a positive and a negative brush, the formula for average torque in an actual machine is

$$T = \frac{N_s p}{\pi}\Phi i = K\Phi i \qquad (73\text{-}3)$$

In the last form, just for convenience, we let $N_s p/\pi = K$, another

(73)

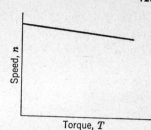

Figure 73a. Speed-torque characteristic of a shunt motor, equation 73-4.

design constant. We now substitute i from equation 73-3 and e from equation 73-2 into equation 73-1, and rearrange to get an explicit expression for speed n:

$$n = \frac{v}{k\Phi} - \frac{RT}{kK\Phi^2} \tag{73-4}$$

This equation may be applied to a shunt motor by letting the main field flux Φ be constant. With constant Φ, the speed n is merely a constant minus a term proportional to torque, and this expresses the same relation that is shown graphically in Figure 73a.

Equations 73-1, 2, and 3 may also be applied to a series motor. This time the flux is not constant but is taken to be proportional to the armature current. Introducing a third design constant that involves the number of series field turns and the reluctance of the magnetic circuit, we write

$$\Phi = k'i \tag{73-5}$$

This equation assumes a linear relation between current and magnetic field; it neglects saturation and is therefore not accurate for a heavily loaded motor. However, it helps us find the general shape of the speed-torque characteristic of a series motor, and it may be corrected for saturation if enough design data are available. The speed-torque characteristic of the series motor is found by solving equations 73-1, 2, 3, and 5 simultaneously, to obtain

$$T = \frac{Av^2}{(n + BR)^2} \tag{73-6}$$

where A and B are design constants (combinations of K, k, and k')
  v is applied voltage
  n is speed of the machine
  R is resistance of the armature and series field windings

(73)

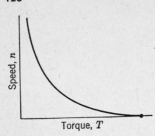

Figure 73b. Speed-torque characteristic of a series motor, equation 73-6.

The shape of the speed-torque characteristic of a series motor is shown in Figure 73b. This curve results from considering all quantities on the right-hand side of equaton 73-6 constant, except n. If n, the speed, is zero, and the machine is stalled, torque has a very large value because current is limited only by the resistance of the machine. As the machine increases its speed, and n increases, torque becomes less.

It is important to notice that there is no upper limit to the speed of a series motor. If an unloaded motor is connected to the supply line it increases in speed without limit, its torque being used to accelerate itself, until the armature is destroyed by centrifugal force. A machine that runs away in this manner will almost literally explode, and it is highly dangerous. For this reason, series motors are almost always used with a permanently attached load, driving a fan or blower, as in a vacuum cleaner, or geared to the axle of a trolley bus or subway car. (Note, however, that the torque of equation 73-6 is the magnetic torque on the armature of the motor, which must supply frictional losses as well as mechanical load; hence it is possible that a small series motor, with relatively large losses, may be limited by friction and windage to a safe speed. A milk-shake mixer is an example; these are reported to have a no-load speed of 20,000 revolutions per minute and are designed to be automatically disconnected when not in use.)

74. Speed Control

For applications requiring convenient and accurate control of speed, the d-c shunt motor is the best type. These applications include many uses in control systems and certain drive motors for manufacturing processes.

No other d-c or a-c motor can compare with the d-c shunt motor

(74)

for service that requires running at a speed that is easily adjusted and, being adjusted, stays constant regardless of load.

In equation 73-4, the first term on the right-hand side gives the no-load speed of a shunt motor, and this is inversely proportional to flux. Hence increasing the field current slows the motor; decreasing the field current gives greater speed. This relation, it will be remembered, is based on the fact that the motor must run fast enough to make the generated electromotive force equal the applied voltage.

The second term in the equation accounts for the slowing of the motor under load (as in Figure 73a), and this term may be made as small as the customer is willing to pay for by reducing the resistance R. If resistance is low, the motor runs at a speed determined almost entirely by the amount of field current. The field current, and hence the speed, can be adjusted by changing the field rheostat, or by quicker and more sophisticated electronic circuitry.

The advantage of a series motor, or a heavily compounded shunt motor, on the other hand, is its great change of speed under load. It is specially suitable for traction purposes, on electric locomotives, subway trains, street cars, trolley busses, and for such industrial uses as steel-rolling mills. When a car driven by a series motor comes to a hill, more torque is needed. While climbing the hill the car slows automatically, and this action accomplishes the same purpose as the automatic transmission of an automobile: it provides more torque without overloading the motor or the power supply. Moreover, series motors are usually designed so that the maximum torque is quite large (for the size of the motor), giving a greater starting torque than would ordinarily be obtained from a shunt motor.

The speed at which a series motor runs under steady load is determined by the characteristic of the load as well as that of the motor. Figure 74a repeats the speed-torque characteristic of a series motor

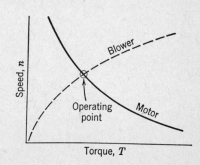

Figure 74a. Graphical determination of motor speed with variable torque load.

(74)

and also shows as a dashed line the speed-torque characteristic of a blower that the motor is driving. The point of intersection is the operating point. It shows the speed of steady operation, the only speed at which the motor produces the amount of torque that the blower requires. The blower, of course, requires more torque at higher speed, whereas the motor produces less.

This same method of determining operating speed, by what amounts to a graphical simultaneous solution of the speed-torque equations of the driving and driven devices, may be applied to any kind of motor. However, for shunt motors, and for a-c motors that run at nearly constant speed, it is usually good enough to estimate that the operating speed will be equal to the no-load speed reduced by some small percentage, depending on the fraction of rated power that is being required. Such an estimate can be aided by knowledge of the speed regulation of the motor (comparable to voltage regulation of a generator), which is defined as

$$\text{Speed regulation} = \frac{\text{No-load speed} - \text{Full-load speed}}{\text{Full-load speed}} \quad (74\text{-}1)$$

Speed of shunt motors is controlled by varying the field current; there is no comparable way of varying the speed of series motors. In practice, resistance can be used in series with the motor. This resistance reduces current when starting and speed when running, and it is the function of the controller on most electric cars and trains. Series resistance is clearly inefficient for speed control, however.

75. Motor Starting

When a d-c shunt motor is started, resistance is switched into the armature circuit before voltage is applied to the machine. This limits the current drawn from the line to a safe value. When the machine has come up to speed the starting resistance is removed from the circuit. Note that current to the shunt field is drawn directly from the line, and not through the starting resistance. The greatest possible starting torque is desired, and this requires maximum current in the field circuit.

Starting and control devices for shunt motors are so designed that the field circuit cannot be opened while the armature circuit is closed, for such operation could result in damage and danger. The weakening of the machine field, caused by interruption of the field current, would result in excessive armature current. If the machine were well protected, this would burn out fuses or trip circuit breakers. If the machine were not well protected, the armature winding itself could burn out or, even worse, the reduced field, combined with heavy armature current, might cause such excessive speed that the armature would burst from centrifugal force.

Series motors, as has been mentioned, are started with resistance in series with the motor. This is satisfactory for starting, although it is inefficient as a means of speed control while running. Series motors are nearly always used for traction purposes, and if there are two motors on a car they may be started in series with each other, and then switched, when they have come up to speed, to run in parallel.

76. Reversal of Motors

To reverse the direction of rotation of a commutator motor, current through the armature must be reversed relative to the direction of the magnetic field, as discussed in Section 59.

In a shunt or series motor, this can be done by reversing connections of either the armature or the field circuit, but not both. In a shunt motor, the field circuit carries less current than the armature circuit, and is easier to switch.

The split-field series motor has two field windings, wrapped in opposite directions on the same poles. Only one is used at a time. If the motor is to turn in one direction, one of the windings is used. If it is to turn the other way, current is supplied to the other part of the field winding; this reverses the magnetic field and hence reverses the torque and direction of rotation of the motor.

77. Alternating-Current Commutator Motors

If the direction of current through *both* the armature and field windings of a commutating motor is reversed (equation 59-2), so that both magnetic fields are reversed, torque remains in the same direction and the motor turns as before. If alternating current is supplied to a series motor, instead of direct current, the direction of current reverses each half cycle. It reverses in both the armature and field windings at the same instants, and the motor torque is continuously in the same direction. Hence a series motor will run on alternating current.

There are disadvantages in a-c operation. Eddy current and

(77)

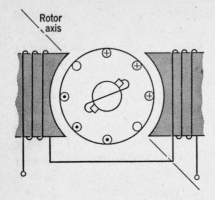

Figure 77a. A repulsion motor has brushes set off the stator axes.

hysteresis loss in the iron are greater than in d-c operation. Motor current, and hence maximum torque, is limited by reactance of the machine as well as by resistance. Commutation is worse, unless a compensating winding is used. Large series motors must be specially designed if intended for a-c operation.

Very small series motors are called "universal" because they will run on either direct or alternating current of the same voltage. They are used in vacuum cleaners, sewing machines, food mixers, and other low-power devices.

A shunt motor does not operate satisfactorily on alternating current. The field circuit is more inductive in relation to its resistance than the armature circuit, and as a result the armature current and field current are not in phase with each other if alternating voltage is applied. The shunt motor is different from the series motor in this respect, for when the armature and field windings are in series their currents cannot be out of phase.

The repulsion motor is a commutator type of a-c motor that has some similarity to a shunt motor. In fact, a d-c shunt motor will run as a repulsion motor if its field winding is supplied with alternating current, its armature terminals are short-circuited, and its brushes are shifted off the neutral axis.

Figure 77a shows a diagram of a repulsion motor. Brushes, short-circuited together, permit current to flow in the rotor winding as indicated by the dots and crosses (it is understood that the current alternates), and the rotor magnetic field is directed along the axis shown. If the brushes are moved around the commutator until the rotor axis is horizontal and in line with the direct axis of the field poles, the rotor winding carries heavy current. If stator current is

i_1 and rotor current i_2 in equation 59-2, these are both large; yet torque is zero for $dM/d\theta$ is zero in this position.

On the other hand, if the brushes are shifted until the rotor axis is vertical, in the quadrature axis of the machine, there is again no torque. In this position the mutual inductance M is zero with the result that i_2 is zero.

In an intermediate position, however, as shown in the figure, i_1, i_2, and $dM/d\theta$ all have values greater than zero. There is then torque, and the machine runs as a motor.

A repulsion motor has operating characteristics similar to those of a series motor. Single-phase a-c motors are sometimes made to start as repulsion motors and to run as induction motors. A repulsion motor obviously will not run on direct current.

78. The General Rotating Machine

Almost all types of generators and motors have much in common. Although they carry different names, such as d-c generator or a-c generator, series motor or repulsion motor, induction motor or synchronous motor, they are basically similar. The most vivid evidence of this basic similarity is the fact that one single machine can be constructed * to behave as a generator or motor of any of the common types. The only alterations necessary to change from one type to another are in the external connections of the windings, and the use of slip rings or commutator. "The various types differ fundamentally only in the distribution of conductors forming the windings and in whether the elements have continuous cores or salient poles." †

A few devices—the Faraday disk of Figure 21b, for instance, and its successor the homopolar generator—do not fall within this generalization, but these are oddities. By and large, the quotation is a fair statement.

Since it is the object of electrical machine design to provide a large torque, there must be (by equation 59-1) a large rate of change of

---

* Described by Brown, Kusko, White, and Woodson; cited in the appendix as References 78A, B, C, D.

† Quoted from Bernard Adkins, Reference 78E. Adkins' bok is recommended to carry the reader further into machine theory than is included in the scope of this present discussion. Fitzgerald and Kingsley (Reference 78F) and Ku (78G) are also analytical. Robertson and Black is an excellent descriptive book (Reference 78H). Also descriptive are Carr (78I) and Fitzgerald and Higgenbotham (78J).

inductance with rotation, and also large currents. This means that rotor current must provide magnetic poles as strong as possible, and they must be as nearly as possible in the quadrature axis of the stator.

Commutator machines, both shunt and series types, have rotor poles in the quadrature axis because of the position in which the brushes rub on the commutator. The brush setting puts the rotor field at the proper angle to the field of the stator.

In synchronous machines and induction motors, however, the position of the rotor field depends on the nature or amount of the load. As we shall see, the same objective is approached by quite different means.

79. The Generator as a Transducer

Dynamic action of control systems or other information systems will be considered in later chapters, in general, but some of the characteristics and transfer functions of control systems can be discussed at once. Commutator machines are quite commonly used in information systems as well as in power systems. Small motors and generators, some hardly larger than a spool of thread, serve as tranducers in control systems.

A tachometer generator is a transducer for changing rotational speed to voltage. With constant excitation (often a permanent magnet) the generated voltage is proportional to speed. By equation 63-1,

$$e = \frac{pN_s\Phi}{\pi}\Omega \qquad (79\text{-}1)$$

where e is induced electromotive force, Ω is speed in radians per second, and p, N_s, and Φ are poles, coil turns in series, and flux per pole. The transfer function relating output (generated electromotive force) to input (speed) is merely a constant:

$$\frac{e}{\Omega} = \frac{pN_s\Phi}{\pi} \qquad (79\text{-}2)$$

80. The Motor as a Transducer

A motor is also useful as a transducer in control systems. As a torque motor, its input may be current and its output mechanical

(80)

torque. As a servomotor, its input may be voltage and its output speed of rotation, or angular position.

Output and input are conveniently related by transfer functions, as with other transducers. One useful arrangement is to supply field current to a motor from a constant source, so that the excitation remains unchanging. The signal current is then put through the armature winding. (This is similar to the Ward-Leonard control system.) Torque of the motor is determined in magnitude and direction by the magnitude and direction of the signal current. From equation 73-3, the transfer function that gives the ratio of output torque to input current is

$$\frac{T}{i} = \frac{N_s p \Phi}{\pi} \tag{80-1}$$

where T is the shaft torque (newton-meters)

i is the signal current in the line to the armature (amperes)

N_s is the number of armature coil turns in series

Φ is the flux entering the armature per pole of the main field of the motor (webers)

p is the number of poles of the main field

It is interesting, and important in control work, that the transfer function relating electromotive force to angular velocity (equation 79-2) and that relating torque to current (equation 80-1) are identical. This fact, discussed in Section 31, indicates that the device is a symmetrically bilateral transducer. (See equations 209-2 and 209-4.)

A transfer function relating rotational speed to applied voltage can also be found for such a motor. This is not a mere constant, however, as is the transfer function of equation 80-1, for speed of the motor involves the moment of inertia and consideration of voltage must include inductance. The transfer function involving speed and inductance must therefore be postponed to Chapter 15, when we shall be prepared to consider the dynamic characteristics of the system.

81. An Electromechanical Amplifier

Used differently, a generator can be an amplifier. The armature is driven at constant speed. The input signal is a small varying current supplied to the field circuit, and the output is the armature voltage, which varies in a similar manner. Since the output power from the armature winding can be much greater than the input power to the field winding, and the small input controls the large output, the device is an amplifier. It is a useful and practical device for some purposes, but has two drawbacks.

First, the output signal may not be a faithful reproduction of the input signal. A sudden increase of voltage applied to the field winding, for instance, would result in a more gradual increase of field current because of the inductance of the field winding, and hence in a gradual increase of flux and of armature voltage. If this results in appreciable delay the device is said to have slow response, a long time constant. The second difficulty is that the amount of amplification is somewhat limited.

The transfer function is easily found if we may assume, for simplicity, that there is no saturation of the magnetic circuit. Flux is then proportional to field current. Let R represent the entire resistance of the armature circuit, including the armature winding and the load. Armature current is i_a. Then the electromotive force generated in the armature is

$$e = Ri_a \qquad (81\text{-}1)$$

Assuming that flux is proportional to field current i_f we can lump all the constants of proportionality in equation 79-1 and get

$$e = ki_f \qquad (81\text{-}2)$$

Equating 81-1 and 2 gives

$$\frac{i_a}{i_f} = \frac{k}{R} \qquad (81\text{-}3)$$

and this is the transfer function relating output current to input current. It is a current amplification factor. To get large amplification, the constant k can be made large by design of the generator (as indicated by equation 79-1) but only within practical limits. Also, the current can be increased by decreasing R. Although decreasing R increases output current, it does not necessarily increase output power. In practice, power gains of the order of ten to twenty times can readily be obtained. (See also Section 212.)

However, more than this is often wanted. An obvious solution is to cascade two or more generators. The input signal current is supplied to the field winding of the first machine, and the output from the armature of the first machine goes to the field winding of the second machine. The armature current of the second machine is then the output of the amplifier. Such a two-stage electromechanical amplifier may supply power some hundreds of times as great as

(81)

the power input to the field winding of the first of the two cascaded generators. (See also Section 213.)

82. An Amplifier with Feedback

One way to obtain large amplification (although at the expense of slower response *) is to use feedback. *Feedback* means that part of the output is returned to the input, as in a compound-wound generator.

Figure 82a shows a generator with feedback. Whether it is looked

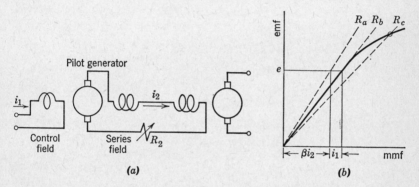

(a) (b)

Figure 82. (a) Showing a generator with feedback as the first stage of a two-stage amplifier (Rototrol). (b) R_1 gives amplification, R_2 on the verge of instability, R_3 self-excitation.

upon as a series generator with an additional winding called the control field, or as a separately excited generator with extreme over-compounding is immaterial.

Consider its operation. The generator is turning at constant speed, being driven by a motor that is not shown. At first there is no current in the control-field circuit. There is no current in the armature circuit (for R_2 is set high enough to prevent self-excitation). The system is at rest.

Now let current i_1 be supplied to the control circuit. It will cause electromotive force to be generated in the armature winding, and if there were no armature current we would write, as in equation 81-2,

---

* This is a usual dilemma. To obtain large amplification is easy, but to obtain both large amplification *and* rapid response is difficult and expensive.

(82)

$$e = ki_1 \qquad (82\text{-}1)$$

But there will, in fact, be armature current i_2. This, flowing in the series field winding, strengthens the total field; introducing a constant β to account for the different numbers of turns in the control field and the series field, we write

$$e = k(i_1 + \beta i_2) \qquad (82\text{-}2)$$

But $e = R_2 i_2$, with R_2 the total resistance of the armature circuit. Thus R_2 includes the resistance of the armature winding itself, the series field coil, and the load—which is illustrated in the figure as the field coil of another (second-stage) generator. Hence

$$R_2 i_2 = k(i_1 + \beta i_2) \qquad (82\text{-}3)$$

We now solve for the transfer function i_2/i_1, the output current over the input current. Writing A instead of k/R_2, we find the transfer function to be

$$\frac{i_2}{i_1} = \frac{A}{1 - A\beta} \qquad (82\text{-}4)$$

(This may be recognized as the basic feedback formula. A is the amplification that would exist in the absence of feedback, as in equation 81-3; β is the relative effect of the output on the input.)

In our device, $A = k/R_2$, and A can therefore be varied by adjusting the resistance in the armature circuit of Figure 82b. Note that we can increase the transfer function, the current amplification factor, as much as we desire by adjusting R_2 to make the value of $A\beta$ approach 1, for doing so makes the denominator of equation 82-4 approach zero, and the amplification approach infinity. As long as $A\beta$ is less than 1 the generator operates as a stable amplifier. It may have as much amplification as desired. But if $A\beta$ reaches 1 the machine becomes self-excited as a series generator (see Section 72), and its voltage starts to rise without regard to whether there is any input signal. Having reached this unstable condition, the voltage rises by itself and would continue to rise without limit (corresponding to the infinite value of the ratio of equation 82-4) except that the magnetic circuit of the machine becomes saturated and an operating equilibrium is reached.

Figure 82b shows this action graphically. The magnetization curve of the generator is shown, and three dash lines correspond to three values of R_2. If $R_2 = R_a$, the device is a stable amplifier. One point of operation is shown: with current i_1 in the control circuit, the electromotive force generated is e. The diagram shows that the necessary

(82)

magnetomotive force is provided partly by current i_1 in the control field, but mainly by current i_2 in the series field. Thus most of the magnetomotive force is provided by feedback, and amplification is high.

By reducing R_2 toward R_b the amplification can be made greater, for the distance representing i_1 becomes less. When R_2 equals R_b the generator is on the verge of instability. If R_2 is further reduced until $R_2 = R_c$ the machine has become unstable as an amplifier and is running as a self-excited series generator. Its generated voltage is limited only by saturation, and the operating point is the point of intersection shown (see Section 68). In this self-excited condition the presence or absence of an input signal makes hardly any difference; the machine is not an amplifier.

It is interesting to consider that when feedback increases the amplification of the generator it slows the response. If amplification is high, a small signal causes a small electromotive force to be generated in the armature. This armature electromotive force causes a small armature current to flow, which, passing through the series coil, strengthens the field and produces more armature current, which produces more field current and hence more armature current, and so on. Since the field circuits are inductive, there is some delay between the generation of an electromotive force and the resulting flow of current. It is not quite right to think of the process as going forward by successive steps, with a delay between each increase of electromotive force and the succeeding increase of current while the output current builds up, for actually the process is gradual and continuous, but it is entirely right to deduce that the process of build-up is slow. (See Section 214.)

The two-stage electromechanical amplifier shown in Figure 82a is a simplified version of Rototrol. A similar system that uses a feedback field winding in parallel with the load, instead of a winding in series with it, is called Regulex.

83. A Two-Stage Amplifier

Another two-stage electromechanical amplifier, called the Amplidyne, is distinguished by having both stages of amplification built into one machine. It is reasonably correct to think of the Amplidyne as an ingenious way of having two stages of amplification connected in cascade, with a single machine providing electric and magnetic circuits for both.

(83)

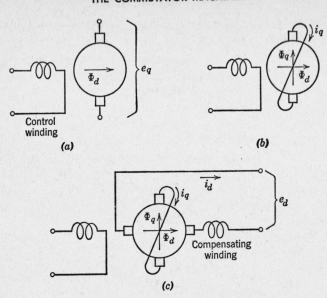

Figure 83. (a) A d-c generator, giving one stage of amplification. (b) When short circuited, there is a strong quadrature-axis field of armature reaction. (c) The reaction field Φ_q generates e_d and i_d. The compensating winding prevents armature reaction from i_d.

The first stage of amplification is provided by a generator acting in the ordinary way, as shown in Figure 83a. The signal voltage or current is applied to the control field winding, producing a flux Φ_d in the direct axis of the machine, which causes an electromotive force to be generated in the constantly rotating armature winding. This electromotive force appears as a voltage between the brushes of the machine (which are shown in the position that is conventionally adopted in diagrams, although as a matter of fact the brushes are physically located under the poles of the control field).

For Amplidyne action, these brushes are short-circuited together, as shown in Figure 83b. A heavy current results. This current produces a strong armature reaction in the machine, causing flux Φ_q in the quadrature axis. Since current in this circuit produces magnetic field in the quadrature axis of the machine, the circuit is referred to as the quadrature circuit, and its electromotive force and current are called e_q and i_q.

The short-circuit current i_q produces a flux Φ_q of armature reaction. Since the armature winding is turning in this quadrature axis field,

(83)

the electromotive force e_d is generated in the armature winding and can be collected by a second pair of brushes as shown in Figure 83c. Here we have the second stage of amplification. Its magnetic field is produced by i_q, which is the output current of the first stage, and its electromotive force is brought out through the second pair of brushes. Current will flow in this second stage if a load is connected to the second pair of brushes. Such a load current produces armature reaction in the direct axis of the machine, so this second-stage circuit is called the direct-axis circuit and its electromotive force and current output are e_d and i_d.

Actually, it would be highly undesirable to have armature reaction result from the second-stage circuit, for it would be directly opposed to the magnetomotive force of the control field. Acting as strong negative feedback, it would sharply limit the possible output of the machine.* To prevent this effect, a compensating winding is used (as shown) in the direct-axis circuit of an Amplidyne to balance and cancel the direct-axis magnetomotive force of the armature (see Section 70).

Such a machine is designed to make Φ_q large, and to make the resulting e_d and i_d large. It is possible in this way to get very substantial amplification from the Amplidyne. Because it combines two stages in one machine, and requires less iron and copper, it is lighter than a pair of separate generators cascaded.†

84. Summary

A commutator machine is an example of a doubly (or multiply) excited device in the sense of Chapter 5. Its torque, either as motor or generator, is proportional to field current, armature current, and rate of change of mutual inductance.

The purpose of the commutator is to reverse the armature current when the armature conductor is between field poles, as the rate of change of mutual inductance is being reversed by rotation. A simple example of a commutator is given.

Electromotive force in the armature winding is given in equation 63-1 for operation of the machine as either a generator or a motor.

---

* Operated in this way without a compensating winding, the device is essentially the Rosenberg railway lighting generator with such strong negative feedback that output current is substantially independent of speed.

† Gibson and Tuteur, Reference 83.

As a *generator,* it may be separately excited or self-excited. The excitation is further classified as shunt or compound (or, rarely, series). Compounding is obtained by using a series winding in the direct axis. Compensating windings or commutating windings are series windings in the quadrature axis. Voltage regulation is discussed briefly.

Self-excited generators operate stably because of magnetic saturation. Stable operation requires that field-circuit resistance be below a critical value, and if this value is exceeded the generated voltage drops to zero (or to the value determined by residual magnetism).

Armature reaction is in the quadrature axis (in the usual machine) because of the position of brushes on the commutator. Armature reaction distorts the magnetic field, and may weaken it if there is saturation.

As a *motor,* the commutator machine may be shunt, compound, or series excited. Speed of a shunt motor is controlled by varying the field-circuit resistance. Speed of a series motor depends greatly on the load. The speed of any motor is such that its generated electromotive force is just enough less than the applied voltage to allow necessary armature current to flow.

Problems of motor starting are mentioned.

Motor torque reverses if field polarity is reversed relative to armature polarity. However, if both are reversed at once, direction of torque remains unchanged. Therefore series motors operate on alternating current. Another type of a-c commutator motor is the repulsion motor.

Motor torque is maximum if the armature field is in the quadrature axis of the machine. In a commutator machine the correct angular relation is maintained by the position of brushes on the commutator.

Direct-current motors and generators are used as *transducers* in control systems. A motor may change current input to torque output. A generator may change speed input to electromotive-force output. In each case the transfer function is $N_s p\Phi/\pi$. It is important that these inverse transfer functions are equal.

The d-c generator may be used as an amplifier to increase the power of an electrical signal. There may be two (or more) stages of amplification. Several practical devices are mentioned.

This chapter has considered the characteristics of a number of practically useful and important forms of the commutator machine in its *steady state.* However, for all but the simplest operations the *dynamic* characteristics are of at least equal importance with those of the steady state. Since dynamic characteristics require some introductory study of dynamic systems, their discussion will be continued in Chapter 10.

PROBLEMS

6-1. Find a commutator motor (perhaps in a household appliance, or an automobile starter, or a shop tool, or elsewhere *) and learn all you can about it by observation. Write about two pages of description, including a diagram, giving physical size and form, nature of load, nature of power supply needed, rated speed, power, etc. The name plate will probably give some data. Look for the poles, field coils, interpoles, commutator, brushes. Are the brushes opposite, or between, the poles? Is the field structure, or the armature, laminated? Is there a series winding? Write as if for an engineering report.   **(Sec. 67)**

6-2. Sketch the armature and field structures of a six-pole d-c machine, and show the general character of the magnetic field. Mark north and south poles on the surfaces of the iron.   **(Sec. 60)**

6-3. A d-c generator is rated 10 kw, 230 volts, 1,760 rpm, flat compounded. When run as a separately excited shunt generator without compounding, at rated speed, the voltage drops from 230 at no load to 200 volts at rated armature current. If it is run as a compound generator, what fraction of the armature current must be diverted from the series field winding for the generator to be flat compounded: (a) at 200 volts output, 1,760 rpm? (b) at 230 volts output, 2,000 rpm?   **(Sec. 66)**

6-4. Suppose the generator of Figure 68b is generating a voltage higher than v_1. The field rheostat is then adjusted to a value that corresponds to the line marked "Lower R." What happens?

(Sec. 68)

---

* The following (from a student paper, 1961) shows the spirit in which this question is approached: "The motor I chose to examine is the starter motor from a friend's Jaguar Mark VII. He was having some trouble with it and took it out, so I grabbed it and tore it down, examining it carefully as I went."

6-5. A self-excited d-c shunt generator has an armature resistance of 0.12 ohm. The field resistance is 91.2 ohms, and the full-load armature current is 192 amp. The magnetization curve for the generator is shown in the figure. Find the full-load terminal voltage.

(Sec. 68)

6-6. An unloaded self-excited shunt-connected d-c generator is being driven by a motor, but terminal voltage, instead of having its rated value of 120 volts, is either zero or at most a few volts. Assuming that the machine is in good condition, and has no broken wires

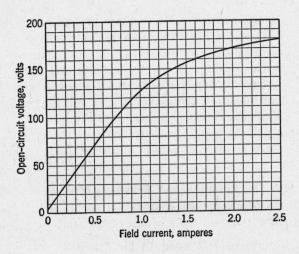

Problem 6-5

or bad brushes, list the possible reasons for this failure to produce voltage. (There are at least four reasons to be listed.) It is your job to produce voltage; what will you do about it? Tell what you will do, what you will then observe, what conclusions you will draw, and what the next step will then be. **(Sec. 69)**

6-7. A d-c shunt motor has an armature resistance of 0.10 ohm and a field circuit resistance of 125 ohms. When operating under load with a terminal voltage of 125 volts, the line current is 51 amp and the speed is 1,500 rpm. If the applied voltage is reduced to 100 volts while the mechanical torque remains constant, what is the new speed? Assume that flux is proportional to field current. **(Sec. 73)**

6-8. A 5-hp (3.73-kw) d-c motor, shunt excited, runs without load at 1,750 rpm with the following conditions:

Applied voltage $\qquad v = 115$ volts
Field resistance $\qquad R_f = 176$ ohms
Armature resistance $R_a = 0.35$ ohm
Armature turns $= 110$, number of poles $= 4$

How fast does this motor run when driving full rated load? **(Sec. 73)**

6-9. A 10-hp (7.46-kw) d-c motor, shunt excited, runs without load at 1,760 rpm with the following conditions:

Applied voltage $\qquad v = 220$ volts
Field resistance $\qquad R_f = 125$ ohms
Armature resistance $R_a = 0.40$ ohm
Armature turns $= 200$, number of poles $= 4$

How fast does this motor run when driving full rated load? **(Sec. 73)**

6-10. A shunt motor is rated 230 volts, 10 hp (7.46 kw), 1,800 rpm. Using rated field current, what will be its speed when line voltage is 210 volts and current is 25 amp? **(Sec. 73)**

6-11. Equations for speed of shunt and series motors are obtained in Section 73. Find such an equation for a compound motor. Draw speed-torque characteristic curves, considering compounding in either direction, and explain the good and bad effects. **(Sec. 73)**

6-12. A shunt-excited machine is generating 240 volts. It is connected to a d-c line on which 240 volts is maintained. What would make this machine become a generator? A motor? Explain changes that would take place in equation 73-1. **(Sec. 73)**

6-13. Express equation 73-4 in terms of N_s and p, eliminating both k and K. **(Sec. 73)**

6-14. A d-c series motor is connected to a load that requires constant torque regardless of motor speed. Neglect armature and field resistance. (a) How much does the motor speed change when the line voltage changes from 230 to 200 volts, saturation being neglected? (b) How would saturation affect the result? What would be changed in the derivation of equation 73-6 by saturation? **(Sec. 73)**

6-15. Derive equation 73-6 for the speed-torque characteristic of a series motor. **(Sec. 73)**

6-16. Apply the method of Figure 74a to show how to find the speed of a streetcar on the level, on a slight hill, and on a steeper hill. (a) Suppose the car to be driven by a d-c series motor, as is common practice. (b) Suppose the car to be driven by a shunt motor; explain why this is impractical. **(Sec. 74)**

6-17. A centrifugal pump is driven by an electric motor. Torque required to turn the pump is $T = 0.059n^2$ newton-meter, where n is speed in revolutions per second. (a) The driving motor is a shunt-connected d-c motor. Its terminal voltage is maintained constant. With field current of 2.3 amp it is known to run at 50 rev/sec (rated speed) when delivering 10 kw (rated power) through its shaft. Its speed regulation is 0.07 (often written 7 per cent). At what speed will it drive the pump, and how much power will it deliver to the pump (field current being still 2.3 amp)? (b) The driving motor is a series-connected d-c motor. Its terminal voltage is maintained constant. It is known to run at 50 rev/sec when delivering 10 kw power through its shaft. Its torque at zero speed is 130 newton-meters. At what speed will it drive the pump, and how much power will it deliver to the pump? **(Sec. 74)**

6-18. Show in a sketch how the direction of rotation of a d-c series motor can be changed. Also, show how the direction of rotation of a shunt motor can be reversed by switching, remembering the danger of having, even momentarily, little or no field. **(Sec. 76)**

6-19. Referring to other books, write a one-page description, with a diagram, of a homopolar generator, explaining its operation. Contrast with Adkins' statement in Section 78. **(Sec. 78)**

6-20. As suggested in the last paragraph of Section 80, write the transfer function relating torque to field current. (a) Assume a linear relation between field current and flux. (b) Discuss what would be changed if this relation were not linear. **(Sec. 80)**

THE SYNCHRONOUS MACHINE

chapter 7

85. Synchronous Torque

We saw in the last chapter, in equation 59-2, that most of the torque in a rotating machine comes from the term

$$T_{\text{developed}} = i_1 i_2 \, \frac{dM}{d\theta} \qquad (85\text{-}1)$$

To obtain steady torque from a commutator machine, armature current i_2 is reversed (by the commutator) at the proper instant; this is necessary each time that rotation of the machine results in reversal of the sign of the term $dM/d\theta$. Current in each armature coil is reversed at the critical moment. The commutator reverses i_2 at the same instant that $dM/d\theta$ is reversed by rotation, so torque remains always in the same direction.

In this chapter we consider another means for obtaining torque in an unchanging direction. We let one of the currents, say i_2, be alternating current. If i_2, the armature current, is an alternating current, and if it reverses at the same instant that $dM/d\theta$ is reversed by rotation of the machine, again the torque is continuously in the same direction though there is no commutation.

If i_2 is a sinusoidal current with maximum value I_a (a for armature), we write

$$i_2 = I_a \cos \omega t \qquad (85\text{-}2)$$

For mutual inductance we use the sinusoidal approximation that was used in equation 59-3. If the armature is turning at angular velocity Ω, the angle θ through which it has turned is $\Omega t + \delta$, and this gives, as an approximation,

$$M = M_{\max} \sin (\Omega t + \delta) \qquad (85\text{-}3)$$

(85)

Torque is then found from equation 85-1 by differentiating M:

$$T_{developed} = i_1(I_a \cos \omega t)[M_{max} \cos (\Omega t + \delta)] \qquad (85\text{-}4)$$

Now the average torque developed is the average, over a cycle, of this expression, and it is evident at once that the average is other than zero only if Ω, the speed of rotation (in electrical radians per second), is equal to ω, the frequency of the applied alternating armature voltage (in electrical radians per second). That is, there is an average torque only if the machine is turning at exactly the speed determined by the frequency of the driving voltage. It is for this reason that a machine operating on this principle is called a *synchronous* machine.

Furthermore, we can see that the phase angle must be right. If δ is zero, the average torque (the average of equation 85-4) is maximum; if δ is 90 degrees, the average is zero. That is, if the rotation of the machine is not in the right phase relation with the armature current, the average torque developed is less than maximum, and it can be zero, or even negative. Hence the synchronous machine must run not only at the correct speed but also at the correct angle.

In the foregoing discussion, i_1 represents constant field current and i_2 represents alternating armature current, but it is not specified which part of the machine must be stationary and which rotating. As a matter of fact, it makes no difference. The armature may rotate, as in Figure 18a, but much more commonly it is stationary, as in Figure 85a, while the field structure rotates. Whichever rotates, the mutual inductance M alternates in equation 85-1, and i_2 alternates while i_1 remains constant.

As a practical matter, of course, it is necessary to conduct current to the coil that is on the rotating element of the machine. If an a-c machine were actually constructed with a rotating armature as shown in Figure 18a, the armature current would be led in through slip rings. These are rings of brass or other metal coaxial with the shaft of the rotor but insulated from it. They turn with the rotor, and blocks of carbon, called brushes, that are held by the frame of the machine, but insulated from the frame, rub on the rings as they turn. These stationary "brushes" are connected by copper wires to the machine terminals. Thus electric current enters at one machine terminal, goes through a brush to a slip ring, through the armature winding, to the other slip ring, and out through the other brush to the other terminal.

The alternative arrangement is indicated in Figure 85a. Armature conductors are in slots in the inner surface of the *stator*, and field coils are wound on *rotor* poles.

(85)

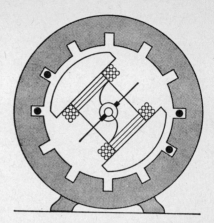

Figure 85a. An a-c machine with rotating field structure (2-pole).

With this construction it is not necessary to bring armature current through slip rings; the armature is not moving and can be connected directly to the machine terminals. On the other hand, the coils of the field poles are now on the rotor and must be supplied with direct current through a pair of slip rings. Thus the rotating-field design has not eliminated slip rings, but field current is much less than armature current and is hence more easily conducted through sliding contacts. Moreover, the d-c field winding can be supplied through two slip rings, whereas there would have to be three or four rings to carry armature current from a two-phase or a three-phase a-c machine.

In this section we have mentioned only one armature coil, and hence a single-phase armature has been assumed. This is quite possible, but a two-phase machine is also used; and indeed the most common machine has three phases in the armature winding.

86. A Two-Phase Armature Winding

It would clearly be extravagant to use only one coil in one pair of slots in the armature of a generator, since the capacity of the machine can be practically doubled by placing another coil in an adjacent pair of slots in the unused armature surface. Two such coils, as in Figure 85a, connected in series, generate nearly twice as much voltage as one. However, there is a limit to the number of coils that can efficiently be connected in series.

Two coils in adjacent slots generate electromotive forces of equal amplitude, assuming the coils are identical, but their electromotive

(86)

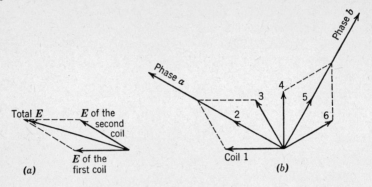

Figure 86. (a) Electromotive forces of 2 adjacent coils. (b) Electromotive forces of 6 coils added to give 2 phase voltages.

forces are not quite in phase with each other. The coil in the first slot generates an electromotive force that leads the electromotive force of the coil in the following slot by a fraction of a cycle. Figure 86a shows phasors for such electromotive forces, assuming them to be sinusoidal. The electromotive force generated by the two coils in series is the vector sum of the two phasors, and, as in the figure, its amplitude is slightly less than twice the amplitude of either alone. If coils are placed in two or three or four pairs of slots and all are connected in series, their electromotive-force phasors will add at continuingly greater angles. Each successive coil contributes less than the one before to the amplitude of the total electromotive force. Therefore, while it is highly desirable to utilize the available surface of the armature by placing coils in all the slots (of Figure 85a), it is not efficient to connect all these coils in series.

Let us suppose that three coils are placed in three adjacent pairs of slots. These coils are connected in series. Three pairs of slots in the armature are thus used, and three pairs remain unoccupied. It would not be efficient to put coils in these unoccupied slots and connect them in series with the others, for the additional electromotive forces would be so much out of phase that they would add little to the electromotive forces of the first few coils. See the phasors for coils 1 to 6 in Figure 86b.

However, there is no reason why three coils in these other three pairs of slots cannot be connected together as a separate group, independent of the first group, with their connections brought out independently to another pair of terminals. In Figure 86b we see six phasors of electromotive force from the six coils that can be placed

(86)

in all six pairs of slots shown in Figure 85a. If coils 1, 2, and 3 are connected in series, their electromotive forces add to give the electromotive force (which is also the no-load terminal voltage) marked *phase a;* coils 4, 5, and 6 in series give the terminal voltage marked *phase b.*

A machine connected in this way is known as a two-phase machine. It generates two voltages that are 90 degrees out of phase, as in Figure 86b. It has two circuits that are electrically separate from each other. (It is possible to connect one end of each circuit to a single terminal, thus having a total of three instead of four terminals, but this is a detail of no significance.)

Two-phase machines are used in control systems. Particularly two-phase induction motors (which are discussed later) are used as torque motors. For primary power generation, however, they are obsolete, having given way to three-phase machines.

87. A Three-Phase Armature Winding

A three-phase machine differs from a two-phase machine only in having three separate armature circuits instead of two. Figure 87a

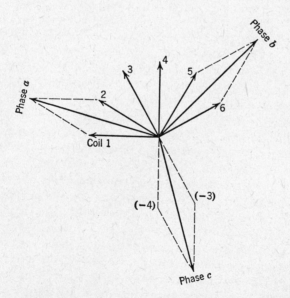

Figure 87a. Electromotive forces of 6 coils added to give 3 phase voltages.

(87)

shows the same six coil voltages added to give three phase voltages. Coils 1 and 2 are connected in series to provide phase a, coils 5 and 6 give phase b, and coils 3 and 4, connected in series (but with the connections to the terminals made in such a way as to reverse the voltage), give phase c. Note that the voltage phasors of phases a, b, and c are 120 degrees apart. Each voltage is one-third of a cycle out of phase with the others, providing a highly desirable symmetry of electrical behavior.

It is evident that armature connections from a three-phase machine can be brought out to six terminals. By connecting one end of each of the phases together it is possible to use a total of only four terminals: one for each phase and one common return. For some purposes it is even permissible to eliminate the common return wire and use only three terminals. However, discussion of three-phase circuitry would be out of place in this book.

88. Excitation of Alternating-Current Machines

A rotating magnetic field structure must be provided to induce electromotive force in the stationary armature windings of an a-c generator. The *salient* pole structure shown in Figure 85a is typical of small machines, although it is rather unusual to have only two poles.

In the large, high-speed a-c generators, driven by steam turbines, which produce most of the world's electrical power, there is field current in a winding on the rotor, but the structure does not have salient poles. There is nothing like the iron spool of Figure 85a with wire wound around it. Instead, the rotor is an iron cylinder with conductors set in slots as shown in Figure 88a. All these conductors (and there are many in a slot, and many slots) are connected in

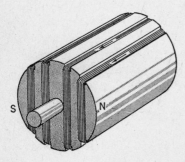

Figure 88a. A non-salient pole or "round rotor" field structure.

(88)

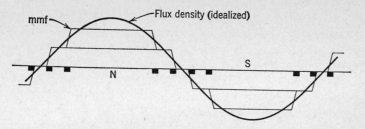

Figure 88b. Magnetomotive force and flux density as functions of distance around the air gap.

series, and direct current passes through them, creating a magnetic field. There will be a north pole at the region marked N, and a south pole on the opposite side, at S.

An advantage of this non-salient-pole construction is that the distributed winding produces magnetic flux at the surface of the armature with a reasonable approximation of sinusoidal distribution. The flux density is greatest near the centers of the poles (marked N and S) and diminishes to zero at the top and bottom of the diagram. See Figure 88b. The magnetomotive force curve has a step at each rotor slot containing a field coil, for magnetomotive force around the flux paths depends on the number of turns of the field winding linked. As in Figure 88b, the sharply stepped magnetomotive force of the field winding is somewhat smoothed by the air gap to an approximately sinuoidal flux density at the armature surface.

Direct current for the field winding must be provided. It usually comes from a small auxiliary d-c generator called an exciter, or possibly from a rectifier fed from an a-c circuit. The amount of d-c power used to excite an a-c generator is a small fraction (perhaps 1 or 2 per cent in a large machine) of the power output of the a-c generator. It is not theoretically necessary that any power be consumed in excitation, for no power is required to maintain a constant magnetic field, but practically there is unavoidable power loss in the field winding owing to resistance of the wire. This resistance loss can be made small by using large wire. From the economic point of view there is an optimum size that balances cost of copper wire (and a larger machine) against cost of power wasted (and additional provision for cooling).

89. Generated Electromotive Force, Alternating-Current Machine

The rms value of induced electromotive force in an armature coil of N turns was seen in equation 30-3 to be $4.44fN\Phi$, where f is frequency and Φ the amount of field flux that links the armature coil in the position of maximum linkages. For practical use in a polyphase a-c machine this formula is slightly modified to give the induced electromotive force per phase:

$$E_{rms} = 4.44k_bk_pfN_{ph}\Phi \qquad (89\text{-}1)$$

where f is frequency (cycles/second)

Φ is flux entering the armature from each field pole (webers)

N_{ph} is number of armature-turns connected in series, per phase

k_b, breadth factor, and k_p, pitch factor, require explanation (given below)

The breadth factor, or distribution factor, is needed because a practical winding is distributed in several pairs of armature slots, as mentioned in Sections 86 and 87, instead of being placed entirely in one pair of slots. Since the electromotive forces of coils in different slots are slightly out of phase (as in Figures 86b and 87a), the total electromotive force is somewhat less than the electromotive force per turn times the number of turns; k_b is a factor that takes this into account.[*]

The pitch factor is needed because the two sides of an armature coil are not usually placed in diametrically opposite slots. In Figures 30b and 85a opposite sides of a coil are shown 180 degrees apart on the armature, so that they occupy corresponding positions under opposite poles of the field structure, but for various practical reasons the two sides of a coil are usually something less than 180 electrical degrees apart. The induced electromotive force of the coil is correspondingly reduced, and pitch factor k_p takes this into account.[†]

---

[*] The numerical value of K_b is very nearly 0.96 for a three-phase armature, or 0.91 for a two-phase armature, of normal design. (From McFarland, Reference 89.)

[†] Fractional pitch coils reduce the emf of harmonics more than the emf of the fundamental, thereby improving waveform; also, fractional-pitch coils require less copper. The numerical value of k_p is commonly between 0.9 and 1.0. See McFarland, Reference 89.

90. Synchronous Reactance

The terminal voltage of an a-c machine is different from the generated electromotive force, mainly because of voltage drop in the reactance of the armature winding. There is voltage drop in the resistance of the armature winding also, as there is in a d-c machine, but in most a-c machines the reactance is much greater than the resistance. This is particularly true in large machines (over 5 kilovolt-amperes) in which resistance is small, and in high-frequency machines (400 cycles per second or more) in which reactance is large. In the small 60-cycle machines that are sometimes used for control purposes, resistance may be appreciable or even predominant.

Thinking in terms of generator action, we may say that terminal voltage is less than generated electromotive force by the voltage drop in armature resistance and reactance. In each phase of the machine,

$$V = E - (R_a + jX_a)I \tag{90-1}$$

V, E, and I are complex quantities, the transforms of terminal voltage, generated electromotive force, and armature current. R_a is the resistance of the armature winding. Specifically, it is the *effective* resistance, which is slightly higher than the ordinary d-c resistance because it includes certain small losses resulting from such a-c phenomena as skin effect. X_a is the *synchronous reactance* of the machine, and it includes both leakage reactance and armature reaction.

Synchronous reactance, like any reactance, is a measure of the voltage induced in a circuit by the alternating magnetic field that surrounds it when alternating current flows. Part of the magnetic field of synchronous reactance is *leakage flux,* which links the armature winding but not the field winding, causing the *leakage reactance* of the machine. The rest of the field of synchronous reactance is *armature reaction flux,* which links the armature winding and also the field winding. It is customary to differentiate between these two, for they are affected differently by magnetic saturation of the iron of the machine. However, for present purposes we shall neglect saturation and assume linear magnetic relations in the machine. Hence we can simply say that synchronous reactance results from all the magnetic flux produced in the machine by armature current regardless of the path followed by that flux.

91. Phasor Diagrams

The usual conceptual model or equivalent circuit of a synchronous machine is shown in Figure 91a. Each one of the three phases of the machine is thought of as if it were a source of constant electromotive force E in series with the synchronous reactance of the winding and also, if it is large enough to be significant, the armature resistance. This extremely simplified concept is adequate for a general understanding although careful work with synchronous machines requires more precise analysis.*

Equation 90-1 is the mathematical model of Figure 91a, and the corresponding phasor diagram is shown as Figure 91b. In words, the terminal voltage plus the voltage drop in armature resistance and synchronous reactance equal the generated electromotive force. Perhaps it should be pointed out that when there is armature current this generated electromotive force is a purely hypothetical concept; it does not then actually exist anywhere, and could not be measured. E is generated in the same armature coils in which the voltage drops IR_a and jIX_a take place, and cannot be separated from them.

A few general comments may be made in connection with Figure 91b. It is evident that E differs from V because of the IZ drop in the armature impedance. If armature resistance is low, as it is in large machines, the difference between E and V is mainly due to the synchronous reactance drop jIX_a. If armature resistance is low, and if armature current I is approximately in phase with the terminal voltage, as in Figure 91b (giving a power factor of approximately unity), the difference between E and V is a phasor nearly at right angles to the V

---

*There is mutual inductance between the phase windings of a three-phase armature, so the voltage of one phase is somewhat dependent on current in the other phases. The simple representations suggested in this section, and most of the discussions in this chapter, relate to machines with balanced currents (currents, that is, equal in magnitude and one-third cycle out of phase) in the three windings.

Mutual inductances and other complicating effects within a synchronous machine are taken into account, when needed, by giving different values to X_a of Figure 91a for positive, negative, and zero-sequence reactance in case of unbalanced currents; steady-state, transient, and subtransient reactance in case of transient disturbances; saturated and unsaturated values depending on the flux density in the magnetic circuit; direct and quadrature axis values depending on reluctance as determined by the relative angle of armature magnetic poles and rotating field structure. This suggests thirty-six different values of X_a, but only a dozen or so are usually distinguished.

(91)

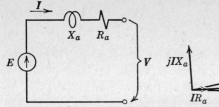

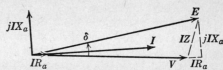

Figure 91a. Equivalent circuit of a synchronous machine.

Figure 91b. Phasor diagram of a synchronous machine running as a generator (producing *P*). *E* is driven ahead of *V*.

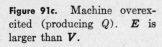

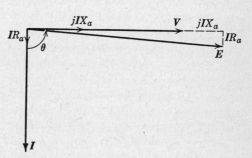

Figure 91c. Machine overexcited (producing *Q*). *E* is larger than *V*.

Figure 91d. Machine underexcited (consuming *Q*). *E* is smaller than *V*.

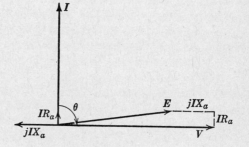

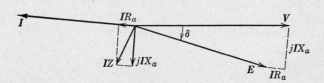

Figure 91e. Machine running as a motor (consuming *P*). *E* is pulled back behind *V*.

(91)

phasor, and hence E has nearly the same magnitude as V. The chief effect of the jIX_a drop is to cause a difference in angle (marked δ) between the E and V phasors.

If, as another possibility, the armature current is nearly 90 degrees out of phase with the terminal voltage, as shown in Figure 91c (the phase angle between V and I is marked θ), there is a large difference in magnitude between V and E, and little difference in angle. Figure 91c is drawn specifically for a machine running as a generator with a load of inductive reactance. Under these circumstances, E is larger than V by (approximately) the numerical value of IX_a. For generator operation, this means that the only way to keep terminal voltage of the machine up to its rated value when it is supplying a heavy inductive load is to increase greatly the field current of the machine in order to give E the necessary large value.

On the other hand, if the armature current of a generator is supplied to a capacitive load, terminal voltage is larger than generated electromotive force, as in Figure 91d. This may be looked upon as an example of resonance between the capacitance of the load and the inductance of the machine. A generator supplying a capacitive load must be given *diminished* excitation if it is to have rated (normal) terminal voltage, for V is larger than E by (approximately) the numerical value of IX_a.

Although the foregoing discussion has been in terms of generator action, the behavior of a synchronous machine as a *motor* is exactly similar. Figure 91e shows an example of motor action. Motor operation may be recognized by the fact that I is opposed to V (or at least has a component opposed to V) instead of being in phase with V (or having a component in phase).†

92. Active Power

If a three-phase synchronous machine is running connected to a three-phase power system, it can be either a generator or a motor. If it is *driven* (as by a steam turbine) it is a generator and supplies electrical power to the system. If it is *driving* a mechanical load attached to its shaft (an air compressor or the propeller of a ship, for instance) it is a motor and draws power from the electrical system.

---

† That positive power is output, and negative power is input, follows from our having drawn the reference arrows for E and I in the same direction in the circuit of Figure 91a. If we had chosen to reverse either arrow (and the choice is quite arbitrary) all the phasor diagrams would have been changed correspondingly, and input power (motor power) would have been positive.

(92)

Figure 92a. There is no armature current when $E = V$.

Whether the machine is running as a generator or a motor, electromotive force is generated in each of the windings of its armature, and current flows in each armature winding. Let us consider the relations that determine the amount and direction of power.

First, let the electromotive force E generated in our machine be exactly equal to the system voltage V (Figure 92a). To obtain this condition, the field current of the machine is adjusted to give the right magnitude of electromotive force, the shaft of the machine is driven at exactly the right speed, and furthermore the angular position of the machine rotor is so adjusted that the generated electromotive force is precisely in phase with the terminal voltage. With this relation the phasors of generated electromotive force and applied line voltage are identical in both magnitude and angle, as in Figure 92a, and $E = V$. There will then be no armature current; consider equation 91-1 and the equivalent circuit of Figure 91a.

Suppose mechanical power is now applied to the shaft of the machine, tending to make it turn faster. The immediate effect is to push the rotor ahead, relative to the line voltage, so E becomes slightly advanced relative to V. This is approximately the condition shown in Figure 91b. Current now flows, driven by the voltage difference between E and V, which is IZ. Because the impedance of the machine is largely reactive the current lags nearly 90 degrees behind $E - V$. It is therefore largely in phase with E, and power is supplied from the machine to the line. The rotor moves far enough ahead of the neutral position shown in Figure 92a to make power output from the machine equal the mechanical power input to its shaft, and equilibrium is established. The rotor advances no farther, for power input is now no greater than power output, and the machine continues to run steadily, in this new position, at exactly synchronous speed.

As another possibility, suppose a mechanical load is placed on the shaft of the machine, instead of a driving torque. This load retards rotation of the rotor, and pulls E back relative to V, as in Figure 91e. Again there is current; again it lags nearly 90 degrees behind $E - V$, which is IZ. But this time current is largely in opposition to E, and power is therefore received by the machine from the line. The rotor falls back in phase, relative to line voltage, until equilibrium between power input and power output is reached. The machine then runs as a motor at synchronous speed.

As in any circuit, the power supplied from the machine to the external circuit is

$$P = |V||I|\cos\theta \qquad (92\text{-}1)$$

where $|V|$ is the rms value of the terminal voltage, $|I|$ is the rms value of armature current, and θ is the phase angle between them. If the angle between V and I is less than 90 degrees, as in Figure 91b, $\cos\theta$ is a positive quantity, and power is positive. Considering the arrows of Figure 91a, positive power corresponds to power output, and therefore to generator action. If the angle between V and I is greater than 90 degrees, $\cos\theta$ is negative, and power is negative, as in Figure 91e. Negative power indicates input power, and hence motor action.

In thinking about synchronous machine action, and particularly motor action, we find it helpful to rewrite equation 90-1 as

$$I = \frac{E - V}{R_a + jX_a} \qquad (92\text{-}2)$$

The numerator is the difference between induced electromotive force and terminal voltage that causes current to flow through the armature winding; it is marked IZ in Figures 91b and e. The denominator is the impedance of the armature winding, and since X_a is usually much greater than R_a, the current I lags nearly 90 degrees behind this difference voltage that produces it, as shown in the figures.

93. Reactive Power

Return now to the neutral condition of Figure 92a and, without any load on the machine, increase the excitation by supplying more field current. This increases E, without changing its phase position. Figure 91c shows the result approximately. E is greater than V, and the armature current, driven by the voltage difference between E and V, is approximately in quadrature with E and V. (We are still assuming small armature resistance.) Although there may be a large current, there is little power, for θ is near 90 degrees.

In this situation the machine is said to be producing a large amount of *reactive* power. The symbol used for reactive power is Q, and by definition

$$Q = |V||I|\sin\theta \qquad (93\text{-}1)$$

where θ is the phase angle as measured from I to V.

(93)

Clearly, Q is large when θ is near 90 degrees. In the phasor diagrams of Section 91, P (which may now be distinguished as *active* power) is proportional to the component of I in phase with V, and Q, the *reactive* power, is proportional to the component of I in quadrature with V.

We say that an *overexcited* synchronous machine *supplies* reactive power, as in the foregoing example. This is comparable to saying that a driven machine supplies active power, as in Section 92.

On the other hand, an *underexcited* machine *consumes* reactive power. If field current is reduced from the value corresponding to Figure 92a, E becomes smaller than V, and the condition of Figure 91d results. Current is again in quadrature, or largely so, with E and V, and there is little active power P either produced or consumed by the machine, but a relatively large amount of reactive power is received by the machine. Q is the reactive power *produced* by the machine, and when equation 93-1 is applied to the situation of Figure 91d, Q is negative because θ, the angle from I to V, is a negative angle. This means that reactive power is being consumed by the machine.

To summarize, a mechanically *driven* machine, such as a generator with a resistive load, produces active power P. A motor, *driving* a mechanical load, receives active power P from the electrical system.

An *overexcited* machine, or a generator with an inductive load, produces * reactive power Q. An *underexcited* machine, or a generator with a capacitive load, receives reactive power Q.

The operation of any synchronous machine can be specified by stating the amounts of P and Q it is producing or consuming. Thus if the machine output is 500 kilowatts and -250 kilovars (the name of the unit is an abbreviation of *kilov*olt-*a*mperes-*r*eactive), it is clearly running as an underexcited generator.

It is a matter of great practical importance that a synchronous machine of normal design, connected to a power system, has the amount of Q adjusted by changing the field current, while the amount of P is adjusted by changing the torque on the shaft. It will be remembered that the power to or from a d-c machine is altered by adjusting the excitation, but changing the excitation on an a-c machine does not have this effect. Power to or from an a-c machine is altered by changing its angle, and this is done by changing the mechanical device (prime mover or load) attached to its shaft.

---

* Physically, Q is a measure of the rate at which energy is delivered to a reactive element in the circuit, to be stored for an instant and then be discharged back into the circuit a quarter of a cycle later. This reactive energy is shuttled back and forth, but is not consumed by the reactive element.

(93)

Another obvious difference between the d-c machine and the synchronous is that a synchronous machine must run at a speed having a precise relation to the system frequency. It does not have the latitude that we found with d-c machines. On a 60-cycle-per-second system a synchronous two-pole machine *must* turn 60 revolutions per second, a four-pole machine 30 revolutions per second, a six-pole machine 20 revolutions per second, and so on.

94. The Armature Field in a Synchronous Machine

Let us consider a machine with a three-phase armature winding. The armature of an a-c generator is stationary, as shown in Figures 85a or 94 a, and the field structure rotates. The direct and quadrature axes of the machine rotate with the field structure; the direct axis is the axis in which the main field winding produces magnetomotive force.

Lines across Figure 94a indicate the three phase belts. Coils in the part of the armature with horizontal shading are connected in series to constitute phase a. Only two coils are indicated in the figure, but there would usually be more. (Several slots per pole, two coil sides per slot, and a fractional pitch winding are almost always used.) Whatever the arrangement of coils in phase band a,

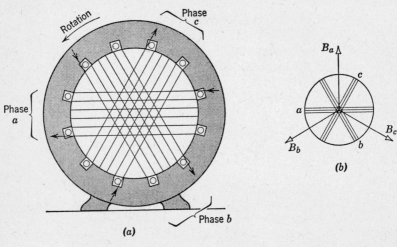

(a)

(b)

Figure 94. (a) Phase belts in a three-phase armature. (b) Positive directions of magnetic fields of the three-phase armature coils.

(94)

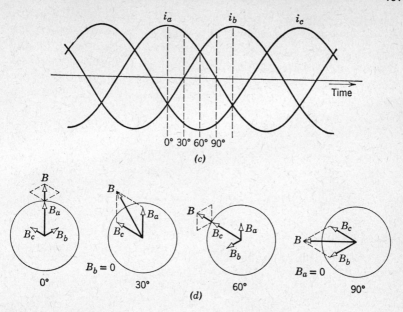

Figure 94. (*c*) Three-phase currents. (*d*) Fields of the three-phase armature coils at several instants, and the resultant "rotating field."

the magnetic intensity H produced by this part of the winding will be vertical, either up or down, and hence the magnetic flux density B produced by phase a will be vertical also. Figure 94*b* shows an arrow marked B_a pointing in the direction that magnetic flux is produced by current in phase a provided the current in phase a is flowing in the circuit in the direction that we shall arbitrarily call positive.

Figure 94*a* shows also the phase belts b and c. Each is spaced 120 degrees from the others, and if all the phase windings are connected similarly and symmetrically, positive current in phase b (acting alone) would produce flux in the direction marked B_b in Figure 94*b*, and the same figure shows the direction in which positive current in phase c (acting alone) would produce flux.

However, as appears in Figure 94*c*, there is never positive current in all three phases at once. When i_a is at its positive maximum, both i_b and i_c are negative, and each has half its maximum value. At this particular instant, then, the three flux densities corresponding to these three currents are as indicated in the part of Figure 94*d*

(94)

that is marked 0°. Assuming linearity and symmetry, these three flux densities add to give the total flux density marked B.

At this instant, as shown, the current i_a is at its positive maximum, so the flux of phase a is positive (upward) and its magnitude is 1 unit. The current i_b is negative and half as great, so the flux of phase b is negative (toward the right and upward) and its magnitude is ½. Current i_c is negative and its magnitude is ½, so phase c flux is negative (toward the left and upward) with magnitude ½. Addition of these three flux-density vectors * gives total flux density directly upward with a relative magnitude of ¾.

95. A Rotating Flux Pattern

Now consider the flux-density vectors a twelfth of a cycle later, at the instant marked 30°. At this instant i_b is zero; i_a is positive and i_c negative, and both have the magnitude of cos 30° or ½√3. The sum of the two is a vector at the angle shown, 30° counterclockwise from the flux at time 0°, and since the component of each of them in this direction is ½√3·½√3 = ¾, the magnitude of the total flux density at this instant is again ¾.

These two diagrams and the two following in Figure 94d suggest strongly that the three-phase currents in the armature winding of Figure 94a produce a magnetic field of constant magnitude but changing direction. We find the magnitude to be ¾ at each instant, while the direction of the field is first at 0°, then at 30°, then at 60°, and so on. The direction of the field appears to be rotating, relative to the armature, at synchronous speed.

This concept of a rotating magnetic field pattern † is tremendously

---

* Note that these arrows represent vectors in the ordinary sense: they show *magnitude* of a quantity and its *direction in space*. They are totally different from the arrows of Figure 87a, for instance, which do not show the direction of anything in space but are to be interpreted in terms of an assumed rotation to give a time relation. These two kinds of arrows are sometimes distinguished by being called "space vectors" and "time vectors," respectively, although the latter are now usually called "phasors."

† Since a magnetic field does not move, being merely a condition of space in the frame of reference of the observer, what do we mean by a rotating magnetic field pattern? We mean, as is seen in the derivation, that magnetic forces in the field are first in one direction, then in another, and so on. The directions of magnetic forces have changed; no physical entity has rotated. To say that "traffic was north and south, but the lights have changed and it has now turned east and west" does not imply that streets have spun around like the spokes of a wheel, but only that there is now a new direction of traffic flow. To speak, as

important. We shall be using it with generators and with synchronous motors, with common three-phase induction motors, and with the two-phase induction motors of control systems, with Selsyn devices in synchro systems, with capacitor motors for refrigerators, for the starting of many single-phase motors and, indeed, for nearly all rotating electrical devices that do not have commutators. The idea needs to be thoroughly understood.

96. Torque in a Synchronous Machine

Looking at Figure 94a or, better, Figure 85a, let us think of the currents in a three-phase armature winding * as they produce a magnetic field. The field pattern produced by the armature rotates at synchronous speed. The iron rotor of the machine also rotates at the same speed. They rotate together.

Let us think of the fields and the field poles as they would be observed by a small but intelligent bug riding on the rotor of the machine. He is shown in Figure 96a. The salient poles of the rotor on which he rides do not seem to him to be moving (even as the turning earth seems stationary to you and me).

If he looks up he can see the armature going by above his head (as we see the stars pass) but—and this is the essential point—if he could measure magnetic fields he would find that the magnetic field produced by the apparently moving armature was, for him, stationary. He would find that a magnetic pole produced by armature current remained in a fixed position in his sky, and he could make a note of its position as being so-many degrees from the direct axis of his field poles. He would find that it was constant (to a first approximation) in both position and intensity.

The bug observes that there is a torque exerted on the field poles by the magnetic field of the armature, and that the amount of this torque depends on both the strength and the position of the armature poles. He observes that the most favorable position for an armature

---

we do, of a rotating magnetic field does not mean that flux lines sweep around, but only that magnetic forces change direction.

It must be noted that the pattern of lines in a magnetic flux plot is meaningful, showing the direction and magnitude of magnetic force, but individual lines have no physical meaning whatever.

* Or in a two-phase armature winding, or an armature winding of any number of phases greater than one. Any polyphase winding can produce a rotating magnetic field of constant magnitude.

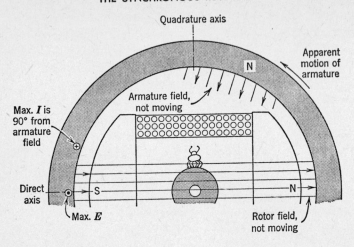

Figure 96a. Bug's-eye view of a synchronous motor with load, as in Figure 91e. (The bug is riding on the rotor at synchronous speed; this is his frame of reference.)

pole of given strength is on the quadrature axis, half way between the poles of the field structure. This is the position in which an armature pole of given strength can exert the greatest torque on the field structure.

He observes conditions as load is gradually applied to the shaft of his motor, starting from the situation shown in Figure 92a when $E = V$. At first, with E equal to V, there is no armature pole, for there is no armature current; consequently there is no torque. With a small load on the shaft, however, an armature pole appears. It is weak because current is small, but it is on (or near) the quadrature axis, and so is favorably located for producing magnetic torque.

As load is increased the armature pole becomes stronger, but at the same time it moves farther from the quadrature axis. The magnetic torque reaches a maximum when the pole has moved some 30 to 45 electrical degrees from the quadrature axis.* With displacement beyond that point the armature pole continues to increase in strength, for armature current still becomes greater, but torque grows less as the position of the pole becomes less favorable.

---

* It would be 45 degrees with a non-salient-pole machine, and approximates 30 degrees for ordinary salient-pole design. See Figure 97a. Note, however, that this angle observed by the bug is not δ, but is the angle between E and I (under the specified conditions this is about $\frac{1}{2}\delta$, as in Figure 91e).

(96)

97. Power-Angle Relation

It will be noted that there is a certain maximum torque, and a proportional maximum power, that cannot be exceeded by a synchronous machine. The amount of this maximum torque is proportional to the strength of the field poles, and to the terminal voltage. With a given amount of field current and a certain terminal voltage, a motor can be loaded to the amount set by this maximum torque, but no more. If an attempt is made to increase the load still more, it will merely bring the motor to a jolting stop.

For the same reason, a generator can supply only a certain maximum amount of power to the system to which it is connected. If an attempt is made to drive it beyond this maximum it loses synchronism with the system. Either motor or generator, when the limit of stability is exceeded, is said to fall out of step.

The relation between power and angle can be expressed quantitatively. If we neglect resistance and losses, magnetic saturation, and saliency of poles, the relation is quite simple:

$$P = \frac{|V||E|}{X_a} \sin \delta \qquad (97\text{-}1)$$

where $|V|$ is the rms value of applied voltage (volts)

$|E|$ is the rms value of generated electromotive force (volts)

X_a is the synchronous reactance (ohms)

δ is the angle from V to E, the so-called power angle or torque angle

P is power output (watts)

This relation is shown in the power-angle curve of Figure 97a. The solid line in that diagram agrees with equation 97-1 and is based on the same assumptions.* The dash line illustrates the type of curve

---

* Equation 97-1 can be shown by a graphical derivation. In Figure 97b, let V be applied voltage. E is electromotive force, and a dashed arc is its locus as mechanical load and hence angle relative to V are changed. The locus of $E - V$ is the circle with center at $-V$ and radius $|E|$. By equation 92-2, neglecting resistance of the machine, armature current is $I = (E - V)/jX_a$. The locus of I is the circle with center at jV/X_a and radius $|E/X_a|$. Power output is $|V|$ times the projection of I on V. The diagram shows P to be equal to $|V|$ times the projection of jE/X_a on V. Algebraically, P is $|V|(|E|/X_a) \sin \delta$, which is equation 97-1. Appropriate modification will take armature resistance into account. (Reluctance torque can be included if direct and quadrature reactances are different, but this is beyond the scope of the present treatment.)

(97)

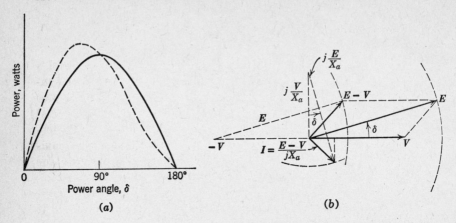

Figure 97. (*a*) Power-angle curves for similar synchronous machines with non-salient poles (solid line) and salient poles (dashed). (*b*) Demonstration of equation 97-1.

to be expected for a machine with salient poles. The machine with salient poles has reluctance torque as well as torque due to current in the field coils, and this has the double advantage of stiffening the machine—producing a given power output with a smaller angle—and of giving a higher maximum or pull-out power.

Reluctance torque is the torque exerted by the magnetic field of the armature on the iron pole of a machine because the pole piece is salient. (Reluctance torque is discussed in Sections 45 and 46.) Inclusion of reluctance torque corresponds to retaining in equation 59-1 the term involving $dL_{22}/d\theta$ as well as the term including $dM/d\theta$; this is required when the self-inductance of the armature winding L_{22} changes (with θ) because of saliency of the field poles. Figure 85*a* shows a field structure in which the saliency of poles is quite marked; Figure 88*a* shows a field structure with saliency reduced to the minimum of mere slots for the windings. When poles are salient the self-inductance L_{22} of an armature circuit is not constant but depends on the relative position of the pole structure. $dL_{22}/d\theta$ is then not zero, and both of the last two terms of equation 59-1 contribute to the torque. The dashed curve of Figure 97*a* then shows the power of the salient pole machine.

(97)

98. Reluctance and Hysteresis Motors

A small synchronous motor with salient poles can run on reluctance torque alone. A fractional-horsepower motor may not even be provided with a field winding. Its salient poles, magnetized by the armature current, are pulled along by the rotating magnetic field of the stator and it turns at synchronous speed on *reluctance torque* alone.

Motors in electric clocks are of this kind. They are, in fact, single-phase synchronous motors, the operation of which is considered in Sections 45 and 127.

Another type of synchronous motor runs on *hysteresis torque*. It will be recalled that hysteresis is the tendency of magnetic material such as steel to retain a magnetized condition that has been imparted to it. Suppose the rotor of a small motor is merely a cylinder of steel, with no winding and no salient poles. A polyphase stator winding (two-phase or three-phase) produces a rotating magnetic field. The rotating stator field magnetizes the steel of the rotor, and then as the stator field continues to rotate it draws the magnetized rotor along with it. The magnetic poles of the rotor are not directly under the poles of the stator; rather, because of hysteresis in the steel, the rotor poles are where the stator poles were a short time earlier. Hence the poles of the rotating stator field are always leading the induced magnetic poles of the rotor surface by a small angle, and because of this angle there is a continual torque on the rotor enabling it to run as a motor.

The amount of torque derived from hysteresis is not very great. Reluctance torque can be provided more cheaply than hysteresis torque. However, hysteresis torque is very steady despite fluctuations of the supply voltage in either amplitude or phase, and this makes it desirable for driving record players.

Also, hysteresis torque is effective when the rotor is running at less than synchronous speed, and reluctance torque is not. At synchronous speed the rotor poles induced in a hysteresis motor remain at fixed spots on the rotor surface as the rotor is pulled along by the rotating field of the stator winding. If the rotor is turning at less than synchronous speed, the induced poles, which must go at synchronous speed, move over the rotor surface at a speed equal to the difference, called the slip speed. Hysteresis torque on the rotor is largely independent of rotor speed. Hence, unlike a motor that depends on reluctance torque, a hysteresis motor is able

(98)

to start itself from standstill and bring itself up to full synchronous speed.

99. Summary

A synchronous machine is another example of a doubly excited device. It differs from the commutator machine mainly in having alternating current supplied to the armature winding. It can operate only at synchronous speed, and only in the correct angular relation.

The armature of a synchronous machine is usually the *stator*, and the field structure is the *rotor*. The armature commonly has a three-phase winding. The field structure may have salient or non-salient poles, and direct current is supplied to its winding.

The generated electromotive force depends on number of armature conductors and on the flux and speed. A synchronous machine is often considered to be equivalent to an electromotive force in series with armature resistance and synchronous reactance. Phasor diagrams show the relationships between the electrical quantities. Active power and reactive power are considered. In an ordinary synchronous machine the flow of active power is governed by shaft torque; the flow of reactive power is governed by the field current.

Three-phase current in the armature winding of a synchronous machine produces a rotating flux pattern. The magnetic force between this armature field and the rotor field provides the mechanical torque of the machine. For an observer having the field structure as his frame of reference, the main field and the armature field are essentially unvarying with time. Torque depends on the main field strength, the amount of armature current, and the angle between the main field and the armature field.

The torque-angle or power-angle diagram shows the relation to angle. There is a maximum power or torque that cannot be exceeded. Salient poles tend to improve machine characteristics by providing reluctance torque.

A synchronous motor will run, if lightly loaded, on reluctance torque alone. Hysteresis torque will also drive a motor at synchronous speed.

(99)

PROBLEMS

7-1. The armature of a 3-phase, 2-pole, Y-connected, a-c generator has 18 slots. If it is wound with one coil-side per slot there are: (*a*) How many slots per phase? (*b*) How many coils per phase? (*c*) If the no-load voltage of one phase is 100 volts (rms), what is the electromotive force (rms) induced in each coil? (Assume that the two sides of each coil are diametrically opposite each other.) Note that this is a possible design, but not very practical. **(Sec. 87)**

7-2. Compute k_b for the windings that give Figures 86*b* and 87*a*. **(Sec. 89)**

7-3. Compute k_p for the armature winding of Figure 61*a*. **(Sec. 89)**

7-4. In Section 92 it is stated that Figure 91*b* shows E with approximately the same magnitude as V, but advanced in angle. Draw a similar diagram in which the magnitude is just the same. **(Sec. 92)**

7-5. Draw phasor diagrams for a generator supplying (*a*) a purely capacitive load and (*b*) a purely inductive load. **(Sec. 93)**

7-6. It is common to plot the line current (alternating current in one of three phases) supplied to a synchronous motor at a steady speed as a function of field current (direct current) supplied to that motor. For each curve drawn, the mechanical load on the motor is constant. The line voltage is constant. (These curves are called, somewhat inaccurately, the V curves of the machine.) Plot three such curves for three different loads, as follows: (*a*) No load. (*b*) Half load. (*c*) Full load. **(Sec. 92)**

7-7. A 3-phase synchronous motor operates at its rated voltage and frequency and delivers rated mechanical power output. The excitation (field current) is adjusted so that the power factor is 1.0. Neglect losses in the motor and assume that the load requires a torque independent of speed. Describe effects, quantitatively if possible, upon the power input, power factor, and current (both in-phase and reactive components) in response to changes of operating conditions as follows: (*a*) Applied (a-c) voltage reduced 10 per cent, frequency and excitation constant; and (b) applied voltage and frequency each reduced 10 per cent, excitation constant. **(Sec. 93)**

7-8. The armature winding of a 2-phase machine consists, essentially, of 2 coils at right angles (instead of the 3 coils shown in Figure 94a). Prove that the magnetic field strength at the center of these coils is a rotating pattern: that is, that H or B is constant in magnitude and rotating at constant angular velocity. This is to be a proof that applies at all times, not merely a series of examples as in the text. **(Sec. 95)**

7-9. Repeat Problem 7-8 for the three armature coils of a 3-phase machine. (*Note:* This is rather more involved, although not basically more difficult.) **(Sec. 95)**

7-10. The third paragraph from the end of Section 91 reads: "For generator operation, this means that the only way to keep terminal voltage of the machine up to its |rated value when it is supplying a heavy inductive load is to increase greatly the field current of the machine in order to give E the necessary large value." When the field current is greatly increased for this reason, compare the magnetic saturation of the iron of the machine (the amount of B) with the magnetic saturation of the iron when there is no load (as in Figure 92a). Is the magnetic saturation of the iron increased greatly, slightly, not at all, or decreased when the field current is increased for this reason? Explain why. Consider magnetic saturation in each of the following parts of the magnetic circuit of the machine, and give separate explanations if they are needed: (a) The iron of the main poles of the machine, inside the field windings. (b) Iron in the armature teeth, between the slots in which the armature winding is laid. (c) Iron in the main body of the armature. **(Sec. 95)**

7-11. A 50-kva synchronous motor driving a constant load is so adjusted that it operates at unity power factor and takes 35 kva. Assume that armature *resistance* is zero. (a) Draw a phasor diagram for this condition of operation. The field current is then increased 20 per cent. (b) Draw a phasor diagram for this changed condition. (c) State what the effect will be on the following quantities and explain in each case why it is so: (1) Speed. (2) Load power. (3) Line current. (4) Power factor. (5) Angle between current and voltage, θ. (6) Torque angle, δ. **(Sec. 97)**

7-12. When a synchronous generator is supplying a capacitive load (Figure 91d), E may be less than V. Suppose the terminal voltage V is to be held constant. The load is almost pure capacitance. Can the capacitance of the load be so great that E becomes zero? What is then the correct field current? Explain how the generator operates in such a case. If the capacitance of the load is even greater than this value, can the field current be reversed? Is the generator then stable? Does saliency of poles affect the answer? (*Note:* This is a problem of practical importance when a long transmission line without load is connected to a generator.) **(Sec. 97)**

7-13. In Section 96, use phasor diagrams to show with what magnitude and in what position the field of the armature winding will appear. (*a*) Explain why, "with a small load on the shaft . . . an armature pole appears . . . on (or near) the quadrature axis." (*b*) Also show why, "as load is increased the armature pole becomes stronger, but at the same time it moves farther from the quadrature axis." **(Sec. 96)**

7-14. Explain the dashed curve of Figure 97*a* in terms of equation 59-1. In terms of the equation, what happens to the curve when (as in an electric clock) there is no field current? **(Sec. 98)**

7-15. A 3-phase, 60 cycle/sec synchronous motor has 30 poles. Rated voltage and current, each per phase, are 1,330 volts and 375 amp. Synchronous reactance is 2.0 ohms per phase. Resistance and other motor losses are negligible. (*a*) The motor is running at rated load, unity power factor. What is the induced electromotive force per phase? (*b*) Line voltage and field current remain the same. What is the greatest power (in all 3 phases) that the motor can develop? (Assume non-salient poles.) (*c*) In Part *b*, what is the greatest torque that the motor can develop? **(Sec. 97)**

TRANSFORMERS
chapter 8

100. Transformers

Induction of electromotive force by a changing magnetic field is well exemplified by transformers. There are many kinds of transformers. An extremely large example is a power transformer of the kind used in electric generation and distribution stations. Its main purpose is to change voltage, either "stepping up" from the voltage of the generators to the much higher voltage of the transmission lines, or "stepping down" at the receiving end of the transmission line to a voltage low enough to be safe in a city distribution system or on a customer's premises. Electric power is delivered to the transformer at one voltage and is given out by the transformer at a different voltage; efficiency is high and little of the input power is wasted in the process of changing voltage.

Medium-sized transformers are used to reduce voltage again from the distribution system, which may be at about 4,000 volts, to the 120- or 240-volt circuits in residences, offices, shops, and laboratories. Still smaller transformers are used to reduce this voltage to 6 or 12 volts for ringing doorbells and operating furnace controls. Power-supply transformers for radio and television receivers may take power at 120 volts and deliver it to several circuits at different voltages: say 300 volts, 24 volts, and 6 volts.

All transformers so far mentioned are primarily for the purpose of changing voltage in a power system. They operate at essentially constant voltage and constant frequency. The power-system frequency may be 60 cycles per second, which is standard in North America; 50 cycles is standard elsewhere.

Higher frequencies are used in power supply devices for control systems. A frequency of 400 cycles is rather common, especially

(100)

aboard aircraft, for transformers are smaller and lighter and motors run at higher speed.

Transformers are also used in circuits for transmitting information: in telephone lines, in control circuits, in audio, video, and radio-frequency circuits. When transformers are used in these information circuits they do, indeed, change the voltage between input and output terminals, but it is more usual to think of them as transforming impedance. A transformer that "steps up" voltage will correspondingly "step down" the current in the same proportion (approximately), as will be realized when it is considered that power input and power output are approximately equal. The output terminals on one side of a transformer may supply high voltage and low current to a load of high impedance, while the input terminals on the other side receive a large current at low voltage—corresponding to a low input impedance. Thus, by using a transformer, it is possible to supply power to a high impedance load although only a low impedance is inserted in the supply circuit.

It is important in circuits for transmitting information to have impedances of loads *matched* to impedances of sources. This provides *maximum power transfer* and gives a received signal of the greatest possible strength.

A transformer is not an electromechanical device, for it takes in electrical energy and gives out electrical energy. A transformer is not supposed, except very rarely, to have any mechanical motion in its operation. To be sure, there are large mechanical forces in the cores of transformers, resulting from the magnetic fields and made evident by the hum emanating from powerful transformers while they are energized; but the designer takes careful precautions to minimize motion of either the iron core or the insulated copper coils.

Figure 100*a* shows a schematic diagram of a transformer. Two coils are wound on a core of ferromagnetic material. In a power transformer the core is made of laminations of sheet steel, specially prepared to have good properties for this purpose. High permeability and low hysteresis loss are desired.

The coils of a transformer are fitted tightly on the core, and the two coils are placed close together, leaving room only for the insulation that is required between them. Frequently the coils are placed one within the other, or layers of the coils are interleaved in some manner. The reason for fitting the coils so closely together is to keep leakage flux to a minimum. In the ideal transformer all

(100)

the magnetic flux that links one winding links the other also. This flux is called mutual flux. Leakage flux is flux that links one winding but not the other. Illustrative paths for mutual and leakage flux are shown in Figure 100a.

In Figure 100a only two coils are shown, both on the top leg of the rectangular core, but it is usual to have coils on the bottom leg also. Coils containing half the turns of the primary winding (the input winding) and half of the turns of the secondary winding would be placed on one leg of the iron core, and coils with the other half of the primary turns and the other half of the secondary turns would be placed on the opposite leg.

In small transformers the windings are of fine copper wire. Heavier wire is used in transformer coils designed to carry several amperes of current, and in large power transformers the coils may actually be made of heavy strap copper. Insulation is of course provided; the wire may be covered with enamel, or cotton, or a plastic material. Transformers for which the rating is more than about a kilowatt are often immersed in oil (in a steel tank) to improve the insulation and also to help carry heat away from the windings when the transformer is in use.

It is not necessary that the transformer have only two windings. Any number of circuits may be wound on the same core. A power-supply transformer (as mentioned previously) that is designed to give 300 volts, 24 volts, and 6 volts from a 120-volt supply line might have four coils.

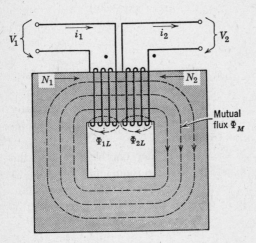

Figure 100a. A transformer.

(100)

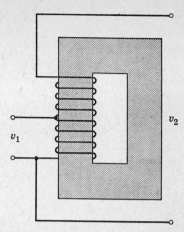

Figure 100b. An autotransformer.

On the other hand, it is not necessary to have a separate coil for each voltage. An autotransformer, as shown in Figure 100b, has only one coil. All the coil is used as the high-voltage winding, while a lower-voltage connection is made between one terminal of the winding and an intermediate tap. It is also possible to have one coil with several taps to give several different voltages. The power-supply transformer that has been mentioned might have only one coil, the full length being used to provide 300 volts, while taps at appropriate positions supplied power at 24 volts and 6 volts and received power at 120 volts. (This would not, in fact, be an entirely practical design, for several reasons, although power-supply transformers often do have tapped windings.)

101. Induced Electromotive Force

Regardless of the construction or purpose of the transformer, its operation is as follows. Suppose, in Figure 100a, that alternating voltage is applied to winding 1. Alternating current then flows in winding 1, producing magnetic flux in the iron core. This flux, which is also alternating, induces electromotive force in *both* primary and secondary windings. In the primary winding the induced electromotive force opposes the applied voltage and limits the flow of current. In the secondary winding the induced electromotive force produces voltage between the output terminals. When a circuit with appropriate resistance is connected as a load to these output ter-

(101)

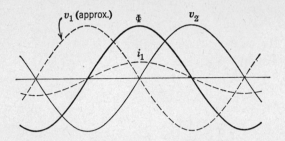

Figure 101a. Phase relations of flux and voltage in a transformer, no load.

minals it receives power from the transformer. We see below in more detail how these things happen.

Consider the alternating flux in the core, shown as Φ in Figure 101a. The amount of flux is

$$\Phi = \Phi_m \sin \omega t \qquad (101\text{-}1)$$

where Φ_m is a constant (the maximum value of flux) in webers
$\qquad \omega$ is a constant, equal to $2\pi f$, f being frequency per second
$\qquad t$ is time, in seconds

This alternating flux, since it is continually changing in magnitude, induces electromotive force in each of the transformer windings.

The electromotive force induced in winding 2 appears as voltage v_2 at the terminals. If winding 2 has N_2 turns, the voltage is (by equation 23-1)

$$v_2 = e_2 = -N_2 \frac{d\Phi}{dt} \qquad (101\text{-}2)$$

The minus sign indicates that an increase of flux, a positive rate of change in the direction shown by the reference arrow, produces a terminal voltage opposite to the reference arrow for v_2 in Figure 100a. This may be verified by the rules of Section 23.

The electromotive force induced in winding 1 opposes the applied terminal voltage v_1. If resistance of the transformer winding can be neglected, the two are equal and opposite, for just enough current flows to produce this balanced condition. The amount of induced electromotive force in the N_1 turns of winding 1 is $-N_1 \, d\Phi/dt$. This being opposed to the applied voltage v_1 we write

$$v_1 = -e_1 = N_1 \frac{d\Phi}{dt} \qquad (101\text{-}3)$$

(101)

This equation relates the applied voltage and the flux in the transformer core. Since the applied voltage is usually known, and the amount of flux is not, the equation is used to find Φ. Then equation 101-2 is used to find v_2:

$$v_2 = -N_2 \frac{v_1}{N_1} \quad \text{or} \quad \frac{v_2}{v_1} = -\frac{N_2}{N_1} \tag{101-4}$$

Note that the two voltages are in direct proportion to the numbers of turns in the windings.

·We now introduce the sinusoidal expression for flux in the core, $\Phi = \Phi_m \sin \omega t$, from equation 101-1. Substituting this into equation 101-2, and differentiating, we find the voltage to be

$$v_2 = -N_2 \frac{d}{dt} (\Phi_m \sin \omega t) = -N_2 \Phi_m \omega \cos \omega t \tag{101-5}$$

This tells us that the transformer secondary voltage is sinusoidal also, varying as minus the cosine of ωt, and that the maximum of the voltage wave is $N_2 \Phi_m \omega$. See Figure 101a.

Similarly, from equation 101-3, the primary terminal voltage is

$$v_1 = N_1 \frac{d}{dt} (\Phi_m \sin \omega t) = N_1 \Phi_m \omega \cos \omega t \tag{101-6}$$

Comparing equations 101-5 and 6 shows again that the primary and secondary voltages are proportional to the numbers of turns in the windings. Figure 101a is drawn for a transformer in which the two coils have the same number of turns; v_1 is marked "approximate" because the impedance of the primary winding has been neglected.

102. Magnetizing Current

The next question is the amount of current in the primary winding. The current must be just enough to produce the necessary flux to induce electromotive force that will balance the applied voltage. This *magnetizing current* and flux are related by the magnetic reluctance of the transformer core. Considering that there is current in the primary winding, and no current in the secondary winding, we write (equation 3-1 in Appendix 1) $N_1 i_1 = \Phi \mathcal{R}$ or

$$i_1 = \frac{\Phi \mathcal{R}}{N_1} \tag{102-1}$$

(102)

We have assumed sinusoidal flux; hence the current would be sinusoidal also *if the reluctance were constant*. Constant reluctance implies linear magnetic relations, with no magnetic saturation of the iron core of the transformer. But transformer cores almost always operate with more or less saturation, so $\mathcal{R}$ is not in fact constant, and the magnetizing current required to produce a sinusoidal flux is not itself sinusoidal. The curve for current i_1 in Figure 101a is drawn as a sine wave, but actually, taking saturation into account, the curve should rise to a higher, sharper peak at its maximum.

Still, for many purposes it is good enough to assume that magnetic relations are linear. In making this assumption, only the fundamental sinusoidal component of magnetizing current is taken into account and $\mathcal{R}$ is assumed to be constant. When equation 101-1 is substituted into 102-1, we obtain

$$i_1 = \frac{\mathcal{R}}{N_1} \Phi_m \sin \omega t \qquad (102\text{-}2)$$

A value of magnetizing reactance can now be found. This is the ratio of the magnitude of the applied voltage, from equation 101-6, to the magnitude of the magnetizing current, from equation 102-2:

$$X_{1\,\text{mag}} = \frac{N_1 \Phi_m \omega}{\mathcal{R} \Phi_m / N_1} = \frac{N_1{}^2}{\mathcal{R}} \omega \qquad (102\text{-}3)$$

The quantity $N_1{}^2/\mathcal{R}$ will be recognized as an inductance. It is the magnetizing inductance of the transformer as seen from the terminals of winding 1.

It is convenient and customary to show transformer relations in a phasor diagram. Figure 102a shows the transforms (or phasors) of the

Figure 102a. Phasor diagram showing the transforms of magnetizing current, flux, and voltages in an unloaded transformer.

waves of Figure 101a. It is clear that the waves for Φ and i_1 are in phase; hence the phasors for Φ and I_1 are at the same angle. Voltages are in quadrature with the flux; they are drawn opposite to each other in the diagram to be consistent with the negative sign in equation 101-4.*

---

* Equation 101-4 indicates that v_2 is negative when v_1 is positive, positive and negative directions being defined by the reference arrows drawn in Figure

It would, of course, be possible to operate the transformer by applying voltage to winding 2 instead of winding 1. If this were done the magnetizing inductance or reactance of winding 2 could be measured. The magnetizing reactance as seen at the terminals of winding 2 would be

$$X_{2 \text{ mag}} = \frac{N_2{}^2}{\mathfrak{R}} \omega \qquad (102\text{-}4)$$

Hence the magnetizing inductance is $N_2{}^2/\mathfrak{R}$. It will be seen that the reactance or inductance of the transformer depends on the winding at which the measurement is made, and the value is proportional to the *square* of the number of turns in the winding.

103. Load Current

We have now seen that when voltage is applied to the primary winding of a transformer there is produced at the terminals of the secondary winding another voltage, similar in form but greater or smaller in magnitude in proportion to the *turn ratio* of the transformer. We have considered that a magnetizing current flows in the primary winding; it is usually quite a small current (compared to the transformer rating).

Next we enquire what happens when the transformer is used to supply a load; when, that is, an impedance is connected between the secondary terminals so that current can flow in the secondary winding of the transformer. Figure 103a shows a transformer with a connected load impedance.

When there is current in the secondary winding of the transformer, the ampere-turns of this winding contribute to the magnetomotive force in the magnetic core (see Figure 100a). When there was current only in winding 1 we wrote (equation 102-1) that $N_1 i_1 = \Phi\mathfrak{R}$. Now, with both windings carrying current, we write

$$N_1 i_1 + N_2 i_2 = \Phi\mathfrak{R} \qquad (103\text{-}1)$$

100a. (It will be recalled from circuit theory that reference directions are arbitrary and may be indicated by arrows, double subscripts, or otherwise. *Positive* then means current, voltage, or flux in the reference direction; *negative* means current, voltage, or flux in the opposite direction.) Similarly, in Section 103, a positive v_2 produces a positive i_2 in a resistive load connected to the secondary terminals in Figure 100a, and a negative v_2 produces a negative i_2. Hence v_2 and i_2 are in phase.

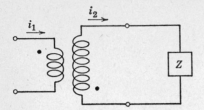

Figure 103a. A transformer with connected load.

or, using transforms of current and flux, we write

$$N_1 I_1 + N_2 I_2 = \Phi \mathcal{R} \qquad (103\text{-}2)$$

However, the flux Φ in the core must be the same with or without load, for the rate of change of flux linkages must still be equal to the applied voltage (equation 101-3). To keep Φ the same when the transformer is loaded, the net magnetomotive force must stay the same, and this requires a change in I_1 when I_2 begins to flow, to counterbalance the magnetomotive force of I_2.

Figure 103b shows waves of voltage and current in a loaded transformer. It is drawn for a transformer with twice as many turns in the secondary winding as in the primary. Thus v_2 is twice v_1. See also the phasor diagram; in Figure 103c, I_{mag} is the component of primary current that provides magnetomotive force to produce flux Φ in the transformer core. I_{mag} is equal to I_1 in Figure 102a.

The load current, flowing in the secondary winding, is shown in Figure 103b as i_2. By assuming a purely resistive load, i_2 is drawn in phase with v_2. Figure 103c shows I_2 in phase with V_2. To keep the flux in the transformer core at the proper value, Φ, despite the magnetomotive force of I_2 in winding 2, there must be an equal and opposite magnetomotive force produced by a component of current in winding 1. Figure 103c shows I_1' as this new component of the primary current. Note that I_1' is directly opposite to I_2, so it produces in the primary winding a magnetomotive force opposing that of I_2 in the secondary winding. Also, since winding 2 has twice as many turns as winding 1, I_1' has twice the magnitude of I_2, thereby providing equal ampere-turns.

Thus I_1 in Figure 103c (or i_1 in Figure 103b) consists of two components. One, I_{mag}, called the *magnetizing* component, has the value that I_1 had when there was no load current. The other, called the *load* component, is exactly enough to counterbalance the ampere-turns of the load current I_2. Expanding equation 103-2, we write

$$N_1 I_{\text{mag}} + N_1 I_1' + N_2 I_2 = \Phi \mathcal{R} \qquad (103\text{-}3)$$

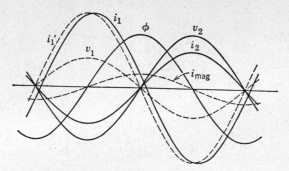

Figure 103b. Transformer voltages and currents.

where

$$N_1 I_{mag} = \Phi\Re \quad \text{and} \quad N_1 I_1' = -N_2 I_2 \tag{103-4}$$

The primary current is thus broken down into two parts, one of which, determined by the applied voltage, is independent of the load current. The other is directly proportional to the load current.

I_{mag} flows in the primary winding whenever the transformer is connected to the line; it furnishes magnetomotive force to provide the necessary flux in the transformer core. Then, when there is load current in the secondary winding, there is also a load component of current in the primary winding. It is just enough to balance out the ampere-turns of the secondary current, and thus to leave the net magnetomotive force undisturbed by the load current. That it is related to the secondary current by the reciprocal of the transformer turn ratio is shown by equation 103-4, for

$$\frac{I_1'}{I_2} = -\frac{N_2}{N_1} \tag{103-5}$$

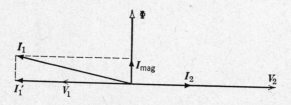

Figure 103c. Phasor diagram of a transformer with load; impedances neglected.

(103)

104. Transformer Reactances

In preceding sections we have neglected resistance of the transformer windings. We have also neglected the fact that there will be some magnetic flux, usually a small amount, linking winding 1 of a transformer but not linking winding 2, and some flux linking winding 2 without linking winding 1.

Figure 100a shows these *leakage* fluxes in a diagrammatical way: Φ_{1L} links winding 1 only, and Φ_{2L} links winding 2 only, so these represent the leakage fluxes as distinguished from Φ_M, which is *mutual* to both windings and is the useful flux of the transformer, until now merely called Φ. Note that any flux that is entirely in the iron core must be mutual whereas all the leakage flux must be at least partly in air. For this reason the reluctance of the leakage paths is much higher than that of the mutual path, and hence in a transformer of ordinary design the leakage fluxes are relatively small.

It is customary to account for leakage flux in terms of leakage inductance and leakage reactance of the transformer winding. Thus it is said that a transformer primary winding has a certain amount of resistance and a certain amount of leakage reactance; similarly, there is a secondary resistance and a secondary leakage reactance. In our previous discussion these have been neglected, but we now consider how to take them into account.

Figure 104a shows a diagram of a transformer. Each winding has resistance and leakage reactance. For convenience of analysis we draw Figure 104b, in which the resistances and leakage reactances are shown separately, in the external circuit, and the transformer symbol represents only an impedanceless transformer.

Figure 104c suggests another step toward making analysis simpler. Not only is the transformer in this diagram assumed to be without resistance or leakage reactance, but it is also assumed to require no magnetizing current. To provide for the magnetizing current that does, in fact, exist, the external reactance $X_{1\,mag}$ is shunted across the primary terminals. The value of $X_{1\,mag}$ comes from equation 102-3.

This arrangement leaves within the box shown in the figure a transformer that has no impedance and requires no magnetizing current. Such a device, purely hypothetical of course, is called an *ideal* transformer. An ideal transformer has a turn ratio, relating voltage and current on one side to voltage and current on the other,

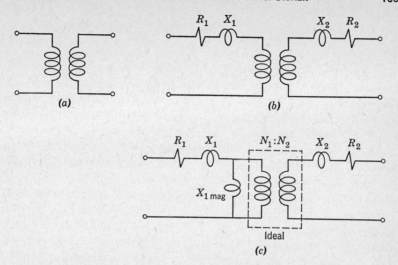

Figure 104. (*a*) An actual transformer. (*b*) R and X have been taken out. (*c*) Magnetizing current is also moved out, leaving an ideal transformer.

but it has no other characteristics. It has no impedance, no magnetizing current, no losses (iron losses of the actual transformer are provided for in Section 107). It retains the one feature of a transformer that is ordinarily useful, the transforming property, and all the regrettable but unavoidable losses and impedances are moved into the external circuit.

But Figure 104*c* is unsymmetrical. Why is it better to put the shunt element that provides for magnetizing current on the primary side of the ideal transformer rather than on the secondary side? To this there is no answer. The shunt element could be put on either side. It would have a different value, $X_{2\ mag}$ instead of $X_{1\ mag}$ (equation 102-4) if it were placed on the secondary side of the ideal transformer, but either representation is valid. The customary and convenient method, however, is to place it on the primary side, and then to bring the secondary resistance and leakage reactance over to this side, too.

105. Equivalent Circuit of a Transformer

It would not, of course, be correct merely to remove X_2 and R_2 from the secondary side of the ideal transformer and insert them on the primary side. In the first place, current is different on the two sides of the transformer because of the turn-ratio factor, so the reactance and resistance elements would not produce the same voltage drop in the new position. And, second, the voltage drop that is produced by them is itself transformed by the transformer. Thus the turn ratio comes into the picture twice. If the turn ratio, N_1/N_2, is called a, as in Figure 105a, the reactance and resistance to be inserted on the primary side of the ideal transformer, to replace X_2 and R_2 on the secondary side and to have the same effect, are a^2X_2 and a^2R_2. These are shown in Figure 105a. These values are called the secondary leakage reactance and resistance *referred to the primary side.*

To see that this multiplying factor of a^2 is correct, consider that R_2 is located on the secondary side, as in Figure 104c. Current through it is I_2, so the voltage drop across it is R_2I_2. However, this voltage drop is produced on the secondary side, and the voltage required on the primary side to overcome the voltage drop R_2I_2 on the secondary side is aR_2I_2.

Now consider Figure 105a. The current on the primary side of the ideal transformer is not I_2, but I_2/a. This primary current passes through a resistance equal to a^2R_2, and the drop across the resistance is $(a^2R_2)\,(I_2/a) = aR_2I_2$. Hence the same voltage drop appears on the primary side whether we consider Figure 104c with R_2 in the secondary circuit, or Figure 105a with a^2R_2 in the primary circuit. A similar statement can be made about reactance. Thus Figure 105a is shown to be equivalent to Figure 104c.

The circuit of Figure 105a is called the equivalent circuit of the transformer with all impedances referred to the primary side. It would be just as satisfactory to refer all impedances, including the magnetizing reactance, to the secondary side, for the transformer is in fact a symmetrical device, and "primary" and "secondary" are only terms of convenience. It will be seen that we have developed, in Figure 105a, a

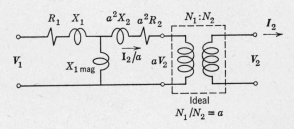

Figure 105a. Secondary impedance is referred to the primary side.

(105)

T network of impedances, in cascade with an ideal transformer, to be a "model" of an actual transformer.

106. The Phasor Diagram

Figure 103c showed a phasor diagram of a transformer that disregarded transformer impedances. Let us now draw a phasor diagram of a transformer taking impedances into account (Figure 106a). It is most convenient to begin with the secondary voltage and current, V_2 and I_2, which we shall suppose to be known. However, instead of drawing phasors for V_2 and I_2, we shall draw aV_2 and I_2/a, which are secondary voltage and current referred to the primary side. This is done with Figure 105a in mind. By thus leaving the transformer turn ratio out of the phasor diagram we can compare primary and secondary quantities more conveniently (and if at any time it is desired to have a diagram to show the actual secondary phasors it is necessary only to multiply all current phasors and divide all voltage phasors in Figure 106a by a).

The induced electromotive force in winding 2 differs from the terminal voltage because of the impedance drop in the winding:

$$E_2 = V_2 + I_2(R_2 + jX_2) \qquad (106\text{-}1)$$

or

$$aE_2 = aV_2 + aI_2(R_2 + jX_2) \qquad (106\text{-}2)$$

Adding aI_2R_2 and jaI_2X_2 to aV_2, aE_2 is drawn. By equations 101-2 and 3, E_1 is equal to aE_2, and this is indicated in the diagram.

Next, $-E_1$ is drawn equal but opposite to E_1 and aE_2, and Φ_M is drawn at right angles. I_{mag} is in phase with Φ_M, and I_1 is equal but opposite to I_2/a. The sum of these current components gives the total

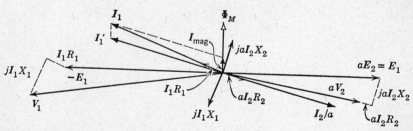

Figure 106a. Phasor diagram of a transformer, including impedances. $N_1/N_2 = a$.

(106)

primary current, I_1. Then the voltage V_1 at the primary terminals is found by adding to the electromotive force the drop in the primary-winding impedance:

$$V_1 = -E_1 + I_1(R_1 + jX_1) \qquad (106\text{-}3)$$

(The negative sign indicates that V_1 is opposite to E_1, as in equation 101-3.) This completes the diagram.

This diagram, although somewhat involved in appearance, is essentially quite simple. It shows graphically the two basic relations of transformer operation:

1. E_1 and aE_2 are equal, and
2. I_1' and I_2/a are equal and opposite.

Everything else about the diagram is evident, and it can be drawn for a transformer loaded with impedance of any magnitude and phase angle without difficulty.

Besides equations 106-1 and 106-3, the other equations used in Figure 106a are

$$E_1 = -j\omega N_1 \Phi_M \qquad (106\text{-}4)$$

$$E_2 = -j\omega N_2 \Phi_M \qquad (106\text{-}5)$$

$$I_{\text{mag}} = I_1 + \frac{I_2}{a} \qquad (106\text{-}6)$$

$$a = \frac{N_1}{N_2} \qquad (106\text{-}7)$$

$$\Phi_M = \frac{I_{\text{mag}}N_1}{\mathcal{R}} \qquad (106\text{-}8)$$

Then if I_2 is to be found in terms of V_1, these seven equations are used to eliminate the following seven quantities: E_1, E_2, V_2, I_1, I_{mag}, a, Φ_M.

107. Iron Loss

One detail that is commonly included in phasor diagrams of transformers has been omitted for simplicity. It is the effect of iron loss in the transformer core. We have neglected iron loss not only in our phasor diagrams but also in our equivalent circuits or models. Iron loss is always kept down by careful design, but there is inevitably some eddy-current loss in an actual transformer despite lamination of the

(107)

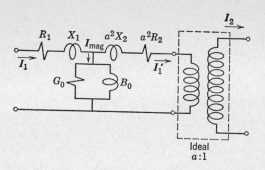

Figure 107a. An equivalent circuit of a transformer. $N_1/N_2 = a$.

core, and there is hysteresis loss in even the best quality of transformer steel.

Hysteresis loss results from cyclic reversals of the magnetization of the iron. When magnetomotive force applied to iron drops to zero the magnetic field within the iron does not fall quite to zero; thus some of the magnetizing energy is not returned to the circuit, and a small amount of energy is lost each time the magnetizing current reverses. Eddy current loss results from circulating currents in the iron or steel laminations of which the transformer core is made.

To represent these iron losses of an actual transformer, we put conductance G_0 into the equivalent circuit as in Figure 107a. It is put in parallel with the shunt element that is marked $X_{1\,mag}$ in Figure 105a and B_0 in Figure 107a, and represents a path for magnetizing current. (By the usual circuit relations, $jB_0 = 1/jX_{1\,mag}$.) Iron losses are so small in a good transformer that G_0 is a very low conductance (a very high resistance) in the equivalent circuit. It is not truly accurate to represent iron loss, and particularly hysteresis loss, by a single value of G_0 at all applied voltages and frequencies, but it is a usual approximation.

To include iron loss in the phasor diagram, it is necessary only to draw I_{mag} at an appropriate angle, leading Φ by a few degrees. It then has a component in phase with E_1, which takes into account the loss of power in the core. The energy lost in the core of a good power transformer is so small that it is hardly noticeable in a phasor diagram drawn to scale, but it is important because this loss continues as long as the transformer is connected to the line, whether it is loaded or unloaded. In distribution transformers it continues day and night.

108. Models of Power Transformers

Simplified models of transformers are often used in power system studies, for the equivalent circuit of Figure 107a is a more precise model of the actual transformer than is needed for many purposes. Sometimes the equivalent circuit of Figure 105a is preferred as being good enough and slightly simpler. For studies of heavily loaded power systems, in which the small magnetizing current of transformers is negligible, B_0 as well as G_0 may be omitted, leaving only the series impedance and an ideal transformer. For studies of short-circuit current, if power is unimportant, even the series resistance may be neglected, leaving the transformer represented by a series reactance and an ideal transformer only.

Simplified models are used when measuring the impedances of transformers. In the *short-circuit* test, the terminals of the secondary winding are short-circuited, and measurements made at the primary terminals (usually using ammeter, voltmeter, and wattmeter) are interpreted as giving the sum of the primary impedance and the secondary impedance referred to the primary side. It will be seen in Figure 107a that this is equivalent to omitting G_0 and B_0 from the equivalent circuit.

In the *open-circuit test*, measurements at the primary terminals, made while the secondary terminals are open-circuited, are interpreted as giving the admittance of the shunt branch consisting of G_0 and B_0. This time the model consists of the shunt branch only, with the series impedances of Figure 107a neglected entirely.

109. Models of Transformers in Communication Systems

Still other simplifications of the equivalent circuit are helpful for transformers used in communication systems, as input, interstage, or output transformers, or for impedance matching. Such audio-frequency transformers must transmit a range of frequencies, and perhaps the most important characteristic of the system is its useful frequency range.

It is found that three different models are useful for a transformer in such a system, one for use in its intermediate-frequency range, one for the highest frequencies, and one for the lowest. They are shown in Figures 109a, b, and c. The load is represented by a^2R, where R is the resistance of the actual load, a is the transformer

(109)

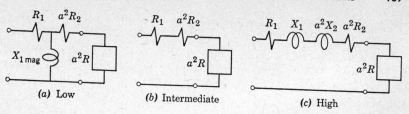

(a) Low

(b) Intermediate

(c) High

Figure 109a, b, c. Convenient models of an audio-frequency transformer in different frequency ranges.

turn ratio, and a^2R is therefore the equivalent resistance referred to the primary side of the transformer.

Figure 109b is for the intermediate-frequency range in which the transformer works more or less ideally except for the resistance of its windings. Communication transformers are so much smaller than power transformers that they have relatively high resistance, compared to leakage reactance, and in the intermediate-frequency range it predominates.

The leakage reactance of the windings is proportional to frequency, however, and at higher frequency it becomes important. Figure 109c is then used. The upper limit of the useful frequency range comes when the sum of X_1 and a^2X_2 is of the same order of magnitude as the total resistance of the circuit, including the equivalent load resistance a^2R, plus the transformer resistance, plus the

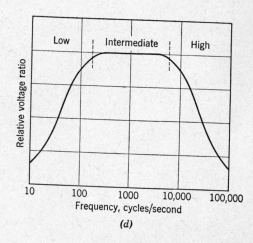

Figure 109d. Variation of amplification with frequency in a typical power amplifier with output transformer. (Courtesy F. E. Terman.)

(d)

(109)

resistance of the input circuit (which is not shown in the diagram).

At low frequencies the leakage reactance is unimportant, but the magnetizing reactance of the transformer becomes small enough to make the shunt element of the model significant. The lower limit of the useful frequency range is reached when $X_{1\,mag}$ is of the same order of magnitude as the equivalent secondary resistance plus load resistance, $a^2R_2 + a^2R$ combined, as if in parallel, with the resistance of the input circuit.

Figure 109d shows the practically constant ratio of output voltage to input voltage obtained in the intermediate frequency range, and the droop of voltage at the load in both high and low ranges.* It is clear that this type of behavior can be predicted from the equivalent circuits of Figures 109a, b, and c, or equally well but with much greater difficulty from the more complete equivalent circuit of Figure 107a.

110. Distributed Capacitance

In some audio-frequency circuits, and when used at radio frequencies, the *distributed capacitance* of a transformer is important. All transformers, and in fact all electrical devices and systems, have capacitance between one part of the device and another. There is capacitance, for instance, between one layer of turns of wire in a transformer coil and the next layer wound on top, or even between one turn and the next. There is capacitance between the primary winding and the secondary winding. There is capacitance between each part of the windings and the iron core.

Exact computation of the effect of distributed capacitance of a transformer is far too involved to be practical. Fortunately, for many purposes it is good enough to assume that the capacitance is not distributed but is lumped in a single element at the terminals of a winding, as in Figure 110a. This model shows why there will be resonant effects. When resonance occurs in the upper part of the useful frequency range it may actually improve the transformer characteristics, but more commonly it produces an undesirable resonance.

Under most practical circumstances the distributed capacitance of power transformers may be neglected. However, if a transformer

---

* This is treated quantitatively in many books; e.g., Terman, Reference 109. See also Section 196 of this book.

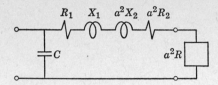

Figure 110a. In the high-frequency range it is sometimes necessary to include transformer capacitance C in the model of an audio-frequency transformer.

is exposed to a lightning wave, the behavior of the wave and the probable damage to the transformer depend primarily on the transformer's distributed capacitance. The steep front of the lightning wave gives it some of the characteristics of a high-frequency wave.

111. Input and Transfer Functions

The terminology of *transfer functions* is particularly simple when applied to ideal transformers. A transfer function relates such a quantity as current or voltage in one part of a system to a current or voltage in another part of the system. The term is used with alternating quantities, and the transfer function is defined as the ratio of the *transforms* of the two quantities, the ratio, that is, of the complex numbers representing the currents or voltages.

Thus the transfer function relating the output voltage of an ideal transformer to the input voltage is

$$\frac{V_2}{V_1} = \frac{N_2}{N_1} \tag{111-1}$$

where N_1 and N_2 are the numbers of turns in the primary and secondary windings. The transfer function relating the output current to the input current is

$$\frac{I_2}{I_1} = \frac{N_1}{N_2} \tag{111-2}$$

These transfer functions are simply constants; indeed, one is the turn ratio a of Section 105, and the other is $1/a$.

A transfer impedance relating input voltage to output current is found by substituting ZI_2 for V_2 in equation 111-1, Z being the load impedance (as in Figure 103a), giving

$$\frac{V_1}{I_2} = \frac{N_1}{N_2} Z \tag{111-3}$$

(111)

Also the input impedance can be found in terms of the output impedance (this is an impedance function but not a transfer function). Z_{in} is V_1/I_1, and using equations 111-1 and 2, we obtain

$$Z_{in} = \frac{V_1}{I_1} = \frac{(N_1/N_2)V_2}{(N_2/N_1)I_2} = \left(\frac{N_1}{N_2}\right)^2 \frac{V_2}{I_2} = \left(\frac{N_1}{N_2}\right)^2 Z \quad (111\text{-}4)$$

In this equation the input impedance is equal to the load impedance times the square of the turn ratio.

It was explained in connection with Figure 105a, and is illustrated in Figures 106a, 109a, b, c, and e, that an impedance Z on the secondary side of an ideal transformer of ratio $a:1$ has the same effect as an impedance a^2Z on the primary side; this is shown again in equation 111-4. Thus if it is desired to supply a 900-ohm load (Z of Figure 103a) without putting much more than 100 ohms impedance into the driving circuit, it is necessary only to connect the load through a transformer with a 1-to-3 turn ratio.

Such an impedance transformation is useful if a piece of equipment with 900 ohms of internal resistance (a telephone receiver, for example) is to be supplied from a source (a transmission line, perhaps) of 100-ohm impedance.

Transformers are used in communication systems for several purposes, the most important being (1) to increase the voltage, (2) to short-circuit direct current while transmitting an a-c signal, and (3) to match impedances of two circuits. The use of a transformer for impedance matching is specially interesting.

Impedance matching of this kind is important in communication work because it provides *maximum power transfer*. That is, the greatest possible amount of power reaches the receiving end of the system from a given transmitter if (assuming the load to be purely resistive) the resistance looking into the load at its terminals is equal to the resistance looking back into the system, toward the transmitter, from the load terminals. In any system transmitting information, it is necessary that enough energy arrive to give an intelligible signal. Maximum power transfer is therefore desired, and it is usually worth while to provide at least an approximate match of impedances. Transformers are often used for this purpose, as a step-up transformer between a microphone and a vacuum-tube amplifier, or a step-down transformer between the output of the amplifier and a speaker.

(111)

112. Summary

Transformers, although *not electromechanical* devices, are discussed in this chapter because of their importance. The first section of the chapter is descriptive.

Alternating magnetic flux in the transformer core induces electromotive force in the transformer windings, proportional to the numbers of turns. The magnitude of the primary-winding electromotive force is nearly equal to the applied *voltage*. The *magnetizing current* of the transformer depends on the magnetizing inductance. The transforms of the alternating quantities are shown in phasor diagrams.

When there is *load current* in the secondary winding, there must be a counterbalancing component of current in the primary winding, the currents being inversely proportional to the numbers of turns. This load component, added to the magnetizing current, gives the total primary current.

Transformer windings have resistance and *leakage reactance*. In *equivalent circuits* these and the magnetizing reactance are conveniently considered as if they were separate from an *ideal transformer*, which is conceived to have transforming properties consistent with the turn ratio of the actual transformer, but none of its impedances, admittances, or losses. In the equivalent circuit (or model), it is convenient to "refer" all impedances to one side of the ideal transformer.

Load currents and impedance drops are readily included in the *phasor diagram* of the transformer. Core losses can also be included if desired.

For many purposes, *simplified models* of a transformer are adequate. This is true for both power and communication uses. Three different models are used for an audio-frequency transformer, the choice depending on the frequency range under consideration. Distributed capacitance is sometimes important; an equivalent lumped capacitance can be added to the model to explain resonance and other phenomena.

Transfer functions are ratios of transforms of voltages and currents. A few examples are given for ideal transformers.

Input impedance is given in terms of load impedance. They are related by the square of the turn ratio. This expresses the *impedance transforming* characteristic of a transformer, valuable in impedance matching.

(112)

PROBLEMS

8-1. Find a transformer and learn all you can about it from observation. Any kind of transformer may be used: power, audio-frequency, doorbell, impedance-matching, power-supply, etc. Write about two pages of description, including a diagram. (Write as if for an engineering report.) Give its purpose, its general size, shape, and construction, provision for cooling. Give information about its electrical operation that is available from the name plate, with any deductions that you are able to make. Possible data to include are voltage, current, power ratings; number of windings, number of turns, size of wire; number and thickness of core laminations, estimated weight, insulation; turn ratio, input and output impedance, etc.

(Sec. 100)

8-2. A silicon-steel transformer core is 2.0 by 2.5 cm in cross section. The *maximum* flux density in the core may be 1.20 webers/m^2. A coil to be connected to a 120-volt a-c circuit (an ordinary lighting circuit) requires how many turns? If the average length of flux path in the core is 16 cm, what is the no-load primary current with 120 volts rms, 60 cycle/sec alternating voltage applied to the coil? (Use average $\mu/\mu_0 = 3,000$.) **(Sec. 102)**

8-3. Give the core cross-sectional area, the flux density (using a reasonable value, see Appendix 1), and the number of turns necessary for the tapped autotransformer described in the last paragraph of Section 100. **(Sec. 101)**

8-4. The figure shows an iron core for a transformer for a power supply, transforming from 120 volts input (rms) to 6 volts output, 60 cycles/sec. Use maximum $B = 0.6$ weber/m^2, $\mu/\mu_0 = 6,000$. Find: (a) Number of turns in each winding. (b) Reactance of primary winding with secondary open. (c) Reactance of secondary winding with primary open. (d) Input impedance to primary (120-volt) winding with 6-ohm resistive load on the secondary. In (d), neglect iron loss and resistance of the transformer coils. Take magnetizing

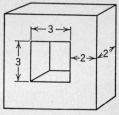

Problem 8-4   Dimensions in cm

current into account if it is appreciable compared to the total primary current.   **(Sec. 104)**

8-5. What are the advantages of 60-cycle/sec current for electric power systems compared with 400-cycle? Explain why the lower frequency is usually best for ordinary industrial power, and the higher for use aboard aircraft. Consider motors and generators as well as transformers.   **(Sec. 104)**

8-6. Draw equivalent circuits for the following transformer, giving numerical values, with (a) all quantities referred to the primary side, and (b) all quantities referred to the secondary side. Rated values: $V_1 = 42,000$ volts, $V_2 = 2,400$ volts, kva = 500. Impedances: $R_1 = 19.0$ ohms, $R_2 = 0.051$ ohm, $X_1 = 39.0$ ohms, $X_2 = 0.11$ ohm. Neglect magnetizing current.   **(Sec. 105)**

8-7. The load impedance Z on a transformer is a pure resistance and is the rated load of the transformer. The resistances and leakage reactances of the transformer are the following percentages of Z: $R_2 = 5$ per cent, $X_2 = 7$ per cent, $R_1 = 4$ per cent, $X_1 = 7$ per cent. Magnetizing current of the transformer is 10 per cent of rated current. Rated voltage is applied to the primary terminals. Draw a phasor diagram, drawing carefully, to scale, showing V_1, V_2, I_1, I_2, Φ, and any other phasors you wish to include. You may assume a turn ratio of one.   **(Sec. 106)**

8-8. Draw a phasor diagram for a transformer with such a load that the voltage regulation (as defined in Section 65) is zero. (a) Neglect magnetizing current. (b) How serious is the neglect of magnetizing current? Explain.   **(Sec. 106)**

8-9. An ideal transformer is connected between the output of a power amplifier and the input to a speaker. Speaker impedance is 16 ohms, pure resistance. It is desired to have input impedance to the

transformer be 5,000 ohms.   There are 25 turns on the secondary
winding of the transformer.   (a) How many primary turns are
needed?   (b) If the speaker receives 1.0 watt, what is the transformer
primary current and voltage?   (c) What cross-sectional area of core
material is required if $\mu/\mu_0 = 5,000$?   **(Sec. 109)**

8-10. A triode amplifier can be represented by the equivalent circuit shown, in which the generator resistance R_g is 2,000 ohms.   The

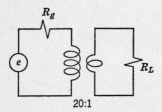

20:1   **Problem 8-10**

load resistance R_L is seen by the triode tube through a transformer
having the following characteristics: $N_1/N_2 = 20$, $R_1 = 800$ ohms
(a-c resistance of the primary winding), $R_2 = 1.0$ ohm (a-c resistance
of the secondary winding).   (a) Draw an equivalent circuit in which
all quantities are referred to the secondary side of the transformer.
(b) Calculate R_L for maximum power transfer (that is, with R_L equal
to the sum of the other resistances).   **(Sec. 111)**

8-11. An audio-frequency transformer has a primary winding of
90 turns and a secondary winding of 800 turns.   Consider operation
at 1,000 cycles/sec.   Assume a well-designed transformer (reasonably
low losses, etc.).   The secondary winding is connected to a resistance
of 500 ohms.   (a) Find the input impedance to the primary winding.
(b) The ratio of the output voltage to input current is called a transfer
impedance; find this ratio.   (c) The ratio of the output voltage to
input voltage is called a transfer function; find this ratio.   Find this
transfer function also when the output terminals are *open*-circuited,
and when *short*-circuited.   **(Sec. 111)**

THE INDUCTION MOTOR

chapter 9

113. Polyphase Rotor and Stator

In preceding chapters we have discussed machines that have direct current in one winding and alternating current in the other. It will be remembered that the d-c machine has direct current in the field winding and, by virtue of the commutator, alternating current in the armature winding. The synchronous machine also has direct current in the field winding and alternating current in the armature winding.

Now we consider a machine that has alternating current in *both* windings. To refer yet again to equation 59-2 (or 85-1), the torque developed within such a doubly excited machine is

$$T = i_1 i_2 \frac{dM}{d\theta} \tag{113-1}$$

Let us write $i_1 = I_1 \cos \omega t$ and $i_2 = I_2 \cos \omega_s t$; this means that we assume alternating currents in both windings, but their frequencies and amplitudes are as yet arbitrary.

We know that the mutual inductance between stator and rotor windings is alternating when the machine is turning, and approximately sinusoidal. If Ω_r is the speed of rotation of the rotor (electrical radians/second) we can write

$$M = M_{max} \sin \Omega_r t \tag{113-2}$$

(To make the algebra easier, phase angle is not included in either of the expressions for current, or in equation 113-2, which is otherwise the same as equation 85-3.)

Now, inserting these expressions in equation 113-1, we have

(113)

$$T = (I_1 \cos \omega t)(I_2 \cos \omega_S t)(M_{max} \cos \Omega_r t)$$

$$= \tfrac{1}{2} I_1 I_2 M_{max} \cos \omega t \, [\cos (\omega_S + \Omega_r)t + \cos (\omega_S - \Omega_r)t] \quad (113\text{-}3)$$

But this torque has an average value different from zero only if

$$\omega = \omega_S + \Omega_r \tag{113-4}$$

or if $\omega = \omega_S - \Omega_r$, or if ω is the negative of either of these. The possibility in which we shall be interested is that given by equation 113-4, which is that there can be average torque in our motor if the speed of revolution of the motor Ω_r, plus the frequency of the current in the rotor ω_S, is equal to the frequency ω of the current in the armature. Consequently, if this condition regarding frequency can be met, torque can be developed in the motor.

This condition regarding frequency is, in fact, met by the induction motor. Rotor current is induced by motion, and its frequency is necessarily ω_S, which is equal to the *slip* as will be explained. The symbols of equation 113-4 can be identified as

Ω_r is speed of rotation of the rotor (electrical radians/second)
ω_S is frequency of rotor current (radians/second)
ω is frequency of the applied current (radians/second)

Equation 113-3 is written for a machine with only two windings, one on the rotor and one on the stator. It applies, therefore, to a single-phase induction motor. It indicates the necessary frequency relation for a motor with two or three phase windings on the stator, but if there were other windings, other terms would be needed. Obviously equation 113-3 would be rather lengthy if this mathematical treatment were extended to give a full account of polyphase induction motor action.

The fact of the matter is that the polyphase induction motor is a highly sophisticated device. Nothing could be simpler to operate, and the counterpart of this simplicity of operation is a theory of considerable elegance. The interrelations among the voltages and currents and the speed and torque of the machine are fascinating.

Because it can be so simple if properly treated, the usual approach to an induction motor is to think first of the magnetic field produced by its *polyphase* stator winding. This is a magnetic field of constant magnitude (at least to a good approximation) that appears to rotate at synchronous speed. To view the results of this magnetic field from an advantageous frame of reference, the observer should be rotating at synchronous speed. We, therefore, again enlist the services of our

(113)

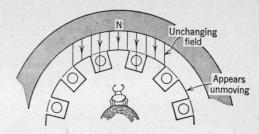

Figure 113a. Bug's-eye view of an induction motor with no slip. (The bug is riding on a frame of reference that turns at synchronous speed.)

small but intelligent and rather hardy bug. He will have to ride on the rotor of another motor turning at synchronous speed in the same direction as the induction motor, independently, but close enough to give him a good view (Figure 113a).

114. Slip

First, suppose that the rotor of the induction motor is somehow being driven at exactly synchronous speed. To our bug the rotor will seem to be standing still, and the stator will seem to be turning backward at synchronous speed. When he makes magnetic measurements he will find a magnetic field, a field produced by current in the armature windings. Although the stationary armature windings seem to him to be moving, he finds that the field they produce is not moving, and is unchanging (at least to a first approximation) as seen by him, and relative to the rotor of the machine that he is watching.

He sees, then, as suggested in Figure 113a, a stationary central structure (the rotor) and a backward-rotating outer structure (the stator). He finds a stationary and constant magnetic field produced by current in windings on the outer structure. Windings on the inner structure are carrying no current; no electomotive force is being induced in them by the magnetic field. As our bugs sees them, they are not moving through the magnetic field, nor, in his view, is the field changing with time. Hence there is no induction.

Now we stop driving the rotor of this machine at exactly synchronous speed. Let the rotor slow a little, and then hold it at a speed that is, let us say, 1 revolution per second less than synchronous speed. (This difference of 1 revolution per second we call the *slip* speed.)

Our bug (riding on the nearby synchronous motor) continues to watch and measure. What the bug sees, as in Figure 114a, has changed in only one significant way: the central structure of the

(114)

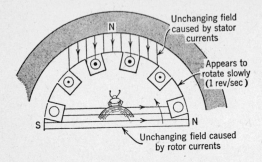

Figure 114a. Bug's-eye view of an induction motor with 1 rev/sec slip. (The bug is riding on a frame of reference that turns at synchronous speed.)

machine he is observing (the rotor) has now begun to move slowly past him. It turns toward the left at the slow rate of 1 revolution per second. Thus the bug sees the rotor turning at the speed of slip, and he sees the rotor windings moving through the magnetic field at a speed of 1 revolution per second. He sees—or could measure with a voltmeter—an electromotive force generated in these windings. It is an electromotive force that alternates as the rotor slips around, and its frequency (in a 2-pole machine) is 1 cycle per second.

As seen by the bug, the rotor is now running as an a-c generator. It is turning (as he sees it) at 1 revolution per second in a constant magnetic field, and hence electromotive force is being generated in its conductors. The rotor conductors are connected as a polyphase winding (so we have assumed), but until now we have supposed that they carried no current.

Now let the ends of these rotor windings be short-circuited together, so that current can flow through them quite freely. Since electromotive force is being generated in the winding, current does now flow. This current has a frequency of 1 cycle per second.

The polyphase currents in the rotor conductors, acting together, produce a magnetic field. They are 1-cycle-per-second currents, and they produce a field of constant magnitude that is "rotating relative to the rotor windings" at 1 revolution per second.

To our synchronously rotating bug (Figure 114a), the rotor structure appears to be going toward the left at the slip speed of 1 revolution per second, and the magnetic field produced by the rotor currents appears to be standing still. The magnetic field produced by the rotor currents and the magnetic field produced by the stator currents both appear to the bug to be stationary and constant in magnitude, though not necessarily at the same angle. Thus the bug sees the necessary condition for steady torque to be exerted on the rotor (equation 113-4).

(114)

115. Torque

Consider this torque in more detail. In the first place, it results from rotor current, which results from generated electromotive force. In which direction is the electromotive force? Referring to Figure 114a, we see that the rotor appears to be moving toward the left (counterclockwise). The magnetic field in which the rotor conductors are moving is directed downward. The electromotive force is therefore (by Figure 20a) out of the page. If current flows in phase with the electromotive force that produces it, current in the rotor conductors is also out of the page (as shown by dots).

Next, there is a force on these conductors because they are carrying current in the magnetic field of the stator, and the direction of such a force is (by Figure 10a) toward the right (clockwise). This statement might be hard to defend against someone who pointed out that the conductors, being set in slots, are almost entirely shielded from the magnetic field. Look again, from another point of view.

Current is out of the page in conductors at the top of the rotor (Figure 114a) and correspondingly into the page in similar conductors (not shown in the figure) at the bottom of the rotor. Current circulating in this way produces a magnetic field directed toward the right (by the right-hand rule, fingers pointing in the direction of current), and this magnetic field issues from the right-hand side of the rotor, producing a north magnetic pole as indicated by N in the figure. Repulsion between this magnetic pole and the north pole on the surface of the stator, at the top, gives a clockwise torque. This is the same answer that was obtained before. However we may care to think about it, the direction of torque on the rotor is clockwise.

Now returning to the actual facts of the situation, as seen by us who stand on the floor of the laboratory watching the machine, and not from the viewpoint of a hypothetical whirling bug, the stator of the machine is in fact stationary and the rotor is turning toward the right, clockwise, at just a little less than synchronous speed. The rotation of the rotor is clockwise; torque on the rotor is clockwise; the rotor is therefore being driven by the magnetic torque that is exerted on it, and the machine is running as a motor. This is the basic principle of operation of induction motors.

116. The Induction Motor

We describe now, briefly, an induction motor, so that we may have a clearer mental picture of what we are talking about. There is a stator with a three-phase winding, connected to a three-phase power supply, producing a "rotating magnetic field."

Inside the stator is the rotor, which has a polyphase winding. This may be a three-phase winding, but it could be a winding with any number of phases more than one. In practice the rotor winding very often consists merely of copper bars set in the rotor slots, with a copper ring short-circuiting together all the ends of the bars at one end of the rotor, and another copper ring short-circuiting together all the ends of the bars at the other end of the rotor. A motor with such a rotor winding, made of many bars with the ends welded to a pair of rings, is called a *squirrel-cage motor;* the reason is obvious to one who is acquainted with the similarly designed whirling wheel sometimes used to exercise captive squirrels. There are as many rotor phases as there are bars in the squirrel cage per pair of poles, for there are this many independent rotor circuits.

The rotating magnetic field induces electromotive force in the rotor bars. Current flows in the bars. The magnetic effect between rotor current and stator current is a steady torque. With the rotor turning at somewhat less than synchronous speed, the torque is in the direction of rotation and hence the machine is a motor. A mechanical load can be attached to its shaft, and it will supply mechanical power through the shaft to drive the load.

117. Torque-Speed Characteristic

Clearly, the amount of torque in the induction motor is dependent on the speed of slip. Returning to the bug's-eye view of Figure 114a, the electromotive force generated in the rotor winding is proportional to the speed of slip, the speed at which the bug sees the rotor turning through the magnetic field. (This is assuming that the magnetic field is constant, independent of load on the motor; and this is approximately true, for the total strength of the field, as in a transformer, is primarily determined by the voltage applied to the stator terminals.) Finding that rotor electromotive force is proportional to slip suggests that rotor current is proportional to slip also, but this is not true. Another factor enters into the consideration of current:

(117)

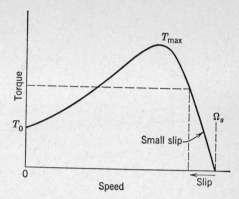

Figure 117a. Torque-speed
curve of a typical squirrel-cage
induction motor.

rotor current is limited by the impedance of the rotor winding, and
the impedance is not constant. One component of impedance is
reactance, and reactance is proportional to frequency. Frequency of
rotor current is proportional to slip. Therefore the impedance is
greater when the slip is greater. As slip increases, generated electromotive force increases, but impedance increases also.

At small values of slip, reactance is quite small because frequency
is low. Rotor current is then limited almost entirely by resistance.
In this low-slip range the motor torque is indeed very nearly proportional to slip. The linear relation is shown by the part of the curve
marked "Small slip" in Figure 117a, slip being the difference between
the speed corresponding to any point on the curve and synchronous
speed, marked Ω_s. No actual induction motor can ever quite reach
synchronous speed, for at that speed torque would be zero, and there
must in fact be at least enough torque to overcome friction and windage.

In this small-slip region the torque-speed curve is nearly a straight
line. However, as slip increases, and reactance becomes larger
compared to resistance, the rotor torque no longer increases in proportion to slip. There are two reasons for this. One is that the
increasing amount of rotor impedance, which we have discussed,
limits the amount of current. The other is that the rotor current,
when limited by reactance, is no longer in phase with the generated
electromotive force, but lags.

The result is shown in Figure 117a; torque reaches a maximum
value, and then actually declines.

The reason can easily be seen by our cooperative bug, watching
the rotor from his synchronously rotating perch nearby, as suggested

(117)

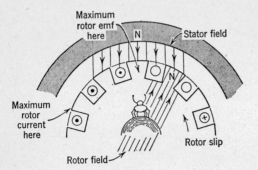

Maximum
rotor emf
here

Stator field

N

Maximum
rotor
current
here

Rotor slip

Rotor field

Figure 117b. Bug's-eye view of an induction motor with large slip, and hence with rotor current lagging rotor emf.

in Figure 117b. He sees the rotor slipping toward the left, and this time the rate of slip is much more rapid than before. The electromotive force that he sees generated in the rotor is correspondingly high. Rotor current is large, too, but not as great in proportion. Moreover, the current lags behind the electromotive force (as in any inductive circuit), and therefore any particular rotor bar is not in the same position when its current is at the maximum value as when its electromotive force is at maximum. The bug in the figure sees maximum electromotive force in the bars directly above his head, for there the rotor field is strongest and the rate of cutting magnetic field is greatest. But the current does not have its maximum value until a later instant (see Figure 117c), and by that time the same rotor bar has moved toward the bug's left, and the bug sees maximum current in the rotor conductors marked with dots.

These dotted rotor bars, with maximum current, are not in the strongest part of the rotor field, so the magnetic torque on the rotor

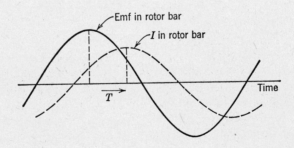

Emf in rotor bar

I in rotor bar

Time

T

Figure 117c. *T* is the time between maximum rotor emf and maximum rotor current; during this time *T* the rotor conductor is carried by slip to a less favorable position in the stator field.

(117)

is now less because of the unfavorable phase-angle relations. Another way to look at the same thing is that the rotor field is no longer at right angles to the stator field, as it was in Figure 114a, but has turned into a less favorable position in Figure 117b. As a result, rotor torque is reduced. This reduction takes place when the rotor current has relatively high frequency, resulting from increased slip.

Figure 117a shows the torque reaching a maximum value T_{max} and then, with still greater slip (lower rotor speed) decreasing to T_0 which is the zero-speed torque or starting torque of the motor. The starting torque is usually a small fraction of the maximum torque of a squirrel-cage induction motor.

The curve of Figure 117a is typical of such a motor. The motor normally runs in the small-slip region, with torque nearly proportional to slip. The *rated* power as given on the name plate of the motor, the power that the motor is designed to develop safely for an un-limited time, may correspond to about half of T_{max}. (Alger, Reference 117.)

118. Starting

Small squirrel-cage induction motors, in sizes up to a few horse-power, can be started by merely connecting them to a power-supply line of rated voltage. Current is very large while the motor is ac-celerating, but the motor comes rapidly up to speed with no damage to either itself or the power system.

If such "across-the-line starting" were attempted with a really large motor it might possibly damage the motor, and it would be likely to draw such heavy current from the power system that protec-tive relays and circuit breakers would operate. At the least, the line voltage would dip and fluctuate, making electric lights blink and flicker and causing distress to customers.

The usual way to avoid such trouble is to start induction motors on reduced voltage. The motor is not connected directly to the line but is fed through a transformer bank (usually of autotransformers), which reduces the voltage. The transformer acts in two ways to avoid excessive line current. Starting current in the motor is pro-portional to the voltage applied to the motor terminals, which is reduced by the starting transformer by a factor equal to the trans-former turn ratio. But also the supply-line current is less than the motor current by the transformer turn ratio. As a result, starting current in the supply line is reduced by the *square* of the turn ratio

(118)

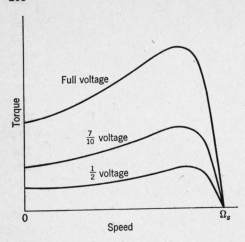

Figure 118a. Torque is proportional to the square of voltage.

from what it would have been if "across-the-line starting" had been used. (See Chapter 8 on transformers.)

By thus starting with reduced voltage the line current can be held to a satisfactorily low value. Unfortunately, however, the torque of the motor is also reduced by using lower voltage. Since both stator current and rotor current are reduced in proportion to the turn ratio of the starting transformer, the torque (propotional to their product) is reduced by the square of the turn ratio. As shown in Figure 118a, torque is reduced to one-fourth of its normal value if terminal voltage is reduced to one-half. A reduction of voltage to seven-tenths reduces torque to about half; it also reduces line current to about half, a compromise value that is often found to be convenient in practice.

The nature of the load determines whether a greatly reduced starting torque is acceptable. It is evident that a squirrel-cage induction motor is not suitable for a load that requires a high starting torque. A rock crusher, for example, cannot well be driven by a squirrel-cage motor unless there is a mechanical clutch that permits the motor to start without driving the crushing rolls until the motor has come up to speed. As another example, an electric locomotive could hardly be powered by squirrel-cage motors, for they would be incapable of starting a heavy train up a hill. A blower, on the other hand, requires little starting torque, and a squirrel-cage motor is quite satisfactory.

(118)

119. Wound-Rotor Motor

It is common for an induction motor to have a squirrel-cage winding on the rotor, but some induction motors have, instead, a three-phase rotor winding quite similar to the stator winding. The conductors of the three-phase rotor winding are insulated from the rotor iron (which the squirrel-cage bars need not be), and by attaching the ends of the rotor winding to slip rings on which stationary brushes rub, connection can be made from the rotor winding to external circuits.

There are several interesting possibilities in the use of such a wound-rotor induction motor. The most important is that the resistance of the rotor circuit can be increased by closing the rotor circuits through external resistors instead of short-circuiting the rotor-winding terminals. Increasing the rotor resistance in this way, with the use of external resistors, makes it possible to improve phase-angle relations in the motor when the slip is relatively high, for it makes the rotor reactance less important. Maximum torque is attained, as shown in Figure 119a, at a lower speed (a higher slip) when the rotor resistance is high. Inserting resistance in the rotor circuit does not greatly change the value of the maximum torque, but it does change the speed at which the maximum occurs.

It is possible by adjusting the resistance to have maximum torque at any speed. Consequently, by inserting the right amount of resistance, maximum torque can be provided at zero speed, to start a motor from standstill.

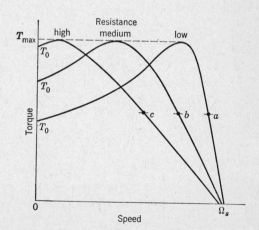

Figure 119a. The speed of maximum torque depends on rotor resistance.

(119)

This means of obtaining high starting torque is sometimes of real practical value. Not only is the starting torque increased, but a high value of rotor resistance also reduces the starting current, holding it to a safe value. Then, after the motor has started, and has reached normal speed, the additional resistance is removed by short-circuiting the rotor terminals, and the motor runs with minimum resistance in the rotor circuit.

The steady speed of a loaded motor can also be controlled by inserting more or less resistance in the rotor circuit. In Figure 119a, points a, b, and c show three different speeds at which a load of constant torque can be driven by a wound-rotor induction motor when the corresponding low, medium, and high values of rotor resistance are used. However, this kind of speed control is inefficient and not very satisfactory.

Wound-rotor motors are more expensive than squirrel-cage motors of the same power rating, and so are not very common. It is only for certain applications, usually of large-size motors, that the advantages of (1) higher starting torque, (2) lower starting current, and (3) possible though inefficient speed control outweigh the advantages of the squirrel-cage motor, which are (1) lower first cost, (2) higher efficiency, and (3) simplicity and corresponding low cost of maintenance.

120. Effect of Rotor Resistance

The torque-speed curves of Figures 117a, 118a, and 119a are most readily explained for a balanced polyphase motor in terms of an equivalent transformer diagram. Consider an induction motor for either power or control. Consider also that polyphase voltage is applied to the stator, producing a magnetic field of approximately constant magnitude that is changing in direction within the stator so that it appears to be rotating at synchronous speed. The mutual flux entering the rotor from this rotating field is Φ_M. The rotor may be either of squirrel-cage (or drag-cup) design, or it may be wound with N_2 turns.

Consider for the moment that the motor is not turning; it is held stationary. The mutual flux links the rotor winding, and electromotive force is induced in the rotor by the rate of change of flux linkages. According to Faraday's equation 23-1, induced electromotive force is then

(120)

$$e_2 = -N_2 \frac{d\Phi_M}{dt} \tag{120-1}$$

Supposing variation of the flux to be sinusoidal (and this is true for the fundamental component at least), we obtain

$$\Phi_M = \Phi_{M(max)} \sin \omega t \tag{120-2}$$

The rate of change of flux is then

$$\frac{d\Phi_M}{dt} = \omega \Phi_{M(max)} \cos \omega t \tag{120-3}$$

and the electromotive force induced in the rotor is

$$e_2 = -N_2 \omega \Phi_{M(max)} \cos \omega t \tag{120-4}$$

Written in terms of phasors, with j showing the 90-degree phase difference between electromotive force and flux,

$$E_2 = -j\omega N_2 \Phi_M \tag{120-5}$$

This electromotive force is entirely used in sending current through the resistance R_2 and reactance X_2 of the rotor winding (or bars) if the rotor is short-circuited; or if additional resistance is added to the rotor circuit, this additional amount of resistance is to be added as part of R_2. Then

$$E_2 = I_2(R_2 + jX_2) \tag{120-6}$$

where R_2 is the resistance of the rotor plus added resistance if any, and X_2 is the reactance of the rotor when current has the frequency under consideration, which, with stationary rotor, will be synchronous frequency. The expressions of equations 120-5 and 120-6 are, of course, equal, so that

$$-j\omega N_2 \Phi_M = I_2(R_2 + jX_2) \tag{120-7}$$

Since the stationary motor is to all intents and purposes exactly like a short-circuited transformer, each phase of it can be represented by Figure 120a. This is similar to Figure 104c, but short-circuited.

Consider next that the motor is no longer stationary, but turns with velocity Ω. The slip of the motor is S (the symbol S will be used for slip in this chapter, to be consistent with common practice). With Ω_s representing synchronous speed of the motor, the definition of slip is

$$S = \frac{\Omega_s - \Omega}{\Omega_s} \tag{120-8}$$

$$\tag{120}$$

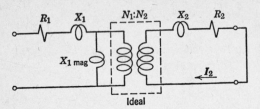

Figure 120a. Diagram of a stationary induction motor with secondary resistance R_2.

When the motor is stationary, slip is one. When the motor is turning, slip has a value less than one. Since the rate of change of flux is correspondingly reduced, the electromotive force induced in the rotor is reduced from E_2 to SE_2. At the same time the frequency of electromotive force in the rotor is reduced by the same fraction, so reactance of the rotor is reduced from its value of X_2 at standstill to the smaller value SX_2. As a result of motion equation 120-7 becomes

$$-j\omega S N_2 \Phi_M = I_2(R_2 + jSX_2) \qquad (120\text{-}9)$$

or

$$-j\omega N_2 \Phi_M = I_2\left(\frac{R_2}{S} + jX_2\right) \qquad (120\text{-}10)$$

121. The Equivalent Transformer

It will now be shown that a short-circuited transformer, if the load is properly adjusted, has the same equation and hence is equivalent to the induction motor. In the diagram of Figure 120a, or the phasor diagram of Figure 106a, the electromotive force E_2 is induced in the secondary winding. The secondary winding is short-circuited. The total secondary resistance is R_2 and the secondary reactance is X_2. The diagram of Figure 120a applies to either a short-circuited

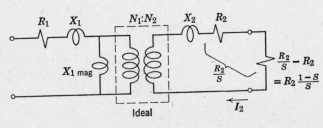

Figure 121a. Diagram of a short-circuited transformer with secondary resistance R_2/S.

(121)

transformer or a stationary induction motor, and so do equations 120-5, 6, and 7.

Let this transformer be changed by altering the secondary resistance to R_2/S, as in Figure 121a, and equation 120-10 applies. In this short-circuited transformer, S has no physical meaning; it is merely a mathematical constant. Nevertheless, the same equation applies that was derived for the induction motor.*

122. Equivalent Load

We can go a step farther and divide the resistance R_2/S into two parts as shown in the diagram. One is R_2; the other is $(R_2/S - R_2)$. When the proper voltage (that of one phase of the motor stator) is applied to the transformer, the power of one phase will flow. Power transferred by the magnetic field is the same in amount whether it goes to the secondary winding of the transformer or to the rotor of the motor. In both transformer and motor, the part of this power lost in heating is $|I_2|^2 R_2$. In the motor the rest of the power transferred to the rotor is mechanical power developed in the rotor, whereas in the equivalent transformer the rest of the secondary power is that which goes to the other resistance, and it is equal to $|I_2|^2 (R_2/S - R_2)$. Hence, if g is the number of stator phases, the mechanical power developed in the motor is

$$P_{\text{developed}} = g|I_2|^2 \left(\frac{R_2}{S} - R_2 \right) = g|I_2|^2 R_2 \frac{1-S}{S} \qquad (122\text{-}1)$$

The torque is mechanical power divided by the speed of the rotor. Since $\Omega = \Omega_s(1 - S)$,

$$T = g|I_2|^2 \frac{R_2(1-S)}{\Omega S} = g|I_2|^2 \frac{R_2}{S\Omega_s} \qquad (122\text{-}2)$$

The secondary current I_2 can now be computed from Figure 121a and the applied voltage. It is not necessary in doing this to neglect the magnetizing current, but it is usual and convenient. In a motor of several horsepower, designed to deliver power, the magnetizing current is commonly small compared to the rated load current. In a small con-

---

*This leads to a useful circle diagram; see, for instance, Alger (Reference 117). The induction-motor circle diagram is a special case of the more general circle diagram for constant reactance and variable resistance (Chapter 8 of Reference 7A).

trol motor this is not necessarily true, but the final outcome is reasonably correct and will be justified later. We therefore let $X_{1\,mag} = \infty$. In addition, for convenience, let $X_1 + (N_1/N_2)^2 X_2 = X$, and $(N_1/N_2)^2 R_2 = R_2'$ (the effective value referred to the primary side). Then the input current is

$$|I| = \frac{|V|}{\sqrt{(R_1 + R_2'/S)^2 + X^2}} \qquad (122\text{-}3)$$

and when the turn ratios are properly sorted out,

$$T = \frac{g|V|^2}{\Omega_s} \frac{R_2'S}{(R_1 S + R_2')^2 + X^2 S^2} \qquad (122\text{-}4)$$

This is the torque shown in Figure 117a. It will be seen from the equation that for very small values of slip the torque is approximately proportional to slip. Moreover, there may be a value of slip so large that the torque passes a maximum and becomes small again as $X^2 S^2$ in the denominator becomes great. All of the curve of Figure 117a can be computed from this equation, within the approximations that apply to the equation. It is interesting to notice that the equation has meaning for negative slip. With negative slip the speed of the machine is greater than synchronous, it must be driven mechanically, and it acts as a generator instead of a motor.

The curves of Figure 118a also come from equation 122-4. These show that torque is proportional to the square of voltage V, speed and hence slip being constant, a fact that is obvious from the equation.

123. Maximum Torque

With the approximations that have now been made, the largest being the neglect of magnetizing current, it is not difficult to find the maximum torque, and the speed or slip at which maximum torque occurs. They are found in the usual manner by differentiating T with respect to S and setting the result equal to zero. After differentiation most of the terms cancel and we obtain

$$S = \frac{R_2'}{\sqrt{R_1^2 + X^2}} \qquad (123\text{-}1)$$

Here we have the value of slip at which torque becomes maximum. Note that this slip for maximum torque is directly proportional to rotor resistance R_2 and compare this with Figure 119a. Remember

(123)

that in a wound-rotor induction motor the rotor resistance R_2 may be adjustable by means of an external resistor, and if so the external resistor may be set to give maximum torque at any speed including the zero speed of starting.

To find the value of torque at its maximum, equation 123-1 is substituted back into equation 122-4, leading to

$$T_{max} = \frac{g\,|V|^2}{\Omega_s} \frac{1}{2(\sqrt{R_1{}^2 + X^2} + R_1)} \tag{123-2}$$

Perhaps the most interesting aspect of this equation is that the maximum torque is not at all a function of the rotor resistance; R_2 does not appear in this formula. The same maximum torque is reached regardless of the rotor resistance, but at a slip proportional to the resistance, and this also is shown in Figure 119a. It must again be remembered, however, that certain assumptions have been made, and if magnetizing current is taken into account this conclusion is not quite true.

124. Amortisseur Winding

It has been mentioned that a synchronous motor can run only at exact synchronous speed. How, then, can a synchronous motor be started?

The answer is that a squirrel-cage winding (or at least a partial squirrel cage) is built into the rotor, and the machine starts as an induction motor. In a synchronous machine the rotor is the field structure (Figure 85a). Short-circuited copper bars are placed in slots in the pole faces. These short-circuited bars are called an amortisseur winding.

While the machine is starting, no direct current is supplied to the main winding on the field poles, but current is induced in the short-circuited bars of the amortisseur squirrel cage. The machine comes up to speed like a rather poor induction motor. Then, when the motor speed is as near synchronous speed as friction and windage losses will permit, direct current is put through the main field winding. The direct-current rotor field will then "lock in" with the rotating field of the stator winding, and the rotor will be carried on to run at exactly synchronous speed. (The motor will "fall in step" only if the rotor is so near synchronous speed before the main field winding is energized that a single pull from the stator field will bring the rotor to full synchronous speed.)

(124)

The amortisseur winding is also called a *damper winding,* because in addition to its use for starting the motor it is also helpful in damping out mechanical oscillations of the synchronous-machine rotor. Oscillations may arise from a periodic disturbance on the line, or may appear spontaneously if the resistance of the armature circuit is too great. A damper winding of low resistance will stop such oscillations, for the circulating currents induced in the squirrel-cage bars produce a torque always tending toward synchronous speed, as in equation 122-4.

125. Single-Phase Induction Motors

The expression for torque in equation 113-3 is obtained by considering an induction motor with a single-phase stator, rather than a two-phase or three-phase stator, and millions of single-phase induction motors are in every-day use. Yet these single-phase stator windings cannot actually produce a rotating magnetic field; this requires a polyphase winding. How, then, does the single-phase motor run?

The best understanding of a single-phase induction motor (or a single-phase synchronous motor, as in an electric clock) comes from a bit of analytical legerdemain. A single-phase magnetic field can be considered to be the sum of two polyphase magnetic fields. The polyphase fields do not exist except in imagination, but the single-phase motor runs just as if they did.

Figure 125a shows a single-phase induction motor. The stator has a pair of salient poles (a four-pole motor, with two pairs of poles, is more common, but the principle is the same), and the cross-hatched area indicates a cross section of the coil that is placed in the motor to magnetize the poles. The coil carries alternating current, which

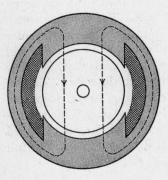

Figure 125a. Magnetic field in a two-pole single-phase motor.

(125)

produces an alternating magnetic field that goes vertically through the rotor.

Consider the magnetic field in the rotor. It is at all times vertical. It is not a rotating field, but alternates between being directed upward and being directed downward. Its magnitude varies sinusoidally with time, or approximately so. We now show that this is exactly the result that would be obtained if we had two rotating magnetic fields, superimposed, each constant in magnitude, with one rotating clockwise and the other counterclockwise.

126. Oppositely Rotating Field Components

Figure 126a shows the vectors representing two oppositely rotating magnetic fields, each having constant magnitude of one half. (These may be visualized as fields of magnetic intensity H that apply at the center of the rotor.) When they coincide in direction, as in the diagram marked 0°, the total magnetic field is 1 unit, vertically upward. When each has turned 45°, the sum is $1/\sqrt{2}$, still vertically upward. As they continue to turn, the total field diminishes to zero and then increases in a downward direction, which may be called negative, until its magnitude becomes -1. Then the total field shrinks again to zero, and after one full cycle returns to its initial value of $+1$. This alternating variation of the total field continues as the component fields rotate; the total field varies sinusoidally.

But this total field is just the kind of magnetic field that exists in a stationary single-phase induction motor. Whether the motor is standing still or running, the total field is equivalent to two op-

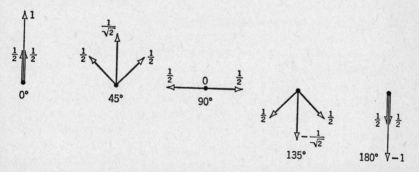

Figure 126a. A pulsing field can be considered to be the sum of two oppositely rotating fields of constant magnitude.

(126)

positely rotating fields of constant magnitude, and we are justified in saying that the single-phase induction motor operates *as if* its stator winding were producing two oppositely rotating fields of constant magnitude.

127. Application to a Synchronous Motor

The application to a single-phase synchronous motor is obvious. Suppose the rotor in Figure 125a has salient poles, and the rotor is running one way or the other at synchronous speed. It will then be running in synchronism with one of the rotating magnetic fields, which we may call the *positive-sequence* component, and the magnetic flux of this field will exert on the rotor a steady torque that drives it as a synchronous motor. To this extent the operation is similar to that of a polyphase motor.

But there is also the effect of the oppositely rotating magnetic field called the *negative-sequence* component. This negative-sequence component will also exert torque on the rotor, but it will pull it first one way and then the other as the field and the salient poles pass each other. Thus the second part of the field, the negative-sequence component, produces an alternating torque on the rotor with an average of zero. The first component is effective in driving the motor; the second component pulls it first one way and then the other, making the motor hum and vibrate, but neither adding to nor subtracting from the average torque. The second component is useless; it is somewhat wasteful of power and inefficient; it may produce unwanted noise and heat; but despite it the motor runs. As has been said, electric clock motors are of this kind.

128. Application to an Induction Motor

Single-phase induction motors operate in a somewhat similar manner. The component of magnetic field that rotates in the same direction as the rotor of the motor, the *positive-sequence* component, exerts through its flux a relatively large torque on the rotor. The oppositely rotating component, the *negative-sequence* component, exerts a relatively small torque in the other direction. The total result is a substantial net torque in the positive direction, and the machine runs as a motor.

This action is best studied with the aid of a torque-speed diagram. Let the rotor of Figure 125a have a squirrel-cage winding; the torque

(128)

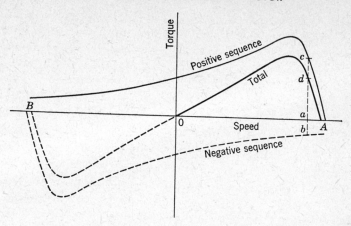

Figure 128a. Torque in a single-phase induction motor.

produced by the positive-sequence component alone is given by a curve similar to Figure 117a. This is shown as the "positive sequence" curve in Figure 128a. Also, the torque-speed curve is extended to the left into the region of negative speed, showing torque that would have to be overcome if the motor were to be driven mechanically in a backward direction. A dash line is shown for torque that would be produced by the negative-sequence component of field alone; this is similar to the positive-sequence curve but with both torque and speed reversed in direction.

When the motor is running near synchronous speed in the positive direction it has a small slip relative to the positive-sequence component of field. An example is shown as *A–a*. Positive torque results, as shown by the ordinate *a–c*. At the same speed it has a slip *B–a* relative to the negative-sequence component of field. This slip is nearly twice synchronous speed. The corresponding negative torque is *a–b*. The net torque on the rotor is *a–d*, the algebraic sum, and, since *a–b* is much smaller than *a–c*, the net torque is only a little less than the positive-sequence torque alone. Thus *a–d* is the effective torque on the rotor, the torque that it will be able to exert as a motor at the indicated speed and slip.*

---

* If Figure 128a were copied directly from Figure 117a it would assume that the positive-sequence and negative-sequence fields were unaffected by rotation of the machine. This is not true. Actually, if positive speed is great the positive-sequence torque is higher and the negative-sequence torque lower than would be

Similar conditions exist at other speeds, as shown by the torque curve marked "total." Notice that when the motor is running in a positive direction there is a positive torque to drive it, and when the machine is running in a negative direction there is a negatve torque to drive it; but when the motor speed is zero there is no net torque.

This condition indicates that a single-phase induction motor will run in either direction, whichever way it happens to be started, but that it has no starting torque. Such a motor could be connected to the line and, given a whirl in either direction, it would run the way it was started, but it would not start by itself. A practical motor, however, must be self-starting, so some means must be provided to give torque at zero speed.

129. Starting Single-Phase Motors

There are several ways to make single-phase induction motors self-starting. Most of them involve the artificial production of a second phase.

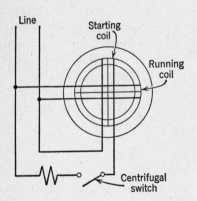

Figure 129a. A split-phase motor.

The distinctive characteristic of a two-phase motor is that the currents in its two coils are in quadrature with each other. How can we provide a single-phase motor with two currents in quadrature?

One solution is to connect one coil of a two-phase motor winding directly to the line. This motor coil, when the motor is connected to

---

predicted by Figure 117a or equation 122-4, considering equal fields. Figure 128a is nevertheless correct, due modification having been made for rotation. See Section 228 and also Reference 78F.

the line for starting, is a highly reactive circuit and the current in it lags nearly 90 degrees behind the applied voltage. The other coil of the two-phase motor is connected in series with a rather high resistance, as indicated in Figure 129a. Current in this circuit is mainly limited by the resistance, and hence is largely in phase with the applied voltage. Since current in one coil is more or less in phase with the voltage, and current in the other is more nearly in quadrature, these two currents approximate a two-phase system. Together they produce in the motor a semblance of a rotating field, and the motor is able to start.*

As soon as the motor has come up to speed the resistor and the motor coil that provide a second phase for starting are disconnected, for it would be inefficient to allow current to flow continuously in the resistor. This is usually done automatically, by some kind of centrifugal switch within the motor. Such a motor is called a *split-phase* motor. Its characteristics are not very good, but it is cheap.

130. The Capacitor Motor

A better arrangement is the *capacitor motor*. The starting resistor of the split-phase motor is replaced by a capacitor, as shown in Figure 130a. By proper choice of the size of the capacitor, taking into account the resistance and reactance of each winding of the motor, the designer can provide for the currents in the two motor coils to be truly in quadrature and of the same magnitude. See Figure 130b. In this way a single-phase motor can have starting characteristics as good as those of a polyphase motor.

As the motor comes up to speed the currents in the two coils do not remain properly balanced. Therefore some motors open the circuit of the starting coil with a centrifugal switch, as do split-phase motors, and run as single-phase induction motors. They are called *capacitor-start* motors. Others do not open the circuit, but merely reduce the amount of capacitance to a value that will provide reasonably well-balanced two-phase currents while running at normal speed with normal load. These are called *capacitor-run* motors. Having two capacitors, they are somewhat more expensive than capacitor-start motors, but their characteristics while running

---

* In practice the additional resistance is most cheaply obtained by merely using finer wire in the starting coil than in the running coil. No external resistor is then needed.

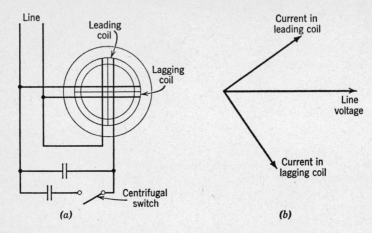

Figure 130. (*a*) A capacitor motor. (*b*) Currents in a capacitor motor can be truly in quadrature.

under load are rather better. Note that the running capacitor can be left in the circuit during continuous operation without loss of efficiency, whereas the resistor of a split-phase motor could not.

Capacitor-start motors are typically used in household refrigerators, and they are useful for many applications that require fractional-horsepower motors with more starting torque than split-phase motors can provide. Capacitor-run motors are used in sizes up to several horsepower; they are probably the best single-phase motors. In the larger sizes they are more expensive than three-phase motors, but three-phase power is not always as readily available as single-phase.

131. Shaded-Pole Motors

One other ingenious starting device should be mentioned. Like the split-phase motor, it works by causing two components of magnetic field to appear in the single-phase motor, out of phase in time and displaced in angle. It is called a shading coil, or ring, and the motor a *shaded-pole motor*.

As shown in Figure 131*a*, the shading coil is a collar of heavy copper or brass placed around part of the iron pole of a single-phase induction motor. When the main winding of the motor produces alternating flux in the pole, some of the flux links this shading coil

(131)

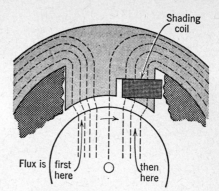

Figure 131a. One pole of a shaded-
pole motor.

and induces electromotive force and hence circulating current in the collar. This circulating current opposes (by Lenz's law) change of the linking flux, with the result that magnetic field in this banded tooth is later in phase than the field in the rest of the pole. In each cycle, the field in the main part of the pole reaches its maximum strength slightly before the field in the banded part of the pole reaches its maximum. Hence the greatest strength of the field is first through the main part, later through the banded part, of the pole. This condition produces an effect, sometimes called a shifting field, that has enough similarity to a rotating field to produce a small torque on the squirrel-cage rotor of the motor. The rotor is carried along in the direction of "shifting" of the field, and once started by this means it will pick up speed and run as a single-phase induction motor. However, the torque produced by a shaded pole is very slight, and only the smallest motors, as for electric fans, electric clocks, and phonograph turntables, can be started by this means.

132. Servomotors

The induction motor has a number of applications in control systems. Two-phase and three-phase servomotors are used to drive various mechanisms, and although they are likely to be small, with a rated power output of only a few watts, their action is similar to that of induction motors rated in kilowatts. Their resistance is always relatively high, however, which results in their having the characteristics typical of a high-resistance motor, including low efficiency.

For the transmission of signals, as in control systems, an induction

(132)

motor is used dynamically. Its periods of starting and stopping, of change of speed, are as greatly needed as its torque or speed under steady running conditions. It will be best, then, to postpone the study of induction motors as elements of control systems until the dynamic operation of devices has been considered.

Dynamic operation is the subject of the next chapter, and consideration of induction motors is resumed in Chapter 16.

133. Summary

The induction motor has alternating current in both its windings. Current in the *stator* winding is at line frequency; current in the *rotor* winding is at *slip* frequency. There is torque because rotor speed plus slip speed must equal the synchronous speed determined by the applied line frequency. Rotor current results from induction, and its frequency is necessarily the frequency of slip.

The *torque* of an induction motor depends on the speed of slip. At zero slip (synchronous speed) there is no torque. As slip increases with load, torque increases until a maximum is reached, and thereafter torque decreases with increasing slip. Maximum torque is produced at a value of slip that depends on rotor resistance; a low-resistance rotor gives maximum torque with small slip, a high-resistance rotor with large slip.

The most common type of induction motor has a *squirrel-cage* winding on the rotor. Squirrel-cage motors in large sizes are usually started with reduced voltage. Other induction motors have *wound rotors*. The rotor resistance of these can be adjusted during operation; they are started with high resistance and run with low resistance in the rotor circuit.

For analysis, an induction motor is often represented by the equivalent transformer. An induction motor and a transformer are rather similar in operation. An induction motor at standstill is like a short-circuited transformer. Similarity of the equations shows that there is analogy between an induction motor with mechanical load and a transformer with electrical load equal to $R_2(1 - S)/S$.

Single-phase induction motors will run, but they will not start. When they are running, positive-sequence torque is greater than negative-sequence torque. At zero speed the two torque components are equal and opposite, so special devices are required for starting. Split-phase, capacitor, and shaded-pole motors are common examples of self-starting single-phase induction motors.

(133)

Symmetrical components of voltage are applied to the single-phase induction motor, and the total torque of the motor is computed from the torque of the symmetrical components individually.

Since synchronous motors, as such, have no starting torque, they are commonly equipped with *amortisseur* windings so that they will start as induction motors. These amortisseur or *damper* windings also serve to damp mechanical oscillations of the machines.

Two-phase and three-phase induction motors of small size are commonly used in control systems. Their discussion is postponed until Chapter 16, after a discussion of dynamic elements, which is the subject of the next chapter.

PROBLEMS

9-1. Find a squirrel-cage induction motor, three-phase or single-phase, and learn all you can about it by observation. (They are used on machine tools, pumps, some household appliances; nearly any a-c drive from $\frac{1}{4}$-horsepower up.) Write about two pages of description, including a diagram, giving physical size and form, nature of load, power supply, speed, etc. Determine number of poles, per cent slip on full load, method of starting. Count, if possible, the bars in the rotor. **(Sec. 116)**

9-2. "The possibility in which we shall be interested is that given by equation 113-4." The three other conditions under which torque has an average value different from zero have physically possible meanings; they are practical conditions. What are they? **(Sec. 113)**

9-3. An electric motor is driving a constant load at constant speed. Neglect all power loss (as heat) in the motor. Input current has a constant value, either the actual current if direct or the rms value if alternating. Steady state has been reached. Consider the statement in the last paragraph in Section 55, that under certain circumstances half of the input power is stored in the field and half is converted to mechanical power. Consider motors of the following types: (*a*) Shunt, d-c. (*b*) Induction, a-c, single-phase or polyphase. (*c*) Synchronous. For each of these types of motors: (1) Does this statement apply? (2) If not, why not? (3) If so, during what time?

(Sec. 113)

9-4. The magnetic field of an induction motor is estimated to be 0.6 weber/m² (maximum). The motor, a 2-pole machine, has synchronous speed of 3,600 rpm. The rotor of the machine is 20 cm long and 30 cm in diameter. There are 52 bars in the squirrel cage, each 1.0 by 2.0 cm. (a) What is the frequency of the line voltage? (b) Find the rms electromotive force induced in a rotor bar at standstill. (c) Find the rms electromotive force induced in a rotor bar with the machine running under full load at 3,520 rpm. Make what approximations and assumptions are necessary and reasonable.

(Sec. 117)

9-5. The magnetic field of an induction motor is estimated to be 0.8 weber/m² (maximum). The motor, a 4-pole machine, has synchronous speed of 1,800 rpm; speed under load = 1,760 rpm. Length of rotor = 5.0 cm; diameter of rotor = 15 cm; number of bars = 45; each bar is 0.5 cm wide by 1.0 cm radially. (a) What is the frequency of the line voltage? (b) Find the rms electromotive force induced in a rotor bar at standstill. (c) Find the rms electromotive force induced in a rotor bar at full load. Make necessary and reasonable approximations.

(Sec. 117)

9-6. A squirrel-cage induction motor has direct current supplied to 2 of the 3 stator terminals. How will the motor behave? If possible, try it; use about rated current in the stator, from a low-voltage d-c supply.

(Sec. 117)

9-7. Extend Figure 117a so that the torque-speed curve is shown from speed = −1 to speed = +2 times rated speed. Explain how the machine can be made to operate in the ranges of speed from −1 to 0, from 0 to +1, and from +1 to +2. Is power in or out on (a) the electrical side? (b) the mechanical side?

(Sec. 117)

9-8. Torque required to drive a centrifugal pump is $T = K_p n^2$ (K_p is a constant, n is rev/sec). An induction motor is used to drive the pump. In the practical operating range the torque of the motor is $K_m S$ (where S is slip in revolutions per second). At what speed will the motor drive the pump?

(Sec. 117)

9-9. Figure 117a shows a maximum of torque in accordance with equation 122-4. Rotor current does not have a corresponding maximum. Show: (a) That it does not. (b) How torque can become less as rotor current becomes greater. **(Sec. 122)**

9-10. A 3-phase, 60-cycle, 6-pole induction motor is rated 220 volts line-to-line or 127 volts per phase. Stator resistance is 0.20 ohm, stator reactance at 60 cycle/sec is 0.50 ohm, and rotor quantities referred to the stator are 0.14 ohm resistance and 0.20 ohm reactance at 60 cycles/sec. Magnetizing reactance referred to the stator is 20 ohms. When the slip is 0.020, what is (a) the motor speed? (b) mechanical power to the shaft of the motor? (c) torque developed? (d) electrical power input? **(Sec. 122)**

9-11. In the foregoing problem what (approximately) is the maximum torque that can be obtained from the motor? How much must the rotor resistance be changed to make this the starting torque?

(Sec. 123)

9-12. Compute the value of rotor resistance to give maximum starting torque of a motor in which magnetizing current may be neglected. Express this resistance in terms of the other resistances and reactances of the motor. **(Sec. 123)**

9-13. A 6-pole, 60-cycle induction motor runs on 220 volts line-to-line (this is 127 volts across each phase). First it is run without load, and current to each phase is 3.5 amp lagging 74 degrees behind the voltage. Then it is stopped, and the rotor is blocked so it cannot turn. Rated voltage is again applied, and, with rotor blocked, the current is 90 amp in each phase with a power factor of 0.45. Draw an equivalent diagram as in Figure 121a except that rotor quantities may be referred to the stator and the turn-ratio omitted. Neglect the voltage drop in the stator caused by magnetizing current (this is equivalent to placing $X_{1\,mag}$ to the left, rather than to the right, of R_1 and X_1). Also, assume that the losses at no load are independent of speed, and hence may be represented by a resistance parallel to $X_{1\,mag}$. Give numerical values for each element in the diagram, assuming $R_1 = R_2'$ and $X_1 = X_2'$ (the primes indicating rotor quantities referred to stator). What is the maximum torque to be obtained from this motor, and at what speed will the torque be maximum? (*Note.* This problem is nicely solved graphically with a circle diagram; it can equally well be solved analytically with the equations of this chapter.) **(Sec. 123)**

9-14. A 12-pole, 400-cycle induction motor runs on 50 volts line to line, or 29 volts across each phase. Running without load the current to each phase is 1.7 amp lagging 75 degrees behind the voltage. With blocked rotor the current is 30 amp, lagging 80 degrees. The same assumptions can be made as in Problem 9-13. As in that problem, draw an equivalent diagram with numerical values; also, find maximum torque and the speed of maximum torque. **(Sec. 123)**

9-15. Derive equation 123-2. **(Sec. 123)**

9-16. It is stated in Section 123 that "the same maximum torque is reached regardless of rotor resistance," but that "if magnetizing current is taken into account this conclusion is not quite true." When magnetizing current is taken into account will an increase of rotor resistance increase or decrease the maximum torque? Why? **(Sec. 123)**

9-17. An a-c pump for liquid metals is described in Chapter 18. Devise a practical form of such a pump. **(Sec. 123)**

9-18. Section 105 states that starting torque of an induction motor is proportional to the square of the applied voltage. From which equation does this statement follow? What approximations are involved? **(Sec. 124)**

9-19. How can you reverse the direction of rotation of a given motor? Discuss for the following types of motors, showing connection diagrams and explaining reasons. (a) A shunt-excited d-c motor. (b) A series d-c motor. (c) A 2-phase induction motor. (d) A 3-phase induction motor. (e) A repulsion motor. (f) A split-phase motor. **(Sec. 129)**

9-20. Section 129 says that the split-phase motor provides, for starting, "a semblance of a rotating field." Show from phasor diagrams why a capacitor motor can be better. **(Sec. 130)**

9-21. Tell how you would most satisfactorily start the following motors under the given conditions. Line current is direct or 60 cycles/sec alternating as would be appropriate. Answer (a) and (b) for the 9 uses. (a) Starting the machine from standstill, what is to be done to bring it up to speed, and how is speed then adjusted (if adjustment is wanted)? (b) What auxiliary equipment, not part of the motor, is needed for starting and for adjustment of speed? (Resistors, transformers, etc.) (1) Single-phase induction motor for running a household refrigerator. (2) Three-phase 5-horsepower induction motor, connected to a fan on the same shaft, for ventilating a classroom. (3) 500-horsepower, three-phase induction motor with wound rotor, for running a fan in a wind tunnel for aircraft testing.

(4) Series d-c motor for running a street car in a city. (5) Series a-c motor for running an electric train between cities. (6) 3-horse-power, 1,400-rpm shunt motor for running a lathe in a machine shop. (7) A motor in an electric clock. (What type of motor?) (8) A motor in a toy electric train. (What type of motor?) (9) A motor on an air compressor in an ordinary gasoline filling station. (What type of motor?) **(Sec. 133)**

ELECTRICAL AND MECHANICAL RELATIONS
chapter 10

134. Simultaneous Equations

Electrical energy is changed to mechanical, or mechanical to electrical, according to the *electromechanical* relations of our first few chapters. Examples are given from microphones and speakers, generators and motors.

An electromechanical device, however, is always part of a system, and cannot be considered alone. Its operation is affected by the electrical elements of the system on one side, and by the mechanical elements on the other. Figure 3a in the first chapter showed the reaction of these elements on each other, with a short discussion of the way each affects the other.

Electromechanical relations were then discussed through several chapters, and we are now ready to consider the electrical and the mechanical relations that are a necessary part of the operation. Only after this is done can a complete dynamic system be considered; only with mechanical and electrical as well as electromechanical elements can a system be operative.

135. Electrical Elements

According to Kirchhoff's voltage law (as stated in Section 5), *Electromotive force = sum of the opposing voltages*, including voltage across resistance, voltage across inductance, and voltage across capacitance. It is expected that the reader is acquainted with these voltages. Very briefly, they are the following.

Voltage across *resistance* is proportional to current in most conductors, including metals. Hence in Ohm's law,

(135)

$$v = Ri \tag{135-1}$$

the resistance R is a constant, and not a function of current i. The value of R is usually dependent on temperature, and perhaps to a slight extent on pressure or tension in the wire, but experiment shows that over an amazingly wide range R is independent of current.

Voltage across *inductance* is proportional to the rate of change of *electrokinetic momentum:*

$$v = \frac{d}{dt}(Li) \tag{135-2}$$

If inductance L is constant, as it usually is in an unmoving circuit that contains no ferromagnetic material,

$$v = L\frac{di}{dt} \tag{135-3}$$

If there is *mutual* inductance, rate of change of current in one circuit induces voltage in another. If the mutual inductance between circuits 1 and 2 is M, we have

$$v_1 = \frac{d}{dt}(Mi_2) \quad \text{and} \quad v_2 = \frac{d}{dt}(Mi_1) \tag{135-4}$$

Voltage across *capacitance* is proportional to charge and inversely proportional to the capacitance C:

$$v = \frac{q}{C} \quad \text{or} \quad q = Cv \tag{135-5}$$

Since current is the rate at which charge enters the capacitor,

$$i = \frac{dq}{dt} = \frac{d}{dt}(Cv) \tag{135-6}$$

or

$$i\,dt = d(Cv) \tag{135-7}$$

Integrating both sides, we obtain

$$\int_0^t i\,dt = \Big[Cv \Big]_{v_0}^{v} \tag{135-8}$$

where v_0 is the capacitor voltage at the instant when $t = 0$, and v is

(135)

voltage * at the later instant t. Then

$$v = \frac{1}{C}\left(v_0 + \int_0^t i\, dt\right) \tag{135-9}$$

If the capacitor is initially uncharged,

$$v = \frac{1}{C}\int_0^t i\, dt \tag{135-10}$$

These are the essential electrical relations that will be needed when the electrical, electromechanical, and mechanical equations are to be solved simultaneously. The mechanical relations, somewhat analogous, are no doubt familiar, also, but will be reviewed in a little more detail.

136. Reactive Inertial Force in Translation

If force is exerted on a heavy body, in line with its center of gravity, and the body is properly isolated from all other influences, it will be accelerated. Its momentum will change. Momentum is the product of mass and speed, mS. Force is equal to the rate of change of momentum:

$$F = \frac{d(mS)}{dt} \tag{136-1}$$

If mass does not change (and in most of the systems we shall be considering, it will not),

$$F = m\frac{dS}{dt} \tag{136-2}$$

Acceleration a is the rate of change of speed, so with constant mass,

$$F = ma \tag{136-3}$$

In these equations, F is in newtons, m in kilograms, t in seconds, S in meters/second, and a in meters/second^2. $F, S,$ and a are vectors in these equations, with force and acceleration in the same direction.

---

* Lower limits are values of the variables at the same instant; that is, $v = v_0$ when $t = 0$. Upper limits imply that voltage is v at the instant at which time is t.

The upper limits may be written v_1 and t_1 if preferred. The subscripts can then be dropped after the integration has been performed. The result is the same, and perhaps the logic is more satisfying.

137. Rotation

If torque is exerted on a heavy body that is free to rotate, the body will be given angular acceleration. Its angular momentum will change. Angular momentum is the product of moment of inertia and angular velocity, $J\Omega$. Torque is equal to the rate of change of this product:

$$T = \frac{d(J\Omega)}{dt}$$

(137-1)

If moment of inertia is constant,

$$T = J\frac{d\Omega}{dt}$$

(137-2)

Angular acceleration α is the rate of change of angular velocity, giving (for constant moment of inertia)

$$T = J\alpha$$

(137-3)

In these equations, T is in newton-meters, J in kilogram-meters^2, Ω in radians/second, and α in radians/second^2. Torque, angular velocity, and angular acceleration are measured about the same axis, which, for our purposes, may be visualized as the axis of a shaft that is free to turn in bearings.

In general, translation and rotation may be combined in the motion of a heavy body. This combination is treated in any book on dynamics, but will not be included here, for it is unusual in our machines and devices. A machine more commonly has *either* translation *or* rotation.

138. Friction

Ordinary mechanical resistance or friction is a nonlinear phenomenon. That is, the force required to overcome friction is not directly proportional to speed. Thus, when we write that such a force is

$$F = rS$$

(138-1)

where S is speed and r is assumed to be a constant, we are distorting the truth in the interest of simplicity.

Actually, the frictional force of one dry solid surface rubbing on another (Coulomb friction) is practically independent of the speed except at the instant of starting (static friction is somewhat greater than sliding friction). This would suggest that F, not r, equals a constant. However, if the surfaces are lubricated, F is small at low speed, and increases with speed, but something less than proportionally.

On the other hand, the force required to overcome the retarding effect of a viscous fluid (fluid friction, including windage or friction with the air) increases quite rapidly with speed. This suggests that F be set proportional to some power of S higher than the first power.

These remarks are largely by way of warning, for we shall follow the usual custom of using equation 138-1 for frictional force, and assume r to be constant. This is not a bad compromise for many practical devices. For instance, the turning of a machine on well-lubricated bearings, especially if there is some air friction, is reasonably well described by a constant frictional coefficient. Acoustical resistance, also, as in a loudspeaker, is fairly constant. On the whole, a linear relation as in equation 138-1 is acceptable if the frictional force is small compared with other forces acting on a device.

In equation 138-1 F is in newtons and S in meters per second; r is called mechanical resistance and is sometimes measured in mechanical ohms. The mechanical resistance is one mechanical ohm if one newton of force produces a speed of one meter per second.

A similar equation can be written for a rotating device, setting torque T (newton-meters) necessary to overcome friction equal to the product of a coefficient D and angular velocity Ω (radians/second):

$$T = D\Omega \qquad (138\text{-}2)$$

139. Spring Force

The restoring force of a spring or other elastic member of a mechanical system is proportional to the displacement, unless the stress exceeds a certain limit beyond which proportionality is lost. This is Hooke's law.

Compliance is the ratio of displacement to the force producing that displacement; that is, if a spring is stretched through a distance w by a force F, its compliance c is

$$c = \frac{w}{F} \qquad (139\text{-}1)$$

Compliance is the reciprocal of stiffness.

(139)

Since we have expressed inertial force and frictional force in terms of speed, it will be convenient to express spring force in terms of speed also. The distance w that the end of a spring has traveled is the time integral of speed, so equation 139-1 can be rewritten

$$F = \frac{w}{c} = \frac{1}{c} \int_0^t S \, dt \qquad (139\text{-}2)$$

The lower limit of 0 supposes that the spring was unstretched at the reference instant that we choose to call zero time, so that $w = 0$ when $t = 0$. If F in equation 139-2 is in newtons, t in seconds, and S in meters per second, the compliance c is in meters per newton.

A similar rotational compliance relates the restoring torque of a twisted spring to the angle through which it has been twisted. With torque in newton-meters and angle of displacement in radians, the unit of rotational compliance would be radians per newton-meter.

For the materials of which elastic members are likely to be made, strain is accurately proportional to stress, and c is constant, until the elastic limit is reached. At the elastic limit the member is permanently deformed, or breaks. For all normal operation of springs and similar devices, therefore, a constant value of compliance c may be expected. (As a contrary example, however, the compliance of rubber is not constant for large deformations. This may be observed by stretching a rubber band until it no longer stretches easily though it does not break.)

140. Solution by Integration

Figure 140a shows a flywheel. Torque can be applied by means of a shaft. The shaft is mounted in bearings that are not shown in the diagram; it can turn freely in the bearings, but there is friction as suggested by a paddlewheel in a viscous liquid at the bottom.

Torque T is applied to the shaft. Since this torque must overcome both inertia and friction we write the following equation in which each term is torque:

$$T = J \frac{d\Omega}{dt} + D\Omega \qquad (140\text{-}1)$$

The first term gives the torque necessary to overcome inertia; J is moment of inertia and Ω is angular velocity, as in equation 137-2. The second term is similar to the expression for frictional torque in equation 138-2. With Ω as angular velocity and D as the appropriate frictional coefficient, this term represents the torque necessary to overcome friction or damping. The sum of the two terms is the total applied torque.

Assume that torque is zero until zero time, and thereafter has a constant value T. The angular velocity Ω is to be found; it is known to be zero until zero time.

Equation 140-1 is a differential equation to be solved to find Ω. It will be solved by separating the variables and integrating. A little algebraic juggling will put t on one side and Ω on the other:

$$\frac{D}{J}\,dt = -\frac{d\Omega}{\Omega - T/D} \tag{140-2}$$

Since D, the damping, J, the inertia, and T, the applied torque, are all constant, this can be integrated:

$$\frac{D}{J}\int_0^t dt = -\int_0^\Omega \frac{d\Omega}{\Omega - T/D} \tag{140-3}$$

Using ln for the natural logarithm, we have

$$\frac{D}{J}t = -\left[\ln\left(\Omega - \frac{T}{D}\right)\right]_0^\Omega = -\ln\left(\Omega - \frac{T}{D}\right) + \ln\left(-\frac{T}{D}\right)$$

$$= -\ln\frac{\Omega - T/D}{-T/D} = -\ln\left(1 - \frac{D}{T}\Omega\right) \tag{140-4}$$

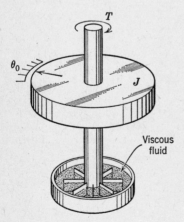

Figure 140a. A flywheel with damping.

(140)

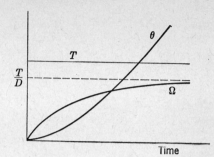

Figure 140b. Velocity and displacement of a damped flywheel with constant applied torque. (Assuming $\theta_0 = 0$.)

Remembering the relation between the logarithm and the exponential, we obtain

$$1 - \frac{D}{T}\Omega = e^{-(D/J)t} \tag{140-5}$$

from which we get an explicit expression for Ω:

$$\Omega = \frac{T}{D}(1 - e^{-(D/J)t}) \tag{140-6}$$

This is our solution; let us see what it means. At zero time the exponential is e^0, which is 1, and $\Omega = 0$, as of course it must. When time is very large the exponential is vanishingly small, and velocity approaches T/D, as shown in Figure 140b. Velocity does not continue to increase without limit, but approaches a steady-state value set by the torque and the damping coefficient.

141. Displacement

We continue the solution to find angular displacement. The increase of angle, from its initial value θ_0, is the integral of angular velocity. From equation 140-6,

$$\theta - \theta_0 = \int_0^t \Omega\, dt = \int_0^t \frac{T}{D}(1 - e^{-(D/J)t})\, dt \tag{141-1}$$

Performing the integration, we find that

$$\theta = \frac{T}{D}\left[t - \frac{J}{D}(1 - e^{-(D/J)t})\right] + \theta_0 \tag{141-2}$$

Angle tends to increase at a constant rate as velocity settles to a steady value, as shown in Figure 140b.

(141)

142. Velocity with Sinusoidal Torque

In the foregoing problem with the flywheel we were given the information that applied torque was constant. If the torque is not constant, but is a known function of time, the method of solution is not different.

As an example of practical interest, suppose the torque varies sinusoidally; that is, torque is applied to the shaft first one way and then the other, so the wheel is not driven to turn continuously in one direction but tends to oscillate, and the driving torque T can be expressed as a sine or cosine function of time. For convenience we write it

$$T = T_m \cos \omega t \qquad (142\text{-}1)$$

T_m is the maximum value of instantaneous torque, and ω is a constant. (Note that ω is quite distinct from Ω, the angular velocity of the flywheel, for ω is merely a constant indicating how frequently the applied torque is reversed.) Figure 142a shows torque T as a function of time t.

Such an alternating torque is rather common in control systems. A device may continually oscillate back and forth past a neutral position of rest. A small motion may set into operation forces that reduce and reverse the applied torque; contacts may be closed and reopened; hydraulic valves may open and close. Perhaps we can conveniently visualize a commutator motor, the moment of inertia of its rotor and shaft being J, with constant field current and therefore with a magnetic field of constant strength. Its armature cur-

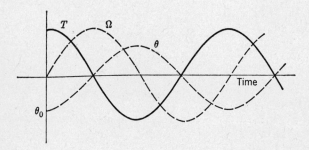

Figure 142a. Angular velocity and displacement resulting from sinusoidal applied torque.

(142)

rent, however, is alternating sinusoidally. The frequency of alternation is rather low * and might typically be once or twice a second, or ten times a second in a small device. Torque then varies sinusoidally also, and can be described by equation 142-1.

To find the angular velocity of the rotor when this alternating torque is applied to it, and considering the inertia of the rotor but neglecting any damping, we integrate equation 137-2 which is $T = J \, d\Omega/dt$. If applied torque and velocity of the rotor are both zero until $t = 0$, integration with T as a function of time gives

$$\Omega = \int_0^t \frac{T}{J} \, dt = \int_0^t \frac{T_m}{J} \cos \omega t \, dt = \frac{T_m}{J} \left[\frac{1}{\omega} \sin \omega t \right]_0^t$$

$$= \frac{T_m}{J\omega} \sin \omega t \tag{142-2}$$

Thus we find that angular velocity varies as a sine function of time. Velocity is first one way, and then the other, as one would expect and as is shown by the dashed line marked Ω in Figure 142a. The ω appearing in the denominator of the coefficient indicates that the more frequently the applied torque is reversed the less the velocity attained by the flywheel, a perfectly reasonable result.

Note that applied torque T and velocity Ω (shown in Figure 142a) are both sinusoidal, but they are a quarter cycle out of phase. Velocity reaches its maximum when the torque becomes zero, and so on.

143. Displacement with Sinusoidal Torque

The next step is to find the angular position of the wheel as a function of time. As in Section 141,

$$\theta - \theta_0 = \int_0^t \Omega \, dt = \int_0^t \frac{T_m}{J\omega} \sin \omega t \, dt$$

$$= \frac{T_m}{J\omega} \left[-\frac{1}{\omega} \cos \omega t \right]_0^t = \frac{T_m}{J\omega^2} (- \cos \omega t + 1) \tag{143-1}$$

This gives

$$\theta = -\frac{T_m}{J\omega^2} \cos \omega t + \frac{T_m}{J\omega^2} + \theta_0 \tag{143-2}$$

---

* Sometimes a continuous oscillation at relatively high frequency, called *dither*, is provided to avoid static friction in a mechanical device.

It will be remembered that θ_0 is a purely arbitrary value. It is the angular position assigned to the flywheel at the reference time $t = 0$, and it may have any value depending on where we locate the scale on which we measure angle. Equation 143-2 will be particularly simple if we so adjust the angle scale that the initial value of angle is $-T_m/J\omega^2$. We do so, with the result that

$$\theta = -\frac{T_m}{J\omega^2}\cos\omega t \qquad (143\text{-}3)$$

This expression for angular position is plotted in Figure 142a also. Like the other curves, it is sinusoidal. It is 90 degrees out of phase with velocity and directly opposed in phase to the applied torque.

This latter point is worth careful consideration. The rotor is at the extreme left end of its travel at the same instant that torque is exerted most strongly toward the right, and when the rotor has reached its extreme right-hand position the torque is maximum toward the left. Such behavior may seem unreasonable, but that is because we have not usually had much experience with motion that is limited entirely by inertia and not at all by friction. Think about this situation, visualize it, try it out by actually oscillating a heavy wheel on a good bearing, jack up a front wheel of your automobile if necessary and pull it first one way and then the other, until this relation seems right and reasonable to you. A good understanding of this matter is important. Also, visualize the out-of-phase nature of angular velocity.

144. Mechanical Phasors

The use of phasors to represent sinusoidally varying electrical quantities is familiar.* A phasor can equally well represent a sinusoidally varying mechanical quantity. Thus the same information is given by the waves of Figure 142a and the phasors of Figure 144a.

In Section 142, torque applied to a rotor was described as $T = T_m$

---

* The word *phasor* is used to mean a line (as in Figure 144a) that represents by its length the magnitude of a sinusoidally alternating quantity, and by its angular position the phase angle of that quantity. The word *transform* will be used for the complex number with magnitude equal to the value (rms) of the alternating quantity and angle in the complex plane corresponding to its phase angle. Thus a phasor is a graphical representation of a transform of an alternating quantity. It is treated in detail in Chapter 3 of *Electrical Engineering Circuits*, Reference 7A.

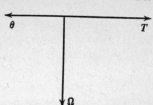

Figure 144a. Phasors representing applied torque, angular velocity, and displacement.

$\cos \omega t$. It would be possible for the line marked T in Figure 144a to have a length T_m. In fact, however, it is customary to make the length of the phasor not T_m, but $T_m/\sqrt{2}$, this being the effective or rms value of the alternating torque. The angle of the phasor T (from the horizontal) is the angle of the cosine function at zero time, which in this case is zero angle. Apart from the scale factor of $\sqrt{2}$, the instantaneous value of T, as plotted in Figure 142a, can be conceived as the projection on the horizontal axis of this phasor while it is rotating with angular velocity ω. We may visualize Figure 144a as turning and Figure 142a as being a plot of the projections of T, Ω, and θ on a fixed horizontal axis as the three phasors turn together like the spokes of a wheel (the factor of $\sqrt{2}$ being duly introduced).

Whether an alternating quantity is mechanical or electrical—a torque, a force, a displacement, a voltage or current—it can be represented by a phasor. Phasors are related to complex quantities that will be called transforms, and these in turn lead to concepts of impedance and transfer functions. We shall work with mechanical impedances as well as electrical impedances, and we shall use transfer functions that are ratios of mechanical to electrical quantities along with those that are ratios of one electrical quantity to another, or one mechanical quantity to another.

145. Sinusoidal Torque and Damping

The rotor or flywheel device is serving us well as an example. Next we shall see what can be done when sinusoidally varying torque is applied to a rotor with damping. We shall find that we cannot separate the variables, and the simple method of solution by integration that we have been using must be given up. This will require that we explore for a new means of solution, and as a matter of fact will lead to a simpler and much more powerful method.

The differential equation is written, as in equation 140-1, by equating applied torque to the torques necessary to overcome inertia

(145)

and friction:

$$T = J\frac{d\Omega}{dt} + D\Omega \tag{145-1}$$

Letting the applied torque be $T = T_m \cos \omega t$, as in equation 142-1, we write

$$T_m \cos \omega t = J\frac{d\Omega}{dt} + D\Omega \tag{145-2}$$

But here we are brought to a stop. There is no apparent way to get the variable t alone on one side of the equation and Ω alone on the other.

The failure of this one method does not mean that we cannot solve equation 145-2. Several other attacks on the problem might be tried.* However, we shall not yet attempt to find a general and complete solution of this differential equation. We shall limit our attention at this time to what is called the *steady-state* solution. (The mathematician calls it the particular integral, and the physicist the forced response.) This steady-state solution overlooks the temporary or *transient* motion of the device when alternating torque is first applied and focuses attention on the steady oscillation of the rotor in response to the alternating applied torque after any transient disturbance has died away.

Our reason for concentrating on the steady-state solution is simply this: the steady-state solution is the first step toward Laplace analysis. In the Laplace method *any* disturbance is looked upon as a sum of steady sinusoidal disturbances.

146. The Steady Solution

The steady-state solution for equation 145-1 with alternating torque is easily found. The differential equation is changed to the corresponding transform (or phasor) equation for the steady state by the usual phasor methods (or by the rule given in the footnote †). The resulting

---

*See Chapters 2 and 16 of *Electrical Engineering Circuits* (Reference 7A) or *Transient Electric Currents* (Reference 145).

† For one not acquainted with phasors, or wishing review, Appendix 2 gives the essential background. Appendix 2 includes this rule for transformation:

1. Write the differential equation.
2. Write another equation, similar except that V replaces v, I replaces i, etc.; also $j\omega$ replaces d/dt, and $1/j\omega$ replaces $\int \cdots dt$.

algebraic equation, which applies only for the alternating steady state, is

$$T = j\omega J\Omega + D\Omega \qquad (146\text{-}1)$$

Solution for Ω then gives

$$\Omega = \frac{T}{D + j\omega J} \qquad (146\text{-}2)$$

where Ω is the transform of angular velocity (rms radians/second)
  T is the transform of applied torque (rms newton-meters)
  D is the damping coefficient (newton-meter-second/radian)
  ω is $2\pi f$, where f is the rate of alternation of the applied torque (per second)
  J is the moment of inertia (kilogram-meters^2)
  j indicates an imaginary quantity; $j1 = \sqrt{-1}$

Thus if the amount of the alternating applied torque is known, the resulting velocity of rotor oscillation is easily found. (Equation 146-2 is written for rms values of the sinusoidally varying torque and velocity. Multiplication by $\sqrt{2}$ would give maximum values.) It must be remembered that this is the solution for the steady state and does not include any transient disturbance.

Notice the analogy between the quantity $D + j\omega J$ and the electrical impedance $R + j\omega L$. From equation 146-2,

$$\frac{T}{\Omega} = D + j\omega J \qquad (146\text{-}3)$$

The quantity T/Ω is analogous to $Z = V/I$, and, because of this analogy, it is sometimes called the *rotational impedance* of the mechanical device.*

The phasor solution is readily extended if the angular displacement of the rotor is to be found as well as (or instead of) the angular velocity. Velocity is the time derivative of displacement, $\Omega = d\theta/dt$, and this expression is substituted into the differential equation 145-1 to give

$$T = J\frac{d^2\theta}{dt^2} + D\frac{d\theta}{dt} \qquad (146\text{-}4)$$

Here we have a second-order differential equation that can be transformed into the algebraic equation

$$T = (j\omega)^2 J\theta + j\omega D\theta = -\omega^2 J\theta + j\omega D\theta \qquad (146\text{-}5)$$

---

* Analogy is helpfully discussed by H. F. Olson in various publications, including Reference 146.

from which

$$\theta = \frac{T}{-\omega^2 J + j\omega D} \qquad (146\text{-}6)$$

Thus we have solved equation 146-4 for displacement (or at least the transform of displacement) in terms of applied torque and the constants of the device, but for the steady state only.

147. Summary

Electromechanical energy conversion comes between an electrical system and a mechanical system. In previous chapters electromechanical equations have been considered.

The *electrical elements* defined in this chapter are *resistance, inductance* including self-inductance and mutual inductance, and *capacitance*. Voltage is equal to current times resistance, the derivative of current times inductance, or the integral of current times the reciprocal of capacitance.

The mechanical elements of *mass, mechanical resistance*, and elastic *compliance* relate force to translatory motion. These are combined with acceleration, velocity, or displacement to give force.

In problems relating to mechanical rotation, the corresponding constants are *moment of inertia*, a coefficient of *friction* or damping, and *rotational compliance*. The differential equations of rotation relate *torque* to angular acceleration, angular velocity, and angular displacement.

If the resulting differential equations are quite simple they can be solved by *integration*. This is illustrated, with a mechanical system as an example, by finding velocity and displacement as functions of applied torque. The equation of torque can be integrated if torque is constant and inertia and damping are both present, or if torque is sinusoidal and there is inertia but no damping.

When torque is sinusoidal, and inertia and damping are both present, the equation of torque cannot be integrated. A complete solution is not obtained, but a solution for the steady state is found by *transforming* the differential equation to an algebraic equation. Torque and other mechanical quantities are readily represented by *phasors*.

This solution, as will be seen, is the first step toward the *Laplace transform*. Chapter 11 will present transfer functions in terms of the steady state, and Chapter 12 will present them in terms of Laplace transforms.

(147)

PROBLEMS

10-1. The device shown on page 83 for Problem 4-9 is a practical form of magnet. It is cylindrical about a vertical axis. The plunger is pulled down by a spring. When the coil current is zero the plunger is withdrawn by the spring until the gap width g is 1.5 cm. Spring tension is then zero. When the coil is energized by direct current the plunger moves to reduce the gap. The coil has 1,000 turns. Assume infinite permeability of the iron, neglect gravity, neglect the gap of 0.02 cm between plunger and shell, and make other suitable assumptions. Find the value of spring stiffness k so that with 3.0 amp in the coil the final value of the gap length is 1.25 cm.

(Sec. 139)

10-2. In the previous problem, what is the stiffness k of the stiffest spring that will permit the magnet to close completely with the given amount of current?

(Sec. 139)

10-3. Accepting as an approximation that torque of a d-c series motor equals $K(v/\Omega)^2$, K being a constant, v the applied voltage, which is constant, and Ω the speed (in radians/second), write a differential equation (somewhat like equation 137-2) in which Ω and t (time) are the only variables. Assume all the torque is used to accelerate the motor; there is no mechanical load. Solve this equation by integration, obtaining Ω as a function of t. The motor has zero velocity when $t = 0$.

(Sec. 140)

10-4. See Problem 4-9 on page 83 for the figure. Force applied to a plunger of mass m is equal to A/S, where S is speed of the plunger and A is a constant. (a) Find S as a function of time t after force is applied. (b) Find g (the distance traveled) as a function of time, t. When $t = 0$, speed is zero, and $g = 0$.

(Sec. 141)

10-5. Examples are given in Sections 140 and 142. For each of these compute the angular acceleration α as a function of time. Sketch α, comparing it with torque.

(Sec. 142)

10-6. If the initial value of angle, θ_0 in equation 143-2, is zero, draw a curve for θ as a function of time.

(Sec. 143)

10-7. The moment of inertia of a small commutator motor is 300 gram-cm². Alternating torque is developed in the motor by alternating armature current; the maximum torque in either direction is 4.0 cm-newtons. The torque varies sinusoidally with time, and has a ½-second period. Compute and sketch the motor angle θ as a function of time (for steady state), showing the phase relation to torque. (There is enough friction to bring the motor to a steady state, but this can be neglected in writing the equation of motion.) **(Sec. 143)**

10-8. Let torque in the motor of Problem 10-7 be a square wave instead of a sine wave; that is, it is 4.0 cm-newtons one way for ¼ sec and then 4.0 cm-newtons the other way for ¼ sec. Compute and sketch the motor angle θ as a function of time (for steady state), showing the phase relation to torque. **(Sec. 143)**

10-9. A mechanical device is described in Section 140. Give an electric circuit that is analogous. "Analogous" means that its equation of action is of the same form but with different letters. Then give a second electric circuit that is also analogous but that is different from the first. (This will be the dual of the first.) **(Sec. 146)**

10-10. Equation 146-2 gives the transform of angular velocity of a device as a function of the transform of applied torque. Knowing that applied torque is $T = T_m \cos \omega t$, find Ω as a function of time. Compare the result with equation 142-2; sketch curves to compare the results. **(Sec. 146)**

10-11. Moment of inertia J of a control motor and attached load is 0.0125 kg-m². Torque developed is $T = 3.41 \cos \omega t$ newton-m; the frequency of T is 1.5 cycles/sec. Compute expressions for the steady-state angular velocity and displacement of the rotor, giving units. (a) Neglect friction. (b) Compute again, letting $D = 0.0125$ newton-meter-sec/radian. **(Sec. 146)**

TRANSFER FUNCTIONS
chapter 11

148. Transmittance

The overall behavior of a system is nicely expressed by its transfer function. Whether the system is electrical, electromechanical, mechanical, or all three, the transfer function gives the output of the system in terms of its input.

The ratio of the transform of a quantity at one point in a system to the transform of a quantity at another point in the system is called a *transfer function* or, by some authors, *transmittance* (Reference 148). This may be the ratio of an output voltage to an input voltage, or of an output voltage to an input velocity, or an output force to an input current. If it is the ratio of a voltage to a current it is called a transfer impedance, for its unit is ohms. Similarly the ratio of a current at one point to a voltage elsewhere is called a transfer admittance, measured in mhos.

As an example, Figure 148a shows a circuit with a pair of terminals at which voltage across the inductance L can be measured. A voltmeter is attached to read v_2; the voltmeter does not draw any current. What is v_2, in terms of v_1?

The voltage v_2 is the voltage across the inductance, that is,

$$v_2 = L \frac{di}{dt} \tag{148-1}$$

This equation can be *transformed* to the algebraic equation

$$V_2 = j\omega L I \tag{148-2}$$

In terms of applied voltage, current is $I = V_1/(R + j\omega L)$, so

(148)

$$V_2 = j\omega L \frac{V_1}{R + j\omega L} \qquad (148\text{-}3)$$

or

$$\frac{V_2}{V_1} = \frac{j\omega L}{R + j\omega L} \qquad (148\text{-}4)$$

This ratio is the transfer function relating output voltage to input voltage (provided current in the output circuit is negligible). Inspection of this complex ratio yields a good deal of information about the relation of the two voltages. In the first place, if R is small compared to ωL, the output voltage approximates the input voltage. If, on the other hand, R is much larger than ωL the output voltage is much smaller than the input voltage and leads it by nearly 90 degrees. The phasors are shown in Figure 148b, and the waves in Figure 148c, for a value of R equal to $4\omega L$.

Transfer functions are often plotted in a non-dimensional diagram with logarithmic scales (known by various names but perhaps most

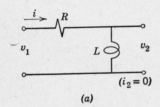

(a)

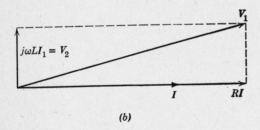

(b)

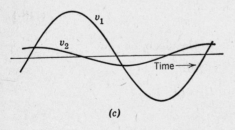

(c)

Figure 148. (*a*) A differentiating circuit. (*b, c*) Phasors and waves representing the input and output voltages of the circuit shown in Fig. 148*a* if $R = 4(\omega L)$. (Different scales.)

(148)

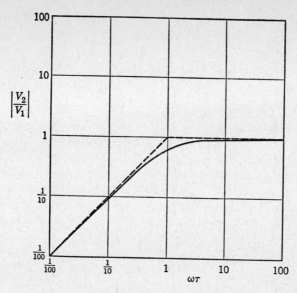

Figure 148d. Frequency-response diagram for the circuit of Fig. 148a (equation 148-5).

commonly called the frequency-response or Bode diagram). Figure 148d shows such a diagram for the transfer function of equation 148-4.

Only the magnitude of the transfer function is shown here; the angle could be shown in a separate curve if desired. The magnitude is computed from equation 148-4. Division by R gives equation 148-5, and τ is substituted for the ratio L/R. (For reasons that will appear in Section 164, τ is called the *time* constant.)

$$\left| \frac{V_2}{V_1} \right| = \left| \frac{j\omega L/R}{1 + j\omega L/R} \right| = \left| \frac{j\omega\tau}{1 + j\omega\tau} \right| = \frac{\omega\tau}{\sqrt{1 + (\omega\tau)^2}} \quad (148\text{-}5)$$

The last form of this equation results from the well-known fact that the magnitude of a complex quantity is equal to the square root of the sum of the squares of the real and imaginary components.

The curve in Figure 148d is computed from this expression. For values of $\omega\tau$ that are very much smaller than 1, the denominator approaches 1, and as a good approximation:

$$\left| \frac{V_2}{V_1} \right| \approx \omega\tau \qquad [(\omega\tau)^2 \ll 1] \tag{148-6}$$

(148)

At the other extreme, if $\omega\tau$ becomes very much greater than 1 the denominator of equation 148-5 approaches $\omega\tau$, and the transfer function approaches 1:

$$\left|\frac{V_2}{V_1}\right| \approx 1 \qquad (\omega\tau \gg 1) \tag{148-7}$$

Equations 148-6 and 7 are plotted as the straight lines in Figure 148d, which are approached asymptotically by the true curve. They are much easier to plot than the true curve and give an approximation that is satisfactory for many purposes.

Note that one of the asymptotes in this diagram is horizontal. The slope of the other is one, so that the transfer function is changed by a factor of 10 when the frequency changes by a factor of 10. The two asymptotes intersect where $\omega\tau = 1$. This form of transfer function is characteristic of simple devices.* Similar and equally simple diagrams will be found for other types of transfer functions in Chapter 13.

149. Phonograph Pickup Transfer Function

As another example, consider the relation of the output voltage of the phonograph pickup device of Section 26 to the input speed of motion of the coil that is driven by the stylus. Induced electromotive force e is given in terms of speed S by equation 26-1:

$$e = BlS \tag{149-1}$$

where B is flux density, and l is length of wire, both constant. Output voltage is practically the same as induced electromotive force if the pickup coil has low resistance or if there is little output current.

This is not even a differential equation; it is a simple proportionality. The transfer function is therefore merely a constant. If E and S are the transforms of e and S,

$$\frac{E}{S} = Bl \tag{149-2}$$

This is a useful though rather elementary kind of transfer function.

It is more interesting to know the relationship between the output voltage and the *amplitude* of the mechanical vibration, the amplitude

---

* This slope of 1 decade per decade is often specified as 20 db/decade, or 6 db/octave.

(149)

of the wave impressed in the phonograph record, for this is a more easily measurable quantity. Also it is a value that is limited by the design of the record. Let us call the displacement of the pickup coil from its central position w. Speed is the rate of change of w, that is,

$$S = \frac{dw}{dt} \tag{149-3}$$

This may be substituted into equation 149-1 to give the necessary relation between e and w:

$$e = Bl\frac{dw}{dt} \tag{149-4}$$

and by transformation

$$E = j\omega Blw \tag{149-5}$$

The transfer function is thence

$$\frac{E}{w} = j\omega Bl \tag{149-6}$$

This function is proportional to frequency ω. The practical meaning is that a given amplitude of mechanical vibration produces a greater output voltage at a higher frequency—or, looked at from another point of view, to maintain the same electrical output at low frequency requires that a wave of proportionately greater amplitude be inscribed in the phonograph record. Since the amplitude of the wave in the record is limited by the spacing between grooves, the low-frequency response of the phonograph is correspondingly limited. (In fact, correction of such a limitation can be provided in the electrical circuit by amplifying low notes more than high ones.)

The j in the transfer function means that the electromotive-force wave e leads the displacement w, as in Figure 149b, by 90 degrees. When the displacement is greatest the speed and hence the electromotive force are instantaneously zero, and when the displacement is zero the speed and electromotive force are at their instantaneous maxima.

Note that equations 149-5 and 6 give electromotive force and not terminal voltage. If there is appreciable current, the output terminal voltage is less than the induced electromotive force by the potential drop in the impedance of the pickup coil. Thus, if resistance is R and inductance is negligible, and the transform of current is I, the terminal voltage transform is

$$V = E - RI = j\omega Blw - RI \tag{149-7}$$

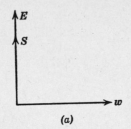

(a)

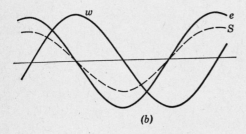

(b)

Figure 149a, b. Phasors and waves representing displacement, speed, and electromotive force of a dynamic pickup device.

We cannot find a transfer function from this equation alone, for there are three variables. It is necessary to have information about the electric circuit into which the phonograph pickup delivers its output signal. Figure 149c shows the pickup device feeding into the input network of an amplifier. Let the input impedance to this network be Z, a complex quantity. Then

$$V = ZI \tag{149-8}$$

and this gives the information needed to find a transfer function.

Equations 149-7 and 8 can now be solved simultaneously. We eliminate I to obtain

$$V = j\omega Blw - \frac{R}{Z} V \tag{149-9}$$

The transfer function is

$$\frac{V}{w} = j\omega Bl \frac{Z}{R + Z} \tag{149-10}$$

It will be seen that this transfer function relating output voltage to amplitude of vibration is a complex function of frequency. Not only does it contain a j, but the impedance Z may be complex. It is a function of frequency because both ω and Z will in general change with frequency. In practice, however, Z is usually a large real number, representing a high resistance. Equation 149-10 shows that the higher the

(149)

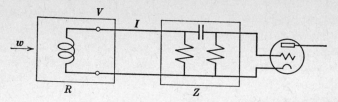

Figure 149c. A phonograph pickup and amplifier input impedance comprise a simple system.

value of Z, relative to R, the greater the transfer function and hence the greater the terminal voltage output for a given input. This, of course, is desirable. If Z is pure resistance, V will be out of phase with w, and the magnitude of the transfer function will be proportional to frequency.

In this example it is not necessary to include in the solution any equations to account for the behavior of the mechanical side of the device, for the amplitude of mechanical vibration is given. The stylus, running in a groove, must vibrate with a certain amplitude regardless of force reacting upon it. Because of this constraint the solution requires only one electromechanical equation solved simultaneously with the electrical equations. The simultaneous equations are 149-5, 149-7, and 149-8.

150. Speaker Impedance Function

A dynamic loudspeaker shows the need for simultaneous solution of *four* equations. (See Section 134.) Consider as an example a speaker in which the voice coil is fed with a steady alternating input voltage of known amount. Figure 150a shows the speaker diagrammatically; physically it looks like Figure 13a. In the diagram of Figure 150a, R is the electrical resistance of the voice coil and L is its inductance. The applied voltage v is known; it is sinusoidal and its transform is V. Mo-

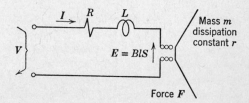

Figure 150a. A speaker system.

(150)

tion of the coil in the magnetic field of the speaker induces an electromotive force e of which the transform is E. Speed with which the coil
moves through the magnetic field is S, with transform S. The moving
coil and cone together have mass m, and the dissipation constant (or
mechanical resistance) of the coil and cone is r. I and F are transforms
of current i and force F.

For the electrical part of the speaker system we write a differential
equation, setting the applied voltage equal to the sum of the quantities
that it must overcome:

$$v = Ri + L\frac{di}{dt} + e \qquad \text{(electrical)} \qquad (150\text{-}1)$$

On the mechanical side, the magnetic force on the coil must overcome
friction and dissipation (this includes the useful output of sound, which
we have not kept separate, in this analysis, from wasted frictional
power) plus the inertia force:

$$F = rS + m\frac{dS}{dt} \qquad \text{(mechanical)} \qquad (150\text{-}2)$$

With B the strength of the magnetic field of the speaker, and l the
length of wire in the voice coil, the two electromechanical equations of
the device are

$$F = Bli \qquad\qquad\qquad\qquad\qquad (150\text{-}3)$$
$$\qquad\qquad \text{(electromechanical)}$$
$$e = BlS \qquad\qquad\qquad\qquad\qquad (150\text{-}4)$$

These four equations are to be solved simultaneously; v is given, and
e, i, F, and S are the four unknowns.

Applied voltage is alternating. We transform the four equations,
using the rule of Section A2-5, and obtain *

$$V = RI + j\omega LI + E \qquad \text{(electrical)} \qquad (150\text{-}5)$$
$$F = rS + j\omega mS \qquad \text{(mechanical)} \qquad (150\text{-}6)$$
$$F = BlI \qquad\qquad\qquad\qquad\qquad\qquad (150\text{-}7)$$
$$\qquad\qquad\qquad \text{(electromechanical)}$$
$$E = BlS \qquad\qquad\qquad\qquad\qquad\qquad (150\text{-}8)$$

With obvious substitutions, we eliminate E and F:

---

* We wish the steady-state solution. If the complete transient solution were
desired, the same four equations would be transformed similarly, but s would
be written instead of $j\omega$, as will be seen in the next chapter.

(150)

$$V = RI + j\omega LI + BlS \qquad (150\text{-}9)$$

$$BlI = rS + j\omega mS \qquad (150\text{-}10)$$

We can now eliminate either S or I. If we eliminate S and keep I it will be easy to find the ratio of applied voltage V to input current I, and since this ratio is input impedance it promises to be useful. We therefore solve the problem that way. A little algebraic juggling gives

$$\frac{V}{I} = R + j\omega L + \frac{(Bl)^2}{r + j\omega m} \qquad (150\text{-}11)$$

This, as has just been said, is input impedance.

This expression deserves careful study. Note that the ordinary electrical impedance of the speaker circuit, $R + j\omega L$, is increased by a term owing to induced electromotive force, which results from the motion of the speaker. This term exists, as we might expect, only if the magnetic field strength B is not zero. Also, if the cone should be infinitely heavy, there would be no such term, or if the cone were infinitely damped (making r infinite).

The speaker cannot be useful unless the real component of the last term is large, for this real component includes the effect of emission of energy as sound (which is the purpose of the speaker) plus any loss of mechanical energy that may be taking place. It is helpful to have the useful part of this term large and all other terms as small as possible.

151. Speaker Transfer Function

Another transfer function of practical importance is the one that relates the motion of the speaker cone to the applied voltage. The output of a speaker is sound, and with sinusoidal motion the average power of radiated sound is (under conditions approximated in practice) proportional to the square of the speed of motion of the cone. Input to the speaker is electrical; perhaps input voltage to the speaker is known. Then the transfer function that relates the rms value of speed S to the voltage V is of particular interest.

The straightforward way to find this transfer function is to solve equations 150-9 and 150-10 simultaneously again, this time eliminating I as the first step. The solution is simple, and we find the transfer function:

$$\frac{S}{V} = \frac{Bl}{(R + j\omega L)(r + j\omega m) + (Bl)^2} \qquad (151\text{-}1)$$

One of several interesting conclusions that may be drawn from this transfer function is that if R and r are small the denominator of equation 151-1 approximates $-\omega^2 Lm + (Bl)^2$. There is a frequency at which this quantity is zero, and hence a frequency of resonance. As a practical matter, such resonance does exist. It may increase the output of a speaker by a number of decibels through a narrow frequency range. If it is too pronounced it decreases fidelity of reproduction.

152. Motional Impedance

The last term of equation 150-11, which results from the motion of the voice coil in a magnetic field, is sometimes called the *motional impedance* of the system. As we should expect, it is a function of the mass m of the moving coil-and-cone, and of the dissipation factor or mechanical resistance r of this moving system. It also depends on the frequency ω.

One who wrote without thinking might be tempted to add $r + j\omega m$ (the mechanical impedance) to $R + j\omega L$ (the electrical impedance) to find the total input impedance of the system. But this would not be correct, and indeed it is obviously illogical. The greater the r or the m (that is, the less the voice coil moves) the less the effect of its motion on input voltage and current. Hence it is really to be expected that $r + j\omega m$ should appear in the *denominator* of the motional impedance term, as our solution of the transformed equations shows that it does.

Note that a strong field magnet (B) and a long wire wound into the voice coil (l) make the effect of motion greater, and the product Bl naturally appears in the numerator of equation 150-11. That Bl is squared results from the fact that it acts twice: first, a large Bl gives a large mechanical force on the voice coil and hence a large motion; and, second, a large Bl gives a large induced electromotive force in the coil for a given motion. Thus motion is proportional to current times Bl, and induced electromotive force to motion times Bl, so electromotive force is proportional to current times $(Bl)^2$.

153. Analogy

One of the useful tools of system study is analogy. We seem to find it easier to think about a system that is composed entirely of the same kind of elements. It is often a help to devise, if we can,

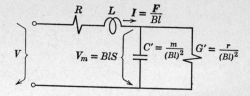

Figure 153a. An electric circuit analogous to the speaker system of Fig. 150a.

an all-electrical system that is analogous to the electromechanical system we are studying.

Analogous systems are those that have equations of identical form, though their symbols have different physical meanings. Thus there is analogy between $T = J\, d\Omega/dt$, relating applied torque, moment of inertia, and angular velocity, and $v = L\, di/dt$, relating applied voltage, inductance, and current, for the forms of expression are identical. Similarly, and for the same reason, $T = J\, d\Omega/dt$ is analogous to $i = C\, dv/dt$, relating current, capacitance, and voltage.* Thus analogs are not unique. We cannot make a blanket statement that current is analogous to velocity; in some analogs it is, and in others it is not.

As an example we try to devise an analog of the speaker system considered in Sections 150 and 152. We want to find an all-electrical system (an electrical network, that is) that has an expression for input impedance identical in form with equation 150-11.

The motional impedance term in equation 150-11 has a complex number in the denominator. A complex number in the denominator of an impedance reminds us of circuit elements in parallel. With a few trials and a few errors, we produce Figure 153a, having G' and C' in parallel, the input impedance to which is

$$Z_{\text{in}} = R + j\omega L + \frac{1}{G' + j\omega C'} \tag{153-1}$$

Now if we choose G' and C' of such size that

$$G' = \frac{r}{(Bl)^2} \quad \text{and} \quad C' = \frac{m}{(Bl)^2} \tag{153-2}$$

equation 153-1 becomes identical with equation 150-11. We are

---

* These formally similar expressions for v and i exemplify a special type of analogy, called *duality*. Though both relate to electrical systems, they describe different physical situations in the same mathematical form.

thereby justified in saying that the systems of Figures 150a and 153a are analogous.

What is the advantage of having devised such an analog? It is mainly that all the system parameters have been put into a system containing only electrical elements, with which we are reasonably familiar, and by inspection of the network of Figure 153a we can tell a good deal about the behavior of a speaker. For instance, it is clear that there may be resonance in the analogous circuit, a fact that is not at all obvious in the electromechanical system of Figure 150a.

Also, remembering that the useful output of the speaker cannot exceed the power going to the conductive element G', we can tell at once that with a given applied voltage there will not be much useful output at high frequency, for input current will be blocked by L, and current to G' will be greatly diminished at high frequency by the shunting effect of C'. If C' can be made small, by making the mass m of the coil-and-cone small, high-frequency output will be improved.*

154. Another Analog

A slight alteration of Figure 153a gives Figure 154a. An ideal transformer (that is, a transformer with a turn ratio but no resistance or leakage reactance or magnetizing current or loss) has been introduced, its turn ratio being Bl to 1. Parallel electrical elements analogous to the mechanical elements are included, but this time

$$G' = r \quad \text{and} \quad C' = m \qquad (154\text{-}1)$$

Thus, at the expense of complicating the circuit by adding a transformer we have simplified the equations of analogy. That the transformer circuit of Figure 154a is indeed analogous to the speaker system of Figure 150a is proved by writing an equation for the input impedance to the transformer circuit. (See Section 111.)

It is interesting to notice that the electromotive force and the current on the secondary side of the ideal transformer of Figure 154a are

---

*Here we are using capacitance as an analog of mass, whereas we often hear that the analog of mass is inductance. As has been said, analogs are not unique. Sometimes mass is analogous to inductance, but in the systems of Figures 150a and 153a, mass is analogous to capacitance. Why? Because with a capacitance in Figure 153a proportional to the mass of Figure 150a *the systems are described by equations of the same form.* That is the necessary and sufficient justification of any analogy.

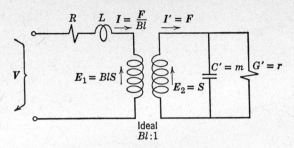

Figure 154a. Another electric circuit analogous to the speaker system of Fig. 150a.

equal, respectively, to speed and force in the mechanical system of Figure 150a, whereas in Figure 153a the corresponding voltage and current are merely proportional.*

One instructive aspect of this second analog is that it shows an analogy between the product Bl in the speaker and the turn ratio in a transformer. The basic reason for the analogy is that each is a transfer function. The turn ratio of a transformer relates the electromotive force in the primary winding to the electromotive force in the secondary winding. The product Bl (as shown in equation 150-8) relates the electromotive force in the winding of the speaker to the speed of motion of the speaker cone.

These are idealized transfer functions. The turn ratio is the transfer function of an *ideal* transformer, for it does not take into account any winding resistance or leakage reactance, hysteresis of the iron or eddy-current loss. Bl is the transfer function across the air gap of the speaker, taking into no account the inductance or resistance of the winding, or the mass or losses of the moving coil-and-cone.

It is interesting to notice that for the idealized speaker the two transfer functions across the air gap are equal. Equations 150-7 and 150-8 show that F/I and E/S are both equal to Bl. As stated in Section 80, such equality is always true of conservative energy conversion, supposing that consistent units are used in the equations.

---

* In all this discussion the mks system of units is assumed. Thus F is in newtons, B in webers per square meter, m in kilograms, etc. Another consistent system might be used, but any inconsistent assortment of units would require proportionality constants in the equations (notably equations 150-9 and 150-10) and the arithmetic would be repulsive.

155. Summary

The ratio of a transform of voltage, current, force, velocity, etc., at one point in a system (usually an output) to the transform of a voltage, current, force, velocity, etc., at another point of the system (usually an input) is called a *transfer function* or transmittance. If the ratio is voltage over current the transfer function is called transfer impedance; if current over voltage, transfer admittance. Transfer functions that relate an output quantity to an input quantity characterize the manner in which the device or system transmits information. In all kinds of information systems the transfer function is exceedingly important.

Generally, but not always, system functions (impedance functions and transfer functions) are found by simultaneous solution of two electromechanical equations, one or more equations for the electrical side of the system and one or more for the mechanical side.

Analogy is helpful in understanding devices and systems. The behavior of an all-electrical system (or perhaps an all-mechanical system) is more easily grasped than is the behavior of an electromechanical system.

A number of examples illustrate the use of these concepts and methods. Examples include a rotating mechanical device as employed in control systems, an electric circuit, a phonograph pickup, and a speaker.

PROBLEMS

11-1. From equation 148-4, compute the real and imaginary components of V_2/V_1 as functions of frequency. This transfer function can be indicated as a point in the complex plane for each value of frequency. Do so, and indicate the locus followed for all frequencies. **(Sec. 148)**

11-2. In Figure 148b, assume V_1 remains constant. Show the locus of V_2 for all values of R with L remaining constant, and also for all values of L with R remaining constant. **(Sec. 148)**

11-3. Draw a phasor diagram, as in Figure 149a, for a pickup device feeding into an impedance Z, in which Z equals twice the resistance R of the pickup and the angle of Z is 45 degrees; that is, $Z = 2R\underline{/45°}$. Show phasors for w, S, E, I, and V. What is the transfer function V/w? **(Sec. 149)**

11-4. Draw a Bode diagram for equation 149-6. **(Sec. 149)**

11-5. Discuss the type of transfer function that would result if, in equation 149-10, $Z = R$. Or if Z were purely inductive. Or purely capacitive. **(Sec. 149)**

11-6. Equation 150-11 is the input impedance to a speaker. Show that resonance is to be expected (resonance is the condition in which impedance is purely real). In terms of the constants of the device, find the frequency at which resonance occurs. **(Sec. 150)**

11-7. A steady musical note is sung into the speaker of Section 13 so that the air produces a force $F = F_m \cos \omega t$ against the surface of the speaker cone. What voltage appears at the open-circuited terminals of the speaker coil as a result? (Express V in terms of the strength of the magnetic field of the speaker magnet; r and m, the components of mechanical impedance; and any other physical quantities needed.) **(Sec. 151)**

11-8. Find a speaker transfer function that relates the displacement of voice coil and cone to the input voice-coil current. Sinusoidal current is assumed. **(Sec. 151)**

11-9. Derive equation 151-1. **(Sec. 151)**

11-10. Discuss the nature and meaning of the transfer function of equation 151-1 at frequencies well above, and well below, the frequency of resonance. Draw an approximate diagram similar to Figure 148d. **(Sec. 151)**

11-11. The electrical analog of Section 153 is found by devising an electrical network with input impedance identical in form with equation 150-11. Show whether or not this circuit also has a transfer function analogous to equation 151-1. **(Sec. 153)**

11-12. Prove that Figure 154a is a correct analog. Consider its application when battery voltage is applied. **(Sec. 154)**

11-13. If the speaker of Section 150 has the cone fastened so that it moves with compliance c meters/newton against elastic restraint, derive the transfer function S/V (similar to equation 151-1). Also, devise an all-electrical analog of this speaker system.   **(Sec. 154)**

11-14. This problem refers to Figure 209a on page 349. The d-c motor has constant field current, while armature current is varied. When the motor is turned at 200 radians/sec with this amount of field current and no armature current the terminal voltage is 100 volts. Parameters are: resistance of the armature circuit $R_a = 0.10$ ohm, inductance of the armature circuit is negligible, J of motor and load is 10 kg m², the damping coefficient of the motor and load is $D = 2.5$ newton-meters/radian per sec.   (a) Devise an all-electric analog of the system.   (b) At $t = 0$, with the rotor at rest, 100 volts direct current is suddenly applied to the terminals as V. Calculate and sketch $\Omega(t)$, the shaft speed as a function of time.   (c) Find the steady-state rpm and output horsepower (746 watts = 1 hp).

(Sec. 154)

LAPLACE TRANSFER FUNCTIONS

chapter 12

156. Laplace Transformation

A transfer function can be usefully written in several ways. In equation 148-4 the transfer function is given as a ratio of a steady-state output voltage to a steady-state input voltage, and it is a function of the applied frequency ω. This is quite correct, and all transfer functions can be so expressed, but it is more convenient (and also more usual) for the transfer function to be the ratio of the Laplace transform of an output voltage to the Laplace transform of the input voltage. The transfer function is then a function of the algebraic variable s (sometimes written p instead of s) that appears in Laplace transformation; s replaces $j\omega$.

Since the reader may very probably not be familiar with Laplace methods and notation, the subject is presented briefly in Appendix 3. Those who have not met the subject before or those seeking a brief review if the elements of the Laplace transformation are not freshly in mind should turn to Appendix 3 before going on to Section 157.

157. A Laplace Transfer Function

The circuit of Figure 157a was discussed in Section 148, and a differential equation was written

$$v_2 = L \frac{di}{dt} \tag{157-1}$$

Now by Laplace transformation (by the rules of Appendix 3) this dif-

(157)

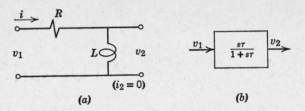

Figure 157. (a) The circuit and (b) the block diagram to represent the circuit (with $\tau = L/R$).

ferential equation is transformed to the algebraic equation *

$$\hat{v}_2 = Ls\hat{\imath} \tag{157-2}$$

In terms of applied voltage, current is

$$\hat{\imath} = \frac{\hat{v}_1}{R + sL} \tag{157-3}$$

Combining this equation with equation 157-2, we obtain

$$\hat{v}_2 = sL\,\frac{\hat{v}_1}{R + sL} \tag{157-4}$$

The transfer function, now in Laplace notation, is

$$\frac{\hat{v}_2}{\hat{v}_1} = \frac{sL}{R + sL} \tag{157-5}$$

If we let $L/R = \tau$, the transfer function is

$$\frac{\hat{v}_2}{\hat{v}_1} = \frac{s\tau}{1 + s\tau} \tag{157-6}$$

Except for notation, these Laplacian equations are the same as equations 148-2 to 148-4.

158. Block Diagrams

A system is often shown in a diagram as a series of blocks. The input to the block is a function of time; perhaps it is a voltage (as in

---

* Notation is discussed in the second footnote to Section A3-2. Note that $\hat{v}$ is used to mean the Laplace transform of v instead of using $V(s)$ to represent the transform of $v(t)$. Similarly, $\hat{\imath}$ is the Laplace transform of i, and so on.

Figure 157b) or a current, a torque or velocity or displacement. The output is another time function, in either the same variable or another. The relationship between the output and the input is the transfer function, conveniently written within the block, as in Figure 157b, in Laplace notation.

The transfer function describes how the block in question affects a signal that passes through it, for the input multiplied by the transfer function gives the output. When there are several blocks in a diagram (as in Figure 161b) the output of one block is the input to the next; then the overall transfer function is the product of the individual transfer functions.

Analysis is particularly simple if it can be assumed that the second block does not load the first block (that is, if its presence does not affect the transfer function of the first block) and that the third block, if there is one, does not load the second, and so on. The solution of a problem can then consider the blocks one at a time. The simplification of analysis that results if succeeding blocks do not load those before them is so great that this condition is commonly assumed even when it is not a very good approximation of the truth.

159. Bilateral and Unilateral Elements

When a system consists of a number of devices connected in cascade, and the operation of each depends on the operation of all the others, the number of equations to be solved simultaneously is very large. The labor of the solution can be depressing.

Fortunately, some devices have one transfer function equal to zero. Such a device is *unilateral;* it carries a signal in one direction but not in the other. A waterfall is unilateral, for the depth of water in the pool at the bottom of the fall does not affect the flow of water at the top. An airplane in flight has unilateral coupling between the wing and tail surfaces, for vibration of the wings may affect the tail, through the air stream, but vibration of the tail cannot, through the air stream, affect the wings.

A generator used as an amplifier is unilateral (Section 81). The input field current produces magnetic flux in the machine. The magnetic flux causes electromotive force to be induced in the armature winding, and output voltage and current result. On the other hand, current in the armature winding does not result in any electromotive force or other signal being induced in the field circuit. Conditions at the armature terminals do not affect conditions at the field terminals.

In Section 81, only one transfer function is computed; the other is zero. A signal cannot go through the device from armature circuit to field circuit, but only from field circuit to armature circuit.

A vacuum-tube amplifier is unilateral. Voltage applied to the grid affects the plate current, but voltage applied to the plate does not affect grid current (at least for low-frequency operation). A signal goes through from grid to plate, and is amplified, but no signal can go from plate to grid.

A *field*-controlled servomotor, like a field-controlled generator, is *unilateral*. Shaft speed is regulated by adjusting the amount of field current (Section 80), but the speed at which the shaft turns has no effect on the field current. This is in contrast to an *armature*-controlled servomoter, which is *bilateral:* voltage applied to the armature terminals affects the shaft speed, and shaft speed affects voltage at the armature terminals.

All ordinary electrical two-port networks (of passive, linear elements) are bilateral and will transmit a signal either way. This is true of transformers as well as all combinations of resistors, capacitors, and inductors.

160. Unilateral Blocks

When a system is composed entirely of bilateral elements, equations representing the behavior of all the elements must be solved simultaneously. Fortunately, when there is a unilateral element in the system it breaks the chain of dependence; the behavior of elements "upstream" from the unilateral element are not affected by conditions "downstream."

Hence a system is analyzed by considering simultaneously the elements from the input port of the system to the first unilateral element, at which point an output is computed. This suggests dividing the system so the connection from one block to the next is unilateral.

An example will no doubt be more helpful at this point than further discussion of general principles. In the next two sections, therefore, we shall consider a field-controlled commutator motor as part of a system. With that motor as an example we shall undertake direct and inverse transformation of a function, find the time constant, compute the forced response and natural response, and see the relation between impulsive disturbance and natural response.

161. A Field-Controlled Commutator Motor

Figure 161a shows a commutator motor driving a load. Constant armature current is supplied to the motor from some independent source, and the motor is controlled by varying the voltage V_f applied to the field circuit. Other symbols are:

I_f is field current (amperes)
R_f is field-circuit resistance (ohms)
L_f is field-circuit inductance (henrys)
$\tau_f = L_f/R_f$, the field-circuit time constant (seconds)
J is moment of inertia of motor and load (kg m^2)
D is mechanical damping coefficient (kg m^2/sec)
$\tau_m = J/D$, the time constant of the rotating system (seconds)

The purpose of the control might be to have the motor turn at a specified speed, as for driving rolls in a paper mill. Another possibility might be to have the motor assume a desired position and stop there. Gun pointing would be an example, or adjustment of a valve, or moving a crane to a certain place.

Consider first that the object is speed control. We need answers to such questions as the following. How much applied voltage is needed for a certain speed? How long will it take the motor to reach this speed,

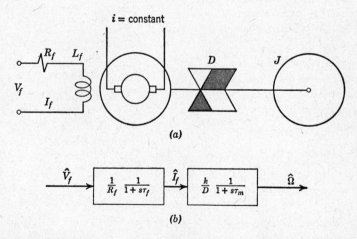

(a)

(b)

Figure 161. (a) A motor with field control (armature current is held constant). (b) The block diagram for the motor speed control system, with transfer functions.

(161)

approximately, starting from standstill? Will speed be an oscillatory function, being first too slow, then too fast, then too slow again, and so on, or will the desired speed be approached monotonically? Is there any chance of speed variations being cumulative so that the whole operation is unstable?

The first step is clearly to find the transfer function that relates speed to applied voltage, $\hat{\Omega}/\hat{V}_f$. Answers to some of the questions will be evident when this transfer function has been found; others will require finding Ω as a function of time by inverse transformation.

It will be convenient to represent this simple system in two blocks, as suggested in Figure 161b. The first block represents the electrical part of the system, which in this case is the field circuit of the machine. The second block contains the mechanical part of the system: the motor armature, shaft, and load. Input to the second block, from the first, is I_f, the field current (or it could be Φ, the main flux of the motor, which we shall assume to be proportional to field current). The first block is quite independent of the second, for the mechanical behavior of the motor does not react on the field circuit; motor speed does not influence I_f.

The transfer function of the first block (see Figure 161b) is $\hat{I}_f/\hat{V}_f$, the relation of output to input. That of the second block is $\hat{\Omega}/\hat{I}_f$. These must now be computed, and it is not difficult. Most of the necessary equations are already familiar. Kirchhoff's law is applied to the field circuit, giving

$$\hat{V}_f = (R_f + sL_f)\hat{I}_f \qquad \text{(electrical)} \qquad (161\text{-}1)$$

from which the transfer function of the first block is

$$\frac{\hat{I}_f}{\hat{V}_f} = \frac{1}{R_f + sL_f} = \frac{1}{R_f}\frac{1}{1 + s\tau_f} \qquad (161\text{-}2)$$

where, as listed above, $\tau_f = L_f/R_f$. (See Figure 161b.)

The mechanical part of the system has inertia and damping. If T is the torque exerted magnetically on the motor armature, the differential equation is (equation 140-1):

$$T = D\Omega + J\frac{d\Omega}{dt} \qquad \text{(mechanical)} \qquad (161\text{-}3)$$

From equation 80-1, torque is computed in terms of armature current i, flux Φ, number of poles p, and number of turns N_s in the armature winding:

(161)

$$T = \frac{N_s p \Phi}{\pi} i \qquad \text{(electromechanical)} \qquad (161\text{-}4)$$

Assuming that flux is proportional to field current (that is, neglecting saturation), we let $\Phi = k_f I_f$ and write

$$T = \frac{N_s p k_f}{\pi} I_f i \qquad (161\text{-}5)$$

It is specified that armature current is held constant (this may not be entirely easy to do, in fact, but it can be approximated), and all these symbols except I_f therefore represent constant quantities that can be lumped in a single constant k, giving $T = k I_f$. Putting this expression for torque into equation 161-3, we obtain

$$k I_f = D \Omega + J \frac{d\Omega}{dt} \qquad (161\text{-}6)$$

This differential equation (in the time domain) is next transformed (into the frequency domain) by the rules of Appendix 3, giving

$$k \hat{I}_f = D \hat{\Omega} + s J \hat{\Omega} \qquad (161\text{-}7)$$

The transfer function of the second block of Figure 161b is thus found to be

$$\frac{\hat{\Omega}}{\hat{I}_f} = \frac{k}{D + sJ} = \frac{k}{D} \frac{1}{1 + s\tau_m} \qquad (161\text{-}8)$$

where $\tau_m = J/D$.

The transfer functions of the two blocks of the diagram are given by equations 161-2 and 161-8. We now wish to find the overall transfer function relating the motor speed (as output) to the applied voltage (as input). Multiplying the transfer functions of the two blocks, we have

$$\frac{\hat{\Omega}}{\hat{V}_f} = \frac{\hat{\Omega}}{\hat{I}_f} \cdot \frac{\hat{I}_f}{\hat{V}_f} = \frac{k}{R_f D} \frac{1}{(1 + s\tau_m)(1 + s\tau_f)} \qquad (161\text{-}9)$$

Interpretation of these transfer functions will be discussed in Section 163.

162. Control of Position

As has been mentioned, there are also applications of the motor of Figure 161a in which the *position*, the shaft angle θ, is the interesting

$$(162)$$

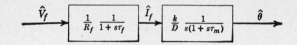

Figure 162a. The block diagram for the motor with angular position as output.

output quantity, rather than speed of rotation. The transfer function $\hat{\theta}/\hat{V}$ can be obtained in various ways. The mechanical differential equation, 161-3, could be rewritten in terms of θ instead of Ω, and this would lead to a transfer function for the second block of our diagram (see Figure 162a) in which the angle θ is the output. However it is easier, and perhaps more instructive, to proceed as follows.

Note that velocity is the time rate of change of angle. That is,

$$\Omega = \frac{d\theta}{dt} \tag{162-1}$$

Transform this equation by substituting s for the derivative: *

$$\hat{\Omega} = s\hat{\theta} \tag{162-2}$$

This gives as the relation between angular position and angular velocity

$$\frac{\hat{\theta}}{\hat{\Omega}} = \frac{1}{s} \tag{162-3}$$

Noting that $1/s$ (in the frequency domain) transforms to integration (in the time domain) we interpret equation 162-3 as meaning that θ is the integral of Ω—which, of course, is quite correct.

Now equation 161-8 is multiplied by equation 162-3, and this gives in a single step the transfer function that we want for the second block of Figure 162a, relating shaft angle to field current:

$$\frac{\hat{\theta}}{\hat{I}_f} = \frac{\hat{\Omega}}{\hat{I}_f} \cdot \frac{\hat{\theta}}{\hat{\Omega}} = \frac{k}{D} \frac{1}{s(1 + s\tau_m)} \tag{162-4}$$

The overall transfer function relating shaft angle to field-circuit voltage is then

---

* The complete statement is that if $\theta(t)$ transforms to $\hat{\theta}(s)$, then $\dfrac{d}{dt}\theta(t)$ transforms to $s\hat{\theta}(s) - \theta(0)$. But we shall stipulate that $\theta(0) = 0$; that is, the initial position of the shaft will arbitrarily be called zero angle.

$$\frac{\hat{\theta}}{\hat{V}_f} = \frac{\hat{\theta}}{\hat{I}_f} \cdot \frac{\hat{I}_f}{\hat{V}_f} = \frac{k}{R_f D} \frac{1}{s(1 + s\tau_m)(1 + s\tau_f)} \qquad (162\text{-}5)$$

163. Interpretation

What, now, can we say from inspection of these transfer functions without going through any further computations? What can we deduce about the response of our electromechanical system without applying the process of inverse transformation to determine the response in detail?

We look first at the transfer function of the first block (equation 161-2), which relates field current to applied voltage:

$$\frac{\hat{I}_f}{\hat{V}_f} = \frac{1}{R_f} \frac{1}{1 + s\tau_f} \quad \text{where} \quad \tau_f = \frac{L_f}{R_f} \qquad (163\text{-}1)$$

The essential thing is that this transfer function contains one factor of the form $1/(1 + s\tau_f)$. This indicates that the corresponding time function resulting from inverse transformation would contain one exponential expression of the form e^{-t/τ_f}. (Pair 2 of Table A3-4 shows that such a term would appear in the time function.) The curve of Figure 164a shows a graph of such a term. We cannot, without detailed computation, say what the magnitude of this component of the system response will be. It could be large or small. It could be displaced upward or downward (having a constant added). It could appear upside down (having a negative sign). But we may be sure that such an exponential component will appear, and that it will have a time constant τ_f equal to L_f/R_f.

Let us now look at the transfer function of the second block of Figure 161b. This represents the mechanical part of the system.

$$\frac{\hat{\Omega}}{\hat{I}_f} = \frac{k}{D} \frac{1}{1 + s\tau_m} \quad \text{where} \quad \tau_m = \frac{J}{D} \qquad (163\text{-}2)$$

Here again we have a transfer function of the form $1/(1 + s\tau)$, and this transfer function, like that of equation 163-1, implies a response that is an exponential function of time. The time constant is, of course, not the same as in the previous example. In this block the time constant is determined by the mechanical parts of the motor; it is $\tau_m = J/D$, the moment of inertia over the damping coefficient. (For devices of ordinary design, this mechanical time constant is probably much longer than the field-circuit time constant τ_f.)

164. Time Constant

Consider more precisely the meaning of the time constant of an exponential function. As we have seen, it is easily determined from the transfer function, and the next several chapters will show its great practical importance. The time constant of a device or system tells whether response will be rapid or slow. In most systems rapid response is highly desirable.

Figure 164a shows the graph of an exponential function with a negative exponent, $e^{-t/\tau}$. When $t = \tau$ the exponential is e^{-1}, which equals 0.368. Hence the time constant τ is the length of time required for the function to diminish to 0.368 of its initial value, as shown in the diagram.

In a time equal to 2τ, twice the time constant, the exponential component of unit height will have diminished to $e^{-2} = (0.368) \times (0.368) = 0.135$. When elapsed time is equal to three time constants the exponential function will be down to 0.0498, or practically 5 per cent, of its initial value.

An exponential function in a system response provides a transition from an initial value to a final value. All but 36.8 per cent of that transition takes place in a time equal to the time constant τ of the exponential. Thus the greater part of the response of a system to an input signal of command has taken place in time equal to one time constant, and nearly all has occurred in three time constants. (The numbers, 36.8 per cent and 5 per cent, are well worth remembering.)

Another aspect of the time constant is that $1/\tau$ is the initial slope of the exponential curve, the slope at $t = 0$. In Figure 164a a dash line is drawn tangent to the exponential curve at $t = 0$. The slope of the curve is

$$\frac{d}{dt} e^{-t/\tau} = -\frac{1}{\tau} e^{-t/\tau} \tag{164-1}$$

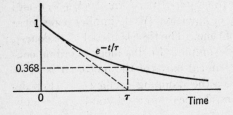

Figure 164a. The graph of an exponential function, showing the time constant.

(164)

which has the value $-1/\tau$ when $t = 0$. The slope of the dash line is therefore $-1/\tau$. As a result, the dash line intersects the horizontal axis at time $t = \tau$. It is useful to remember that τ is the time in which the entire transition of the exponential function would have taken place if it had continued at its initial rate of change.

165. Overall Transfer Function

Each block of Figure 161b is, we see, characterized by a transfer function of the form $1/(1 + s\tau)$. Hence each responds with a time function of the form $e^{-t/\tau}$.

The first block feeds into the second block a field current, a motor flux, that is of exponential form with a time constant τ_f. The second block puts out a mechanical speed influenced by this field-circuit exponential and also influenced by the exponential function that is characteristic of the mechanical component itself, with time constant τ_m. The output, the shaft speed, is therefore a function containing two exponential terms, one of time constant τ_f and the other of time constant τ_m.

Look at the mathematics of this two-block system. Each transfer function has a term of the form $1/(1 + s\tau)$. The overall transfer function, the product, is of the form $1/(1 + s\tau_f) \times (1 + s\tau_m)$ as in equation 161-9. This product of factors in the denominator implies that the time function will contain two exponential terms. That is, the function describing the speed of rotation of the shaft, which is the output of the device, will contain such an expression as $K_1 e^{-t/\tau_f} + K_2 e^{-t/\tau_m}$. (The constants K_1 and K_2 will depend on applied voltage and initial conditions.) This much can be predicted just from inspection of the transfer functions, and this information can be extremely useful, as we shall see.

The statement that two factors of the form $1/(1 + s\tau)$ in the transfer function imply two exponential terms in the response function is perhaps not obvious. Consider, however, that the transfer function can be changed by the method of partial fractions from being a product of two factors of the form $1/(1 + s\tau)$ to be a sum of two terms, each of the form $1/(1 + s\tau)$. Then each of these terms has, as its inverse transform, an exponential time function. This relation can be generalized from two factors and two exponential terms to any number. A transfer function that is the product of three, or four, or n such factors will have in the response time function three, or four, or n exponential terms.

(165)

166. Inverse Transformation

We have derived as equation 161-9 the transfer function relating shaft speed to voltage applied at the field-circuit terminals.

$$\frac{\hat{\Omega}}{\hat{V}_f} = \frac{k}{R_f D} \frac{1}{(1 + s\tau_m)(1 + s\tau_f)} \tag{166-1}$$

We have drawn certain useful conclusions from an inspection of this function, but we have not yet carried our solution to the point of finding precisely the response of the system to some given applied voltage. In fact, a precise and explicit solution is not always necessary, especially in control systems. Nevertheless, it will be well to complete the solution in this simple example to illustrate the process, for it is sometimes needed.

Suppose that constant voltage V_f is suddenly applied to the field-circuit terminals of our motor (Figure 161a), the motor being previously at rest. $V_f(t)$ is therefore a step function of voltage of height V_f, and its transform $\hat{V}_f$ is (by pair 1 of Table A3-4) equal to V_f/s. Introducing this $\hat{V}_f$ into equation 166-1, we have

$$\hat{\Omega} = \frac{kV_f}{R_f D} \frac{1}{(1 + s\tau_m)(1 + s\tau_f)} \frac{1}{s} \tag{166-2}$$

Inverse transformation of this expression is now required. We predict that the result will have two exponential terms and one constant term, corresponding to the two factors of the form $1/(1 + s\tau)$ and the one factor of the form $1/s$, respectively.

Expanding equation 166-2 by the method of partial fractions gives

$$\frac{1}{(1 + s\tau_m)(1 + s\tau_f)s} = \frac{A}{1 + s\tau_m} + \frac{B}{1 + s\tau_f} + \frac{C}{s} \tag{166-3}$$

Each of these terms can be transformed by using pairs 1 and 2 of Table A3-4, and thus the transform of equation 166-2 is found to be

$$\Omega = \frac{kV_f}{R_f D} \left(\frac{A}{\tau_m} e^{-t/\tau_m} + \frac{B}{\tau_f} e^{-t/\tau_f} + C \right) \tag{166-4}$$

To evaluate A, B, and C we multiply equation 166-3 by $(1 + s\tau_m)$, $(1 + s\tau_f)$, and s, respectively. In the first case we let $s = -1/\tau_m$, in the second $s = -1/\tau_f$, and in the third $s = 0$. The three equations then yield

(166)

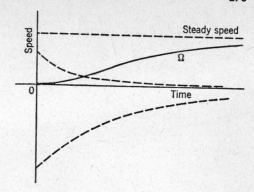

Figure 166a. Shaft velocity of the motor as it comes up to speed, a step function of field voltage being applied.

$$A = \frac{\tau_m^{2}}{\tau_f - \tau_m} \tag{166-5}$$

$$B = \frac{\tau_f^{2}}{\tau_m - \tau_f} \tag{166-6}$$

$$C = 1 \tag{166-7}$$

These values for A, B, and C are now entered in equation 166-4, giving

$$\Omega = \frac{kV_f}{R_fD}\left(\frac{\tau_m}{\tau_f - \tau_m}e^{-t/\tau_m} - \frac{\tau_f}{\tau_f - \tau_m}e^{-t/\tau_f} + 1\right) \tag{166-8}$$

(A new transform pair is thus obtained; it is listed as pair 4 in Table A3-4.)

Equation 166-8 tells how velocity varies as the motor comes up to speed. A graph of this function for one typical set of values of the parameters is shown in Figure 166a. Note that there are one constant and the two exponential components. Note also the remarkable manner in which they combine to satisfy the physical requirements of the system, which are the following: (1) correct steady speed at $t = \infty$, (2) zero speed at zero time, and (3) zero rate of change of speed at zero time. No other combination of one constant term and two exponentials could meet these requirements but only the function that we have computed in equation 166-8.

167. Natural Response

It will be noticed in the foregoing example that two terms in the response (the two exponential terms) are determined, in form, by

(167)

the characteristics of the device (the motor) under consideration, while one of the terms (the constant term) is determined by the applied voltage.

It is evident from the transfer function of equation 166-1 that there will always be two exponential terms in Ω, whatever V_f may be, and that their time constants will be τ_m and τ_f. These exponential terms comprise what is called the *natural response* of the system, for they appear whenever the system is disturbed. Several interesting observations may be made about these terms of the natural response.

First, they are a form of response that requires no driving force for its continuance. If we speak in terms of an electric circuit, the natural response is a form of current that can flow without requiring any voltage to keep it going.

Second, the impedance of the circuit (or mechanical device) to this particular form of current (or motion) is zero. In terms of Kirchhoff's voltage law, the voltage drops produced in the various elements of the circuit by this particular form of current add, when totaled around the circuit, to zero.

Third, these exponential terms of the natural response die away in time; they approach zero asymptotically as time increases. The natural response is therefore called the *transient* component of the response; after a sufficiently long time it disappears.

Fourth, the need for the natural or transient component of response is to provide a smooth transition from the initial conditions to the final or steady-state conditions. In Figure 166a the exponential components of natural response (mechanical speed in this example) provide a smooth transition from the initial speed of zero to the final steady speed, keeping the differential equations of the system satisfied at all times.

168. Forced Response

The final steady response, after all transient components have died away, is determined, in form and magnitude, by the applied driving force or voltage. Hence it is called the forced response. If the driving force is constant, the final response is constant also (as is the steady speed in the system of Figure 166a), or it may be zero. If (in any linear system) the driving force is alternating, a sinusoidal function of time, the final steady response will be a sinusoidal function of time also.

The forced response, by itself, satisfies the differential equations

(168)

of the circuit or system. But in general it will not satisfy the initial conditions in a system at the tme of a disturbance and, since it does not, the total response must contain, in addition to the forced response, a sufficient amount of transient component to satisfy the initial conditions.

In the example of Section 166 the applied voltage is a step function, V_f. It is represented in the transformed equation 166-2 by the factor $1/s$. In equation 166-3, after splitting into partial fractions, the term C/s results, and this leads to the constant term (1 within the parentheses) of equation 166-8. This constant term is the steady speed, forced by the applied voltage, that continues indefinitely.

169. Impulsive Disturbance

A sudden shock to a system, called an impulsive disturbance, excites the natural response of the system without producing any steady-state response. When a croquet ball is struck with a mallet, the disturbance is impulsive. That is, the driving force has ceased before any significant part of the response has taken place—before the croquet ball has moved very far. Thereafter the ball follows its natural pattern of behavior. Since no force is applied after the first instant, the response has no forced component.

An engineer skilled in control systems can study a physical system by prodding it and watching it resile. As we gauge the quality of a wine glass by gently snapping its rim and listening as the ring dies away, or judge the firmness of construction of a car by slamming the door, so a control engineer can put an impulsive disturbance into a system and learn its characteristics by observing the result.

A public address system is crudely tested by rapping on the guard over the microphone. The jingle of a bunch of keys is used as a quick and easy yet rather severe trial of the fidelity of a tape recorder.

All this is impulse testing. It can be done physically to study an existing system, or it can be done mathematically for purposes of analysis.

170. The Impulse Function

Mathematically, the impulsive disturbance is interpreted by Laplace analysis as being a means of applying to a system *all frequencies*

(170)

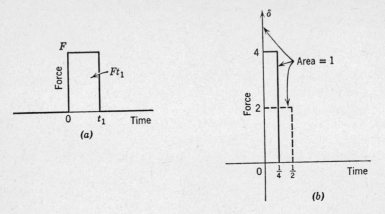

Figure 170. (a) Impulse. (b) The impulsive δ function is the limit as duration is shortened, keeping impulse equal to 1.

at once. To see this we must first devise a mathematical description of an impulsive disturbance.

Speaking in terms of force (although we shall later apply the discussion to voltage and other disturbances), an impulsive disturbance is a large force exerted for a short time. The *amount of the impulse,* as that quantity is defined in mechanics, is the product of force and time.* Thus in Figure 170a the impulse produced by a force F acting for a time t_1 is Ft_1. The amount of the impulse is equal to the area under the graph of force when plotted against time.

Figure 170b shows two forces that provide the same amount of impulse. In one, a force of 2 newtons is applied for $\frac{1}{2}$ second. In the other, a force of 4 newtons is applied for $\frac{1}{4}$ second. Each provides 1 unit (1 newton-second) of impulse. Now consider forces applied for even shorter times, the amount of force being enough to provide in each case 1 unit of impulse. In the limit, as the time becomes vanishingly small, and the force correspondingly great, we approach what is called the Dirac impulse function, usually indicated by the symbol δ. It is suggested graphically by the vertical arrow in Figure 170b.

Mathematically, δ is a function of time [and as such may be written $\delta(t)$] with a value of zero for all times except for an infinitesimal time following $t = 0$, when the value of the function is such

---

* If the force is varying, impulse is the time integral of force.

that the time integral of the function is *by definition* equal to 1. Thus

$$\int_0^{+\infty} \delta \, dt = 1 \tag{170-1}$$

The integral is here written with the limits 0 and ∞, but any limits may be used that contain the impulse between them.

Physically, δ can represent a force or other disturbance that takes place in so short a time that the response of the system during that time is negligible. The δ function is a mathematical idealization of the rap on a croquet ball, the snap on a wine glass, the tap on a microphone, or the click of one key against another.

The Laplace analysis of the impulsive δ function is obtained by substitution into the defining integral, equation 2-1 in Appendix 3. Denoting the impulsive time function by δ and its transform by $\hat{\delta}$, we obtain

$$\hat{\delta} = \int_0^{\infty} \delta e^{-st} \, dt \tag{170-2}$$

The product to be integrated turns out to be simple. Since $\delta = 0$ at all times except $t = 0$, the product δe^{-st} is zero at all times except $t = 0$. When $t = 0$, $e^{-st} = 1$, so the product is δ times 1, or δ. Thus at all times the product is equal to δ, and the integral reduces to

$$\hat{\delta} = \int_0^{\infty} \delta \, dt \tag{170-3}$$

This we know from the integral of equation 170-1 is equal to 1. That is,

$$\hat{\delta} = 1 \tag{170-4}$$

which means that for all values of s the transform of the δ function is 1. Interpreted as a spectrum, this confirms the statement that all frequencies are present, and all with equal intensity.*

Equation 170-4 provides a new transform pair that can be listed for future reference, in Table A3-4, as pair 5.

---

* It is not easy to visualize the infinite spike of the δ function as the sum of an infinity of sinusoidal components, each of infinitesimal amplitude and endless duration. Yet by starting with the Fourier-series analysis of rectangular pulses and working through the Fourier-integral expression for a single pulse that can be allowed to approach zero duration while maintaining constant area, it will be seen that this interpretation is indeed the reasonable outcome. See, for instance, Chapter 15, and particularly equation 15-45, of *Electrical Engineering Circuits* (Reference 7A).

171. Impulse and Natural Response

Now we are prepared to do mathematically what the engineer does physically when he disturbs a system and watches it return to equilibrium. We apply a δ function of force to a mechanical system, or of voltage to an electrical system, and observe the result. Consider an example.

Figure 171a repeats the inductive circuit of Figure 157a. Now find the current i when an impulsive function of voltage is applied; that is, when $v = \delta$.

To find the current (following the rules of Appendix 3), note that the steady-state impedance is $Z(j\omega) = R + j\omega L$. Therefore $Z(s) = R + sL$. The voltage v is a high value applied for a mere instant, a unit impulse mathematically represented by δ. The transform of the applied voltage is, by equation 170-4, $\hat{v} = \hat{\delta} = 1$.

The current transform is the voltage transform divided by the impedance function:

$$\hat{i} = \frac{\hat{v}}{Z(s)} = \frac{1}{R + sL} = \frac{1}{R}\frac{1}{(1 + s\tau)} \tag{171-1}$$

where τ is the time constant of the circuit, L/R.

By using pair 2 of Table A3-4, current is found to be

$$i = \frac{1}{R}\frac{R}{L}e^{-t/\tau} = \frac{1}{L}e^{-t/\tau} \tag{171-2}$$

The exponential form, shown in Figure 171b, is the natural response.

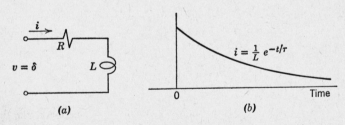

$v = \delta$ R L $i = \frac{1}{L}e^{-t/\tau}$ 0 Time

(a)   (b)

Figure 171. (a) An inductive circuit, and (b) its response to unit impulsive voltage, $v = \delta$.

(171)

172. Summary

A transfer function (or transmittance) is most commonly a Laplace transform, the ratio of the transform of output to that of input. The reader not familiar with Laplace transformation is referred to Appendix 3.

The Laplace transfer function is easily derived from the steady-state transfer function by a change of variable.

A system is often shown as a block diagram; the transfer function of each block is conveniently written within the block.

Analysis of a system is greatly simplified if each block is independent of the other blocks. Independence requires that the transfer function of one block should not contain the impedance or other function of another block.

A field-controlled commutator motor is used as an example of a system of two independent blocks to show (a) direct transformation, (b) interpretation of transfer functions, including time constants, (c) inverse transformation, including (d) natural response, and (e) forced response.

It is shown that only the natural response results from application of an impulse function, symbolized by δ. A sudden disturbance can be used, either physically or mathematically to study a system. The resulting disturbance can be classified, as in the next chapter.

PROBLEMS

12-1. In equation 161-5 a proportionality constant k_f is used. Trace the meaning of k_f back to physical quantities that could readily be evaluated for a given machine.   **(Sec. 161)**

12-2. A mass of 3.4 kg has a damping coefficient of 0.28 kg/sec. An increasing force is applied to the mass until $t = 0$, at which time the mass is moving with a velocity of 8.0 m/sec. At this time, $t = 0$, the force on the mass becomes steady at 7.5 newtons. By Laplace methods, find the velocity of the mass after $t = 0$.   **(Sec. 162)**

12-3. Angular velocity of the rotor of a motor is given by equation 146-2. (*a*) Find the velocity as a function of time, in the steady state, if applied torque is $T = T_0 \cos \omega t$. (*b*) Find velocity as a function of time, both transient and steady state, if applied torque is a step function of height T_s.   **(Sec. 166)**

12-4. In Section 166 a constant voltage V_f is suddenly applied and an angular velocity Ω is found. Now apply the same voltage and find the angular position θ, using equation 162-5. What additional complication is encountered?   **(Sec. 166)**

12-5. The armature of a motor is turning at 11 rev/sec when a step function of torque is applied, the amount being 0.75 newton-meter. Find, by Laplace transform methods, the speed thereafter (a time function). Moment of inertia is 0.05 kg-m², and torque required by a load on the motor is 0.003 Ω newton-meter, Ω being angular velocity in radians/second.   **(Sec. 166)**

12-6. Equation 166-8 gives angular velocity as a function of time. Find the initial rate of change of angular velocity, immediately following the application of torque, (*a*) by differentiation of Ω, and (*b*) by reasoning from the physical nature of the problem.   **(Sec. 166)**

12-7. Equation 162-5 relates shaft angle of a motor to field-circuit voltage. (*a*) Find θ following application of an impulsive δ function of voltage. (*b*) How far will the motor turn before it stops? Discuss the time it will take the motor to reach its final position.   **(Sec. 170)**

12-8. Equation 161-8 gives a transfer function. If I_f is a step function, find Ω. Repeat if I_f is an impulsive δ function.   **(Sec. 171)**

12-9. A dynamic system is described by the following differential equation:

$$\frac{d^2y}{dt^2} + 2\frac{dy}{dt} + y = f(t)$$

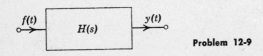

Problem 12-9

(*a*) Find the transfer function of the system, $H(s)$ in the figure. (*b*) Find its impulse response.   **(Sec. 171)**

12-10. Find the transfer function (in Laplace notation) between output speed and input voltage of a speaker. Include the resistance of the electric circuit but not the inductance, or mechanical compliance. (*a*) Compute the time constant (or constants). (*b*) What type of terms (i.e., linear, quadratic, etc.) appear in the transfer function? (But the natural response need *not* be computed.) (*c*) Draw the frequency distribution diagram (log scales) and give values to establish scales.   **(Sec. 164)**

12-11. In Problem 12-10 compute the natural response. **(Sec. 171)**

12-12. A bar of iron with mass of 0.1 kg is attracted toward a magnet. At $t = 0$ the bar is not moving. How long does it take the bar to move 1.0 cm if (*a*) the force is constant at 1.0 newton? (*b*) the force is a unit impulse, $F = \delta$ (use Laplace transformation to solve the differential equation)? (*c*) the force is the following function of time: $F = 1 - e^{-t/2}$?   **(Sec. 171)**

12-13. In Problem 12-12, the bar starts at a distance of 1.0 cm from the magnet, and at this distance the force is 1.0 newton. As the bar moves, the force is inversely proportional to its distance from the magnet, but an exact solution using this function would be difficult. Instead, assume that the force is 1.0 newton from 1.0 cm to 0.9 cm, where it suddenly becomes 10/9 newtons. It remains constant at this value from 0.9 cm to 0.8 cm, where it suddenly becomes 10/8 newtons, etc. Proceeding step by step, find the total time (approximate) for the bar to move through the distance of 1.0 cm to reach the magnet. (*Note to instructor:* This is a relatively long and difficult problem, but highly instructive.)   **(Sec. 166)**

12-14. In Figure 161*a*, the motor with field control is at rest until $t = 0$. Let the applied voltage be the impulse δV_f where V_f is a constant. Find the transform and time function for: (*a*) θ, the angular position, (*b*) $\Omega = d\theta/dt$, (*c*) $\alpha = d\Omega/dt$, (*d*) $d\alpha/dt$. Also, (*e*) draw a sketch, which may be quite rough, showing the time function for each of the above quantities.   **(Sec. 171)**

TYPES OF FUNCTIONS AND RESPONSES

chapter 13

173. Classification of Transfer Functions

Several types of factors have appeared in the transfer functions and the impedance and admittance functions of previous chapters. A factor of the form $(1 + s\tau)$ has been seen frequently; equations 161-2 and 166-1 are examples. Factors of s appeared in some of the functions, as, for instance, in equation 162-4. Furthermore, most of the functions contain a constant factor. There are constant factors in the three equations just mentioned, and indeed the simplest transfer function, as in equation 149-2, is a constant only.

The purpose of this chapter is to classify the factors of transfer functions into types, and to study, for each type of factor:

1. The frequency response (response as a function of frequency).
2. The natural response, a function of time.
3. For some factors, the effect of the factor on a more extensive transfer function (i.e., integration or differentiation by the factor s).

Then, in later chapters, we review a variety of practical electromechanical devices, finding the factors of their transfer functions, and classifying them accordingly.

We give attention to four types of factors of transfer functions, as shown in Table 173. Other factors are possible, but these four are the most common:*

Type I, a constant factor.
Type II, a factor s.

---

*The four types given here are generally recognized, though authors use various schemes of classification. See, for instance, Bruns and Saunders, Reference 173.

Table 173. Types of Transfer Functions

Type of Response	Transfer Function	Frequency Response (Approx.)	Response to Impulse Function δ
I Proportional	k		$k\delta$
II Integral	$\dfrac{1}{s}$		1
II Differential	s		
III Exponential	$\dfrac{1}{1+s\tau}$		$\dfrac{1}{\tau}\,e^{-t/\tau}$
IV Oscillatory	$\dfrac{1}{1+2\zeta\dfrac{s}{\omega_0}+\left(\dfrac{s}{\omega_0}\right)^2}$		$\dfrac{\omega_0^2}{\omega_n}\,e^{-\alpha t}\sin\omega_n t$

283

(173)

Type III, a linear factor of the form $(1 + s\tau)$.

Type IV, a quadratic factor of the form $(1 + bs + as^2)$ in which the constants b and a have values that do not yield real linear factors.

174. A Constant Factor

$$\text{If} \qquad\qquad \frac{v_2}{v_1} = k \qquad\qquad\qquad (174\text{-}1)$$

and k is a constant (not a function of s), the response v_2 is *proportional* to the disturbance v_1. This simple relation applies to such devices as ideal levers, gears, transformers, or purely resistive networks (Figure 174a).

Referring to the purposes tabulated in Section 173, we look first at the frequency response.

(1) When the transfer function is merely a constant, as in equation 174-1, the amplitude of response is independent of frequency. At any frequency the ratio of output v_2 to input v_1 is k. Plotted, as in Table 173, the frequency response is a horizontal straight line.

(2) A device with a transfer function that is a constant can hardly be said to have a natural response. If an impulsive δ function is applied, the output is also an impulsive function, as indicated in Table 173. Whatever the form of the disturbance, the response is of the same form, changed in magnitude by the factor k.

(3) When a constant factor appears as part of some more complicated transfer function, it determines the magnitude of the response. It affects the absolute value of the frequency-response function but does not change the shape of that function. It indicates the size of the natural response that results from a disturbance but does not affect its form.

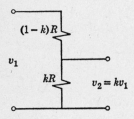

Figure 174a. A resistance network has proportional response.

(174)

175. An Integrating Factor

In equation 162-3 a transfer function that is merely $1/s$ relates angle and speed:

$$\frac{\theta}{\Omega} = \frac{1}{s} \qquad (175\text{-}1)$$

This $1/s$ was interpreted as an integrating factor, meaning that θ is the integral of Ω.

The transform of angle can be written as $1/s$ times the transform of speed:

$$\theta = \frac{1}{s}\,\Omega \qquad (175\text{-}2)$$

176. A Physical Example

The responses of a device with a transfer function $1/s$ are more satisfactorily studied by thinking of such a physical element as the flywheel of Figure 176a. Another device with the same transfer function might be an object with mass only, to which a force is applied, or an electric circuit with a purely inductive element and an applied voltage.

The differential equation of the flywheel is simply

$$T = J\,\frac{d\Omega}{dt} \qquad (176\text{-}1)$$

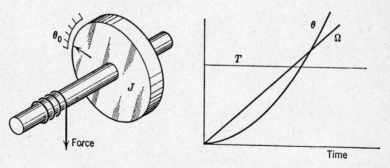

Figure 176a. A flywheel accelerated by a torque.

$$(176)$$

The transform of the equation is

$$\hat{T} = Js\hat{\Omega} \quad \text{or} \quad \hat{\Omega} = \frac{1}{Js}\hat{T} \qquad (176\text{-}2)$$

The transfer function relating the output speed to the input torque is

$$\frac{\hat{\Omega}}{\hat{T}} = \frac{1}{Js} \quad \text{or} \quad J\frac{\hat{\Omega}}{\hat{T}} = \frac{1}{s} \qquad (176\text{-}3)$$

The final form shows the transfer function clearly, and it is often convenient to use. Note that it makes no difference in the present discussion what the symbols T and Ω represent, except that we shall think of T as the input and Ω as the output, with J as a constant of proportionality.

177. Frequency Response

(1) Let us first study the frequency response of a device with a transfer function $1/s$. The frequency response is found by writing the steady-state relation (writing $j\omega$ in place of s):

$$J\frac{\Omega}{T} = \frac{1}{j\omega} \qquad (177\text{-}1)$$

from which we have, for magnitude alone,

$$J\left|\frac{\Omega}{T}\right| = \frac{1}{\omega} \qquad (177\text{-}2)$$

The response is inversely proportional to frequency. When plotted in Figure 177a the graph is hyperbolic. This inversely proportional frequency response is characteristic of the transfer function $1/s$.

Instead of drawing the frequency-response curve, as in Figure 177a, with linear scales, a convenient expedient is to use logarithmic scales. The result is shown in Figure 177b, with reference to scales at the left and bottom of the diagram.

This same diagram may also be considered as being a plot, on linear scales, of the logarithms of the variables. That is, Figure 177b is a plot of $\log |\Omega/T|$ as a function of $\log \omega$, using the linear scales at the right-hand side and top of the diagram.

In Figure 177b the plot of the function is a straight line, instead of the hyperbola seen in Figure 177a. To show that this is correct, the logarithms of each side of equation 177-2 are equated:

(177)

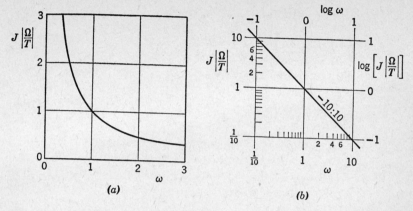

Figure 177. (a) The magnitude of frequency response (equation 177-2) is a hyperbola when plotted on linear scales, and (b) a straight line on logarithmic scales.

$$\log \left[J \left| \frac{\Omega}{T} \right| \right] = \log \left[\frac{1}{\omega} \right] = - \log \omega \qquad (177\text{-}3)$$

With $\log \left[J \left| \dfrac{\Omega}{T} \right| \right]$ as one variable, and $\log \omega$ as the other, this is an equation of the form $y = -x$. Its graph is therefore a straight line with a slope of -1.

Note that in Figure 177b the origin of linear coordinates is at the center of the diagram, at the point (0,0) as read on the linear scales at the right-hand side and the top. This is the point (1,1) as read on the logarithmic scales at the left and bottom.

When the transfer function is $1/s$, as in this example, the response goes down by a factor of 10 as the applied frequency goes up by a factor of 10. We shall find it convenient to refer to this as a slope of -10 in 10, or $-10:10$.*

178. Natural Response

(2) Next we study the natural response of a device with a transfer function $1/s$. The response of a device to an applied δ function is its natural response, and when an impulsive disturbance is applied

---

* Some authors refer to this as a slope of -1, or as an increase of attenuation of 20 decibels per decade, or 6 decibels per octave.

to a device for which the transfer function is $1/s$, the output is a step function.

Equation 176-2 leads to this result. Let $T = \delta$, the impulse function; by pair 5 of Table A3-4 its transform is $\hat{T} = 1$. Substituting this into equation 176-2, we have

$$J\hat{\Omega} = \frac{1}{s}\hat{T} = \frac{1}{s} \qquad (178\text{-}1)$$

Then, by pair 1 of the table, $J\Omega$ is the unit step function

$$J\Omega = 1 \quad \text{or} \quad \Omega = \frac{1}{J} \qquad (178\text{-}2)$$

This natural response can be visualized as the response to an impulsive torque. Suppose a sharp jerk is given to the cord in Figure 176a. This impulse starts the flywheel turning, and since there is no friction it continues to turn thereafter at constant speed. Its speed of rotation is a step function of time.

179. Integration

(3) It has already been pointed out, in Section 175, that $1/s$ is an integrating factor. This is seen again in the flywheel of Figure 176a and equation 176-2. The output time function Ω is proportional to the integral of the input time function T.

When, as in equation 178-2, the input is the impulsive δ function, the output is its integral, a step function. If the input T is a cosine function of time, the output Ω is a sine function. If the input is a step function, the output is a ramp function, the integral of the step function. This is shown in Figure 179a.

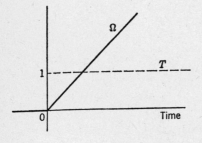

Figure 179a. Response to a unit step-function is the integral of the step function.

(179)

180. A Differentiating Factor

If s is a factor of the *numerator* of a transfer function, it is called a differentiating factor. Consider the equation

$$\frac{\hat{I}}{\hat{V}} = sC \tag{180-1}$$

We should think of this as a formal mathematical relation that is not restricted to any particular physical meaning of the symbols. However, it may help visualization to have in mind the capacitor of Figure 180a.

(1) Frequency response is found by writing $j\omega$ in place of s:

$$\frac{I}{V} = j\omega C \tag{180-2}$$

Then the absolute magnitude is

$$\left|\frac{I}{V}\right| = \omega C \quad \text{or} \quad \frac{1}{C}\left|\frac{I}{V}\right| = \omega \tag{180-3}$$

The output, I, is thus directly proportional to frequency, as shown in Figure 180b and in Table 173. This is the frequency response characteristic of a differentiating factor, an s in the numerator of a transfer function.

(3) The s in the numerator of a transformed function corresponds

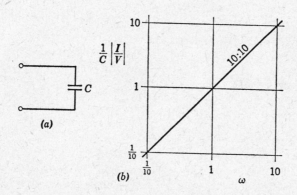

(a)

(b)

Figure 180. A capacitance (a) acts as a differentiating device, and its frequency response (b) is a straight line.

(180)

to differentiation of the time function. If equation 180-1 is written

$$\hat{I} = sC\hat{V} \tag{180-4}$$

the output quantity I is the derivative of the disturbance V, times a constant C. Thus if V is a sine wave, I is a wave of cosine form. If V is a ramp function, I is a step function. If V is a step function, I is an impulsive function.*

181. A Linear Factor in the Denominator

A transfer function is frequently of the form

$$\frac{\hat{V}_2}{\hat{V}_1} = \frac{1}{1 + s\tau} \tag{181-1}$$

(Though this is to be considered a purely formal equation, it may be visualized as the transfer function of the inductive circuit of Figure 181a if $\tau = L/R$.)

(1) Response to alternating excitation as a function of frequency is found, as always, by writing $j\omega$ for s:

$$\frac{V_2}{V_1} = \frac{1}{1 + j\omega\tau} \tag{181-2}$$

The magnitude of this function is found by remembering that the magnitude of a complex number is the square root of the sum of the squares of the real and imaginary components:

$$\left|\frac{V_2}{V_1}\right| = \frac{1}{\sqrt{1 + (\omega\tau)^2}} \tag{181-3}$$

---

*If V is an impulsive δ function, I should mathematically be C times the derivative of the δ function. Can we find the natural response?

(2) The natural response corresponding to a function s is the derivative of the δ function. But what is the derivative of the δ function? The derivative of the δ function is surely zero at all times except $t = 0$, but we are puzzled to say what it is at that precise moment. However, if we consider the δ function to be the limit approached as a high but narrow analytic peak of the variable V becomes still higher and more narrow, we see that the derivative has first a very high positive maximum, immediately followed by a deep negative dip, which, in the limit, tend to infinity. This is suggested in the last column of Table 173. Physically, we may consider the natural response to be approximated by current to (and from) the capacitor of Figure 180a if the applied voltage is made to be as nearly as possible an impulsive δ function, resistance of the capacitor circuit being as nearly as possible zero.

(181)

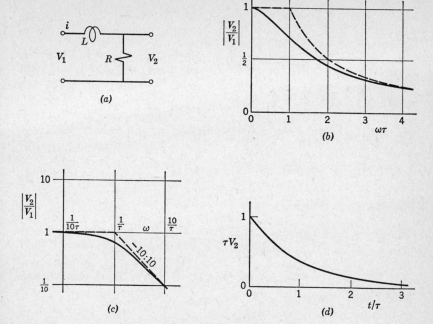

Figure 181. (a) A "low-pass" circuit, (b) its frequency response on linear scales, (c) its frequency response on logarithmic scales, and (d) its natural response as a function of time.

This magnitude, always smaller than 1, is plotted on linear scales as the solid line in Figure 181b, and on logarithmic scales as the solid line in Figure 181c.

(2) The natural response of a device or circuit with a transfer function of this form is found by writing

$$\hat{V}_2 = \frac{1}{1 + s\tau}\,\hat{V}_1 \tag{181-4}$$

and then letting the applied disturbance V_1 be the impulse function δ. The Laplace transform of the impulse function is 1, as in pair 5 of Table A3-4. We know that $\hat{V}_1 = 1$ and write

$$\hat{V}_2 = \frac{1}{1 + s\tau} \tag{181-5}$$

$$\tag{181}$$

Pair 2 of Table A3-4 then gives us the time function for V_2:

$$V_2 = \frac{1}{\tau} e^{-t/\tau} \tag{181-6}$$

That is, if the transfer function is of the form of equation 181-1, the natural response is exponential as shown by equation 181-6 and Figure 181d, and in Table 173.

182. A Linear Factor in the Numerator

Although we have so far seen the factor $(1 + s\tau)$ appearing only in the denominator, transfer functions may also have this factor in the *numerator*. Suppose there were a function of the form

$$\frac{\hat{v}_2}{\hat{v}_1} = 1 + s\tau \tag{182-1}$$

(1) The corresponding response to alternating excitation, as a function of frequency, would be

$$\left| \frac{V_2}{V_1} \right| = \sqrt{1 + (\omega\tau)^2} \tag{182-2}$$

which is the reciprocal of equation 181-3.

This frequency response is plotted on logarithmic scales as the solid line in Figure 182a. It is similar to Figure 181c but inverted. If plotted on linear scales it would be like the reciprocal of Figure 181b. This response increases with increasing frequency, and in Figure 182a it can be seen that the response becomes infinite.

If it is desired to visualize such a response, we can think of the

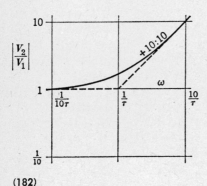

Figure 182a. Frequency response resulting from the factor $(1 + s\tau)$.

(182)

admittance function of Figure 180a with a resistor in parallel with the capacitor shown. Then the ratio of the transforms of entering current and applied voltage is of the form $(1 + s\tau)$. It is apparent that entering current becomes great without limit as the frequency of the applied voltage is raised, the voltage being of constant magnitude, because of the path through the capacitor.

(2) Although $(1 + s\tau)$ is common as a factor in a numerator, it is rarely the whole transfer function. Hence the corresponding time function, the natural response, is not particularly meaningful. The sum of the impulse function and its derivative would be rather unpleasant mathematically. The circuit of the previous paragraph may again help visualization: consider the current that results when an impulse of voltage is applied to a resistor and a capacitor in parallel.

(3) However, when $(1 + s\tau)$ is a factor in the numerator of some more complicated transfer function, as in

$$\frac{\hat{v}_2}{\hat{v}_1} = (1 + s\tau)\hat{f} \tag{182-3}$$

where $\hat{f}$, a function of s, is a fraction with linear factors in its denominator, then the transfer function $\hat{v}_2/\hat{v}_1$ has definite meaning. Now the output is the time function found from $\hat{f}$ plus the *derivative* of this time function (times τ). The derivative term has the effect of increasing the response at higher frequencies.

Such a factor in the numerator and the increased response at higher frequencies raise the response curve of the entire system in which the factor occurs. (See Section 184.) This may be a means of increasing stability in a closed system (Chapter 17).

183. Asymptotic Approximation

In Figure 181c the curve is asymptotic to two dash lines as shown. These dash lines can be drawn more easily than the exact curve; indeed, they can be drawn with almost no computation at all. The only quantity needed to determine them is the time constant τ.

Because these dash lines are so easy to draw they are often used as an approximation of the true curve that is asymptotic to them. The dash lines serve as a fair approximation of the frequency response of any circuit or device characterized by a transfer function $1/(1 + s\tau)$.

Note that one dash line is horizontal, the other has a slope of -1 on logarithmic scales $(-10{:}10)$, and they intersect at the point $(1/\tau, 1)$.

(183)

This point of intersection is called the *break point* or *corner frequency*.

The horizontal line is an approximation of equation 181-3 when the frequency is so low that $(\omega\tau)^2$ is very much less than 1; that is, when ω is very much less than $1/\tau$. In this range it is a good approximation to say that $|V_2/V_1| \approx 1$; this applies for points well to the left of the break point.

The sloping line is an approximation of the same equation when $(\omega\tau)^2$ is so large that the 1 added to it is negligible. In this range, well to the right of the break point, the approximate equation is $|V_2/V_1| \approx 1/\omega\tau$.

The point of intersection is the point at which $\omega = 1/\tau$. This is the value of ω that makes the equation for the sloping line equal 1.

184. Functions with Several Factors

A single transfer function usually has several factors of the types we have been studying, multiplied together. Let us consider, for example, the function

$$\frac{\theta}{T} = c \frac{1}{(1 + s\tau_1)(1 + s\tau_2)} \tag{184-1}$$

Although in the following discussion, physical realization of this function is not limited to any particular device, and the symbols can represent any physical quantities, the example of Figure 190a may be an aid to visualization.

The function of equation 184-1 contains three factors: a constant c and two factors of the form $1/(1 + s\tau)$. It will be assumed that these two latter factors have different time constants, τ_1 and τ_2, and that these time constants are positive real numbers. We find for this function, as we have done for others, (1) the amplitude of response as a function of frequency, and (2) the form of the natural response as a function of time.

(1) This function is a product of three factors. We know the frequency response for each of these three factors. For the constant term it is a constant, shown by the horizontal line at c in Figure 184a. For the factor $1/(1 + s\tau_1)$ it is approximated by the pair of dash lines shown in the figure with the break point at $1/\tau_1$. For the factor $1/(1 + s\tau_2)$ it is approximated by the similar pair of dash lines with the break point, as shown, at $1/\tau_2$. The frequency response for the whole function is the product of these three.

(184)

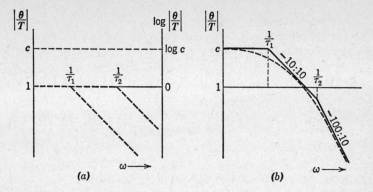

Figure 184. (a) The approximate frequency-response functions of the factors of equation 184-1, and (b) the sum of the three lines which is the product of the three factors. The overdamped case.

The product can be found graphically. Vertical distances in Figure 184a represent logarithms of values of the factors. Adding distances in the diagram is therefore equivalent to adding logarithms of the factors or to multiplying the factors. Hence to find the diagram that represents the whole function we add the diagrams of the three factors. We add vertical distances, referring to the right-hand scale, and measuring from the zero axis marked by a solid line.

The sum is shown in Figure 184b by a solid line of three segments. For frequencies below $1/\tau_1$ it is horizontal. Between $1/\tau_1$ and $1/\tau_2$ its slope is -1 on logarithmic coordinates, which means that response falls off to $\frac{1}{10}$ as frequency is increased by 10. When ω is greater than $1/\tau_2$ the sum is the steeper line with a slope of -2. In this section the response falls off to $\frac{1}{100}$ each time the frequency increases by 10.

A dashed line shows the true frequency-response curve that is approximated by this solid line of three segments.

185. Corresponding Natural Response

(2) When the system function is that of equation 184-1 the natural response is composed of two exponential terms. One exponential term has a time constant τ_1, the other τ_2.

This much can be predicted by a glance at equation 184-1. To find the natural response in full detail we proceed mathematically by letting the disturbing function be an impulse. That is, we let $T = \delta$. The

(185)

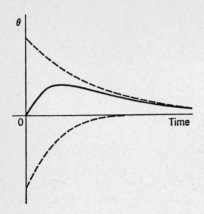

Figure 185a. The natural response of an overdamped device; an example of equation 185-2.

transform of T is then the transform of δ, which is 1. We substitute $\hat{T} = 1$ into equation 184-1, obtaining

$$\hat{\theta} = c\,\frac{1}{(1 + s\tau_1)(1 + s\tau_2)} \tag{185-1}$$

The method of partial fractions will now split the right-hand member into the sum of two terms, each of which has as its inverse Laplace transform an exponential time function. The result is given in pair 7 of Table A3-4. We have not derived pair 7, but this is rather easily done, and the inverse transform of equation 185-1 is found to be

$$\theta = \frac{c}{\tau_1 - \tau_2}\,(e^{-t/\tau_1} - e^{-t/\tau_2}) \tag{185-2}$$

This function is plotted in Figure 185a for one specific set of values of the parameters. It is seen that the two exponential components combine to give a unidirectional pulse of total response.

186. A Quadratic Factor

The transfer function of equation 184-1 can be changed, by multiplication of the factors, to the form

$$\frac{\hat{\theta}}{\hat{T}} = \frac{c}{1 + (\tau_1 + \tau_2)s + \tau_1\tau_2 s^2} \tag{186-1}$$

In Section 184 it was assumed that τ_1 and τ_2 were positive real numbers. This assumption places obvious restrictions upon the possible

(186)

values of $(\tau_1 + \tau_2)$ and $\tau_1\tau_2$ in equation 186-1. Now we remove these restrictions and give equation 186-1 a greater generality than we have previously considered. We shall extend our consideration to the general quadratic denominator, Type IV of Section 173. The discussion will be extended to include three possibilities:

1. The denominator of equation 186-1 can be the product of two real factors, $(1 + s\tau_1)(1 + s\tau_2)$, where (as in equation 184-1) τ_1 and τ_2 are different real numbers. This is the *overdamped* case, Type III, which we have already considered.

2. The denominator can be a perfect square, in which case it can be written $(1 + s\tau)^2$. This is the *critically damped* case.

3. Factors of the denominator can be complex. In this case, Type IV, the denominator is most conveniently not factored but left in quadratic form $(1 + bs + as^2)$. This is the *oscillatory* case.

A quadratic function is characteristic of a physical system that has two elements capable of storing energy, and a damping component. (Such an electrical system might have inductance, capacitance, and resistance; a mechanical system mass, elasticity, and linear friction.) If damping is large, factors of the denominator are real. This is the first of the above three cases, the overdamped case, which has already been discussed.

Next we discuss the oscillatory case, in which the damping is slight. The denominator of equation 186-1 cannot then be factored into real factors. It would still be mathematically correct to use the factored form of equation 184-1, but τ_1 and τ_2 would be complex numbers and would lose their significance as time constants. It is more convenient to use new symbols, writing

$$\frac{\hat{\theta}}{\hat{T}} = \frac{c}{1 + 2\zeta(s/\omega_0) + (s/\omega_0)^2} \qquad (186\text{-}2)$$

In this form there are two new symbols, ω_0 and ζ, not previously defined, but it is clear that if the coefficients b and a of Type IV are known, either as letters or numbers, it is easy to find ω_0 and ζ:

$$\omega_0 = \frac{1}{\sqrt{a}} \quad \text{and} \quad \zeta = \frac{b}{2}\,\omega_0 \qquad (186\text{-}3)$$

The reason for introducing these symbols will soon be apparent; they have physical meaning as coefficients of frequency and damping, respectively.

187. Frequency Response, Quadratic Factor

Figure 187a shows the frequency response for the function of equation 186-2. A family of curves, rather than a single curve, is needed to show the range of responses that can appear in a system with a quadratic transfer function.

Each curve in Figure 187a is for a different value of ζ. The peaked response curve that appears with low ζ indicates resonance; the output of the system is large if the input frequency is in the neighborhood of ω_0; and ω_0 is called the *undamped natural frequency* of the system.

A higher value of ζ corresponds to greater damping in the system, as when $\zeta = 0.5$. The flattish curve for which $\zeta = 1.0$ results when there is critical damping; this is the value that separates oscillatory from overdamped response, for unless ζ is less than 1 the denominator of equation 186-2 can be factored into real factors.

When a quadratic factor of the kind under consideration appears in a system function there are two courses that may be pursued. One is to use exact values of the function. Exact values can be determined by computation from equation 186-2, or they may be taken from published charts. Many books on control systems give charts that are similar to the central portion of Figure 187a, but

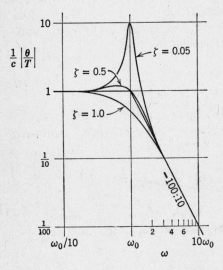

Figure 187a. Frequency response of an oscillatory system, showing curves for three values of damping and the asymptotic approximation (logarithmic scales).

(187)

with scales greatly magnified,* showing curves for many values of ζ.

The other course is to use as an asymptotic approximation a horizontal section of straight line for frequencies below $\omega = \omega_0$ and a straight sloping section for frequencies greater than $\omega = \omega_0$. Figure 187a shows these straight lines to which the exact curves are asymptotic. It will be seen that the approximation is good if the actual frequency is sufficiently far from the undamped natural frequency of the system. Even at frequencies near resonance the approximation is fairly good unless damping is so slight that ζ is much smaller than 0.5.

The curves of Figure 187a are computed from equation 186-2 after replacing s by $j\omega$:

$$\frac{1}{c}\frac{\theta}{T} = \frac{1}{1 + 2j\zeta(\omega/\omega_0) - (\omega/\omega_0)^2} \qquad (187\text{-}1)$$

An interesting and valuable deduction to be drawn from this equation is that the absolute value of the function when $\omega = \omega_0$ (which is the ordinate at which each of the curves of Figure 187a crosses the vertical axis) is $1/(2\zeta)$. Thus the curve for $\zeta = 0.05$ reaches a height of 10, and the curve that crosses the axis at 1 is for $\zeta = 0.5$.

The low-frequency asymptotic approximation is found by neglecting all terms in the denominator that contain ω. This leaves only

$$\frac{1}{c}\frac{\theta}{T} \approx 1 \qquad (\text{for } \omega \ll \omega_0) \qquad (187\text{-}2)$$

The high-frequency approximation comes from neglecting the terms that do not contain ω^2; leaving

$$\frac{1}{c}\frac{\theta}{T} \approx \frac{1}{-(\omega/\omega_0)^2} \qquad (\text{for } \omega \gg \omega_0) \qquad (187\text{-}3)$$

Considering only the absolute magnitude, and taking the logarithm of each side, we have

$$\log\left|\frac{1}{c}\frac{\theta}{T}\right| \approx -2 \log \frac{\omega}{\omega_0} \qquad (187\text{-}4)$$

This is the equation (on logarithmic coordinates) of a straight line with a slope of -2 as shown in the right-hand part of Figure 187a.

---

* E.g., Bruns and Saunders (Reference 173), Bower and Schultheiss, Chestnut and Mayer, Savant, Brown and Campbell (References 187A, B, C, D).

(187)

It will be seen that at frequencies substantially higher than resonance the response drops to $\frac{1}{100}$ as the frequency is increased by a factor of 10.

The corner value or break point in Figure 187a, where the asymptotic approximations meet, is at $\omega = \omega_0$.

188. Natural Response, Quadratic Factor

Next we consider the *natural response* that corresponds to a transfer function of the form given in equation 186-2. As usual, we find the natural response by letting the disturbing force be impulsive. In the notation of equation 186-2, we let $T = \delta$. Its transform, then, is $\hat{T} = 1$, and, from equation 186-2:

$$\hat{\theta} = \frac{c}{1 + 2\zeta(s/\omega_0) + (s/\omega_0)^2} \tag{188-1}$$

The natural response, θ, is the inverse transform of $\hat{\theta}$. How is θ to be found? The most expedient way is to factor the denominator (though we know that these factors will be complex), obtaining

$$\hat{\theta} = \frac{c}{\left[1 + \dfrac{s}{\omega_0(\zeta + \sqrt{\zeta^2 - 1})}\right]\left[1 + \dfrac{s}{\omega_0(\zeta - \sqrt{\zeta^2 - 1})}\right]} \tag{188-2}$$

To simplify this expression we introduce two new parameters, α and ω_n, which we shall call (for reasons that will soon be apparent) the *attenuation constant* and *natural frequency* (radian frequency) of the function. These we define as

$$\alpha = \omega_0\zeta \tag{188-3}$$

and

$$\omega_n = \omega_0\sqrt{1 - \zeta^2} \tag{188-4}$$

It will be noticed that ω_n, the natural frequency, is not quite the same as ω_0, the undamped natural frequency, but that

$$\omega_0^2 = \alpha^2 + \omega_n^2 \tag{188-5}$$

Substituting α and ω_n into equation 188-2 gives

$$\hat{\theta} = \frac{c}{\left[1 + \dfrac{s}{\alpha + j\omega_n}\right]\left[1 + \dfrac{s}{\alpha - j\omega_n}\right]} \tag{188-6}$$

(188)

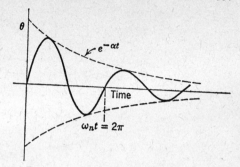

Figure 188a. Natural response of an oscillatory system (equation 188-7).

We now find θ, the inverse transform. Using pair 7 in Table A3-4 (with $\alpha + j\omega_n = 1/\tau_1$ and $\alpha - j\omega_n = 1/\tau_2$), we obtain

$$\theta = \frac{c\omega_0{}^2}{2j\omega_n} [e^{-(\alpha+j\omega_n)t} - e^{-(\alpha-j\omega_n)t}]$$

$$= \frac{c\omega_0{}^2}{\omega_n} e^{-\alpha t} \left(\frac{e^{j\omega_n t} - e^{-j\omega_n t}}{2j} \right)$$

$$= c \frac{\omega_0{}^2}{\omega_n} e^{-\alpha t} \sin \omega_n t \qquad (188\text{-}7)$$

This, a damped oscillation, is the natural response that corresponds to the quadratic transfer function of equation 186-2.

This response, shown in Figure 188a, is oscillatory because of the factor $\sin \omega_n t$. Being multiplied by $e^{-\alpha t}$, it is a damped oscillation; it dies out in time. The natural frequency ω_n gives the actual rate of oscillation, while ω_0 gives the rate of oscillation that would appear if damping were made negligibly small—that is, if α became zero.

It is interesting to compare the physical meanings of α and ζ, both of which have to do with damping. Equation 188-3 shows the relation: α is the attenuation *per second*, and ζ is the attenuation *per radian* of undamped natural frequency. If α is small the oscillation will last for many seconds. If ζ is small the oscillation will last for many cycles.

189. Critical Damping

Finally there remains to be considered, of the three cases listed in Section 186, the possibility of having a transfer function in which the denominator is a perfect square:

$$(189)$$

$$\frac{\hat{\theta}}{\hat{T}} = \frac{c}{(1 + s\tau)^2} \tag{189-1}$$

This can be considered to be a limiting case of equation 185-1 when $\tau_1 = \tau_2$, or, on the other hand, of equation 186-2, with $\zeta = 1$. It is the transitional form between the overdamped and oscillatory expressions that results when there is *critical* damping in the system.

Frequency response of a critically damped system is shown in Figure 189a. This response is the same as the frequency response of Figure 184b if the two break points coincide, and it is the same as Figure 187a when $\zeta = 1$.

The *natural response* of a critically damped system is found by applying an impulsive disturbance. Letting $T = \delta$ we have, in equation 189-1, $\hat{T} = 1$, and

$$\hat{\theta} = \frac{c}{(1 + s\tau)^2} \tag{189-2}$$

The corresponding time function is given in pair 8 of Table A3-4, and θ is found to be

$$\theta = \frac{c}{\tau^2} t\, e^{-t/\tau} \tag{189-3}$$

(Pair 8 can be derived by integrating equation 189-3 in the defining equation of Section A3-2.)

Figure 189b shows the form of the critically damped natural response. It cannot be physically distinguished from an overdamped

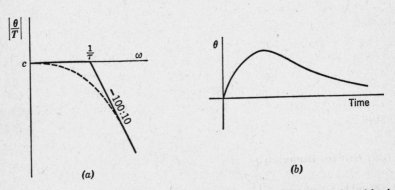

(a)   (b)

Figure 189. (a) Frequency response of a critically damped system; logarithmic scales (equation 189-1). (b) Natural response of a critically damped system (equation 189-3).

(189)

surge (Figure 185a) if the damping of the overdamped system is quite near the critical value. Neither can it be distinguished from an oscillatory response (Figure 188a) if the damping of the oscillatory system is quite near the critical value. The critically damped case is distinct mathematically, but not physically, from its neighbors.

190. Implications of Damping

Since critical damping is merely a transitional form, why need it be given any special attention? There are several answers to this, but perhaps the most interesting is its use in systems designed for quick response.

Visualize a mechanical system, as suggested by Figure 190a. This might represent a device as small and light as the moving element of a voltmeter, with coil and pointer held by a spiral spring, or it might equally well be some heavy industrial or military device, weighing tons, that is to be turned rapidly to a precise position. The question that must be answered by the designer is: How much damping is desired to give rapid response to an applied torque?

The undesirable extremes are evident. If there is too much damp-, ing, the device (the voltmeter, for example) moves too slowly when torque is applied. Such overdamped response is shown in Figure 190b, which is for the same device that produced Figure 185a. If there is too little damping (see Figure 188a), the device is oscillatory. It swings quickly but too far, and then swings back and forth like a pendulum. Some old voltmeters, now obsolete, were like this, and there was annoying delay before the instrument would stop swinging.

Figure 190c shows the response of a device that has a little less than critical damping. There is a small overshoot beyond the steady-state value of θ, indicating that the response is indeed oscillatory; and then the device returns to its steady position. Any modern ammeter or voltmeter illustrates this type of operation, and many quick-response control systems approximate this design.

Mathematically, the steady position, though approached, is never reached, so it cannot be said that a device reaches its steady position in a certain time. It can be stated, however, that the device arrives and remains within a given distance of its final position at a certain time. A voltmeter, for instance, arrives and remains within 1 per cent of its correct reading after a certain fraction of a second. Using this criterion, quickest response is obtained by providing slightly less than critical damping. (See Section 206 for further discussion.)

(190)

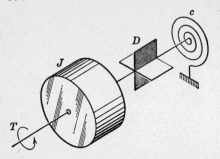

Figure 190a. A rotating device with inertia, damped, and restrained by a spiral spring.

There are, on the other hand, some devices and systems for which a minimum of damping is desirable. Electrical filter circuits of reactive types are built with the least possible dissipation. The ballistic galvanometer should ideally have no mechanical damping. Certain gyroscopic control devices are precise only if friction is absent. These lightly damped devices, if they have both inertia and a restoring force, are highly oscillatory. Their response is extreme, either great or small, at the natural resonant frequency. This is often expressed quantitatively by a parameter Q, which relates the stored energy of the oscillating system to the energy dissipated per cycle. (See Reference 7A, or another book on electrical engineering circuits.) There is clearly a relation between Q and ζ.

In a system of passive elements, there will inevitably be at least

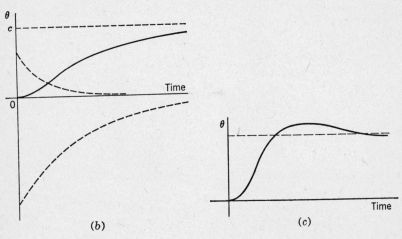

Figure 190. Response to an applied step function of (b) an overdamped device, and (c) an almost critically damped device.

(190)

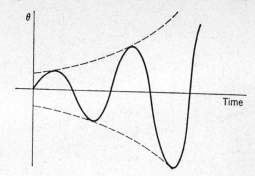

Figure 190d. An oscillation with increasing amplitude (α negative); typical of an unstable device.

a small amount of dissipation, and damping cannot be quite zero. In an active system, however, with power being fed in from some source, it is entirely possible for damping to be zero or even negative. If damping is negative, oscillations grow bigger with time as in Figure 190d, rather than smaller as in Figure 188a. A system in which the oscillations grow bigger is *unstable*.

Oscillations in an unstable system will increase until they result in destruction unless energy dissipation becomes equal to energy input. In the latter case, damping becomes zero.

An ordinary watch is an example of an all-*mechanical* oscillatory system. The balance wheel and hair spring comprise the system shown in Figure 190a. Damping is kept to a minimum, and energy is fed from the mainspring, through the escapement mechanism. Oscillation of the watch does not increase indefinitely but becomes steady when the amount of energy fed in from the mainspring is equaled by the rate of dissipation through friction.

In some rather unusual clocks a magnetic arrangement, replacing the escapement mechanism, gives a slight impulse each time the system oscillates. This arrangement exemplifies an *electromechanical* oscillating system. An all-*electrical* example is the oscillator consisting of inductance, capacitance, and an amplifying element (tube or transistor) that is common in radio circuits.

191. Phase Shift

Throughout this chapter we have been classifying transfer functions according to their natural responses and their frequency responses. With the latter we have given attention entirely to the relative amplitudes of output and input signals as a function of

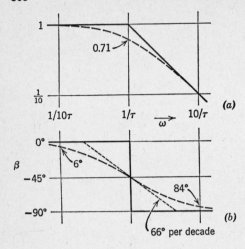

(a)

(b)

Figure 191. Frequency response diagram corresponding to $1/(1 + s\tau)$, showing (a) amplitude, and (b) phase angle.

frequency. In so doing we have neglected an almost equally important aspect of the frequency response, the relative phase of output and input signals. When we discuss the response of a device to a steadily applied alternating driving force we must take into account not only the absolute magnitude of the output signal but also its phase angle.

For a proportional response (Type I), the transfer function being a mere constant, there is no phase difference between output and input. The output voltage from a resistance network, for instance, is in phase with the input voltage.

For an integrating response (Type II) the transfer function contains a factor $1/s$. The steady a-c response therefore contains a factor $1/j\omega$ (equation 177-1, for instance). The plot of amplitude as a function of frequency (on logarithmic scales) is a straight line with a slope of -1, as in Figure 177b. To find the phase relation we write (using the letter V to represent any kind of a signal or disturbance and not necessarily a voltage)

$$\frac{V_2}{V_1} = \frac{1}{j\omega} \quad \text{or} \quad V_2 = \frac{V_1}{j\omega} = -j\frac{V_1}{\omega} \qquad (191\text{-}1)$$

The $-j$ indicates that V_2 is displaced -90 degrees from V_1; that is, the output signal lags 90 degrees behind the input signal. This merely says that the integral of a sinusoidal wave is another sinusoidal wave with a 90-degree lag. For instance, the integral of a cosine wave is a

(191)

sine wave, which is a wave of the same shape but lagging by 90 degrees.

For a differentiating response (also Type II) the transfer function contains a factor s (in the numerator). The plot of amplitude as a function of frequency is a straight line with a slope of $+1$, as in Figure 180b. The a-c transfer function is

$$\frac{V_2}{V_1} = j\omega \quad \text{from which} \quad V_2 = j\omega V_1 \tag{191-2}$$

The j indicates that the output signal leads the input signal by 90 degrees. This, likewise, is substantiated by noticing that the derivative of a sine function is a cosine function, having the same form but leading by 90 degrees.

A transfer function of the form $1/(1 + s\tau)$ (Type III, corresponding to an exponential time function) has the frequency response,

$$\frac{V_2}{V_1} = \frac{1}{1 + j\omega\tau} \tag{191-3}$$

This is the same as equation 181-2, and the amplitude of this response is shown in Figure 181c and again in Figure 191a.

Phase response can be computed from this equation also. By ordinary complex algebra it is found that the output signal lags relative to the input signal by an angle that is plotted as a dashed line in Figure 191b. The extremes of phase are of greatest interest to us. As frequency is reduced the phase shift, which we call β, approaches zero; as frequency is increased far above $1/\tau$, the phase shift approaches -90 degrees.

When the frequency is equal to $1/\tau$, the lag is 45 degrees; this is at the break point in the amplitude diagram. At frequencies 10 times, or $\frac{1}{10}$, the break frequency, the phase shift is within about 6 degrees of its asymptotic limit.

192. Approximation of Phase Shift

There is no simple approximation for phase shift as good as the asymptotic approximation of amplitude. Some authors prefer to use an *exact* computation of β. Some use three straight lines as an approximation; as shown in Figure 191b, two are horizontal, at $\beta = 0$ degrees and at $\beta = 90$ degrees, respectively, and the third is a slanting line through the central point $(1/\tau, -45°)$. This slanting line is given

$$\tag{192}$$

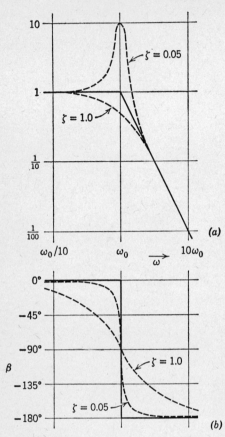

(a)

(b)

Figure 192. Frequency response corresponding to function of $1/[1 + 2\zeta(s/\omega_0) + (s/\omega_0)^2]$, showing (a) amplitude and (b) phase angle.

a slope of 66 degrees per decade, which is the slope of the true β curve at the central point. A very simple but extremely rough approximation is shown by heavy lines in Figure 191b, according to which the phase shift is 0 below the break frequency, and -90 degrees above the break frequency. This approximation gives the right general idea and may be refined as needed.

A factor of the form $(1 + s\tau)$ appearing in the *numerator* of a transfer function (also Type III) has the amplitude response of Figure 182a, which is like that of Figure 191a but inverted, showing increasing amplification instead of increasing attenuaton at hgh frequencies. Its phase response characteristic is like Figure 191b inverted, indicating phase lead rather than phase lag of the output

(192)

signal. It is roughly approximated by a phase *lead* of 90 degrees at frequencies above the break point.

A factor of the form of equation 186-2, corresponding to an oscillatory time function (Type IV), has the amplitude response shown in Figures 187a and 192a. Its phase response is shown in Figure 192b. It is most important to notice that the maximum lag, approached at high frequencies, is 180 degrees—twice as much as for a single-time-constant function. Exact phase response in the frequency region near ω_0 is dependent on the damping parameter ζ, as shown. As a very rough approximation, phase shift is -180 degrees at frequencies above ω_0, and 0 below.

As a better approximation, phase shift can be represented by three straight lines. These are horizontal lines at high and low frequencies, connected by a slanting line through the midpoint. The slope of this slanting line depends on the value of ζ, and the straight line will be tangent to the exact curve at the midpoint if it is given a negative slope of $132/\zeta$ degrees per decade.

These phase-shift diagrams are plotted with a logarithmic frequency scale, as are the amplitude diagrams, but with a linear angle scale. If a transfer function contains several of these elementary factors, the total phase shift is the *sum* of the phase shifts corresponding to the individual factors, so the phase-shift curves for the various factors can be added. Thus the manipulation is similar to that for the amplitude diagrams, which, plotted on logarithmic scales, are added to obtain the *products* of the amplitude functions.

A final summarizing statement will now be made, but with the warning that it must be used with caution. It applies to most systems, but not to all.* As given in the next paragraph, it is extremely rough, but it can be greatly improved by the approximation that uses a sloping straight line, and even more by freehand sketching on the phase-angle plot.

Through the frequency range in which the slope of the asymptotic amplitude diagram, plotted on logarithmic scales, is zero, the phase shift tends to approach zero. Where the slope is -1 (meaning that amplitude decreases by a factor of ten as frequency is increased by 10) the phase shift tends to approach -90 degrees. These and other ranges may be tabulated:

---

* The restriction is to stable minimum-phase systems. All stable ladder networks are included; some bridge networks are excluded. The Bode integral gives an exact relation between slope and phase shift to which the statement given here is an approximation.

(192)

Slope	Phase Shift Approaches
+1	+90 degrees
0	0
−1	−90
−2	−180
−3	−270

A number of examples of the use of this simple relation are found in the next chapters.

193. Summary

Factors of transfer functions are usefully classified according to (1) their forced sinusoidal responses as functions of frequency, and (2) their natural responses as functions of time.

A constant factor is of Type I, *proportional* response. Its presence in a transfer function does not alter the form of the response, but only the magnitude. It is independent of frequency. Phase shift is zero.

A factor $1/s$ is Type II. This factor corresponds to integration; hence the name, *integrating factor*. The natural response is a step function, the integral of the exciting δ function. Whatever the input signal, the output is its integral. Forced response is inversely proportional to frequency; on logarithmic scales this response plots as a straight line with a slope of -1. There is a 90-degree phase lag.

A factor s is also Type II. This factor corresponds to differentiation and is called a *differentiating factor*. Whatever the input signal, the output is its derivative. Forced response is directly proportional to frequency; there is a 90-degree phase lead.

Type III is a factor of the form $(1 + s\tau)$, a *linear factor*. The natural response corresponding to the appearance of this factor in the denominator is of the form $e^{-t/\tau}$. The forced response is a curve approximated, in a logarithmic plot, by two straight lines. One is a horizontal line, the other has a slope of -1, indicating a decrease of response of 10 in 10. The lines intersect at the break point or corner frequency at which $\omega = 1/\tau$. Phase shift approaches zero at low frequency, 90 degrees lag at frequencies well above the break point.

If the factor $(1 + s\tau)$ appears in the numerator, the sloping portion of the frequency response rises with a slope of $+1$, and phase shift approaches 90 degrees lead at high frequencies.

(193)

Type IV is a *quadratic factor*. The natural response corresponding to its appearance in the denominator, as $1/(1 + bs + as^2)$, is a damped sinusoidal oscillation. The forced response as a function of frequency is approximated by two asymptotes at very low and very high frequencies, but in the neighborhood of $\omega = \omega_0$ the approximation may not be close. A damping parameter ζ is an index of the response in this intermediate-frequency range. One of the asymptotic lines is horizontal, the other has a slope of -2 in a logarithmic plot; they intersect at the frequency at which $\omega = \omega_0$. Phase shift approaches zero at low frequency, -180 degrees at frequency well above ω_0.

Increase of *damping* changes overdamped response (Type III) to critically damped, and then to damped oscillatory response (Type IV). If damping becomes zero, sustained oscillations result. If damping is negative, corresponding to amplification in the system, oscillations increase without limit.

The following *parameters* are important and should be understood both mathematically and physically: τ, ω_0 and ζ, ω_n and α.

Transfer functions of systems are usually the product of several of the above factors. The frequency-response curve for the system is plotted by adding the curves corresponding to its factors. For amplitude of response, addition on logarithmic scales is equivalent to multiplication of the transfer functions. Angles are added on linear scales. This method is found useful in coming chapters, and is particularly valuable for the study of control systems.

PROBLEMS

13-1. Describe a mechanical device to fit equation 180-1, and tell how it behaves when the applied disturbance is (*a*) a ramp function, (*b*) a step function, and (*c*) an impulsive function. **(Sec. 180)**

13-2. Devise a system (electrical, mechanical, or electromechanical) to have a factor $(1 + s\tau)$ in the numerator of its transfer function, as in equation 182-3. **(Sec. 182)**

13-3. Show that the factor $(1 + s\tau)$ in equation 182-3 has the effect of increasing the response at higher frequencies. **(Sec. 182)**

13-4. If equation 184-1 is to apply to the device of Figure 190a, express τ_1 and τ_2 in terms of J, D, and c. **(Sec. 184)**

13-5. In Section 185 the natural response is found that corresponds to a given transfer function. Find, similarly, the response resulting from application of a unit step function disturbance. **(Sec. 185)**

13-6. Find an electrical system to which equation 186-2 applies if appropriate symbols are used. **(Sec. 186)**

13-7. It is stated that each curve of Figure 187a crosses the vertical axis at $1/(2\zeta)$. Prove that this is true, and illustrate it by the three curves of the diagram. **(Sec. 187)**

13-8. For the network in the figure, assume current output $i_2 = 0$. Compute V_2/V_1. Draw an asymptotic approximation of the frequency-response curve for V_2/V_1. **(Sec. 187)**

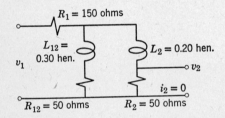

$R_1 = 150$ ohms

$L_{12} = 0.30$ hen.

$L_2 = 0.20$ hen.

v_1

v_2

$i_2 = 0$

$R_{12} = 50$ ohms $R_2 = 50$ ohms   **Problem 13-8**

13-9. A transfer function is given in equation 186-2. The response to an applied impulse function is determined in Section 188. Find its response to an applied unit step function. Sketch the result. **(Sec. 188)**

13-10. If damping of an electromechanical system is critical, compute the greatest error in amplitude of the asymptotic straight-line approximation of the frequency response as compared with the exact curve. **(Sec. 189)**

13-11. Derive, from equation 189-1, the asymptotes shown in Figure 189a. Compute the break point. Show that these asymptotes are the limit approached by those of an oscillatory case as damping is increased to the critical value, and by those of an overdamped case as damping is decreased. **(Sec. 189)**

13-12. Verify equation 189-3, deriving the pair in the table. **(Sec. 189)**

13-13. The function relating angle to torque in a critically damped system is given by equation 189-1. Find angle if the disturbing torque is a unit step function, and sketch the result. **(Sec. 189)**

13-14. (a) Estimate the value of ζ in Figure 188a. (b) Measure the overshoot in Figure 190c and compute ζ. **(Sec. 190)**

13-15. At the resonant frequency, Q of a series RLC circuit is $\omega_0 L/R$ (from any circuits book). Find ζ for such a circuit. Compare ζ with Q. **(Sec. 190)**

13-16. Find the relative times required for a device to arrive and remain within 10 per cent of its steady value if its damping is adjusted to make $\zeta = 0.6$; 1.0; 1.4. **(Sec. 190)**

13-17. Find the relative times required for a device to arrive and remain within 1 per cent of its steady value if its damping is adjusted to make $\zeta = 0.70$; 0.85; 1.00. **(Sec. 190)**

13-18. Figure 190c shows the response of a system to an applied step function. Sketch the response of the same system to an applied impulsive δ function. **(Sec. 190)**

13-19. A phonograph pickup transfer function is given in equation 149-6. Write this function as a Laplace transform. Draw the frequency-distribution diagram (Bode diagram) showing magnitude and phase angle. What is the nature of the output when a disturbance is applied? **(Sec. 192)**

13-20. Repeat Problem 13-19 for the speaker of Section 151. Tell what kind of terms will appear in the output time function when a disturbance is applied to the speaker, giving time constants or natural frequency. **(Sec. 192)**

13-21. If the speaker of Section 151 has the cone fastened so that it moves with compliance c meters/newton against elastic restraint, write the transfer function between output and input (Laplace form). Express numerator and denominator as polynominals, without factoring. Draw an asymptotic approximation of the frequency-distribution diagram, magnitude and angle, including the correct terms although without knowing numerical values. In drawing this diagram assume that the time constants are real and different. Finally, sketch without computation the frequency-distribution diagram, improving on the asymptotic approximation. **(Sec. 192)**

EXAMPLES OF DYNAMIC OPERATION
chapter 14

194. Idealization and Realization

Chapters 6 through 9 presented examples of electromechanical energy conversion. It was better, in those early chapters, to avoid the complications that would have been introduced by a changing speed or transient current, so most of the examples were there taken from the steady state. This meant that devices for carrying information, including control devices, could hardly be considered, since information is transmitted by change.

Now, however, we are prepared to discuss devices in dynamic operation, during change. Only a few of the many devices that are possible and practical can be described. They are chosen as being common and useful, and at the same time typical of a group. The first examples are proportional devices. Then integrating devices and others will be considered. The next chapter goes on to commutating devices, and the following chapter to induction devices.

The first step in analysis of any physical situation is *idealization*. Significant data are sorted out of the general hodgepodge of observed facts. Relatively small effects are disregarded. The essential relations that remain are simplified as much as possible.

For instance, we have in front of us a resistor. The fact that it is painted green we ignore. That the day is warm we neglect, at least as a first approximation, though we know it affects the behavior of the resistor to a small extent. We also neglect the inevitable inductance and distributed capacitance of the resistor. We are satisfied to think of the resistor as if it were a pure, constant resistance and nothing else. That is the idealization we decide upon for our present purpose; for another purpose we might prefer a different idealization.

This process of idealization, sometimes called abstraction, or the making of conceptual or mathematical models, is carried rather far in electromechanics, for the observed data are usually pretty complicated. Saturation of iron and non-linear friction are present in most devices, and when we linearize these camels why should we object to gnats? It is often necessary to be satisfied with approximations that involve possible errors of a good many per cent; examples are seen in later chapters.

Idealization provides us with a set of concepts or mathematical models that can be handled analytically. We then proceed with analysis of the ideal situation, working toward a solution of our problem. The solution is often a design, perhaps the design of a control system, or the design of some kind of device or network. But the design is still in the ideal world of mathematics. Its *realization* in the physical world of hardware must next be undertaken. This realization requires knowledge of practical devices and their characteristics, and in the next chapters we see what can, in fact, be done to realize our ideal designs.

195. Gears

Gears, of course, are not electromechanical; they are mechanical on both sides. They are really nothing more than a form of lever that can operate continually as one tooth succeeds another. At all frequencies a gear train is a proportional device, with output speed or angle directly proportional to input speed or angle.

The ratio of speeds in a gear train is its most important parameter. Also, at high frequency, the moment of inertia of the gear may be considerable. It is sometimes for this reason that the gears in control systems are undercut and made lighter than economy alone would require. Aluminum or even nylon gears can be used for lightness, although strength is never to be forgotten.

The moment of inertia of a gear is added to other moments of inertia on the shaft to which the gear is attached. It is often convenient to refer all moments of inertia to a common speed for easier computation. Thus in Figure 195a the effective moment of inertia at the speed of shaft No. 1 is

$$\text{Effective } J \text{ (at } \Omega_1) = J_1 + \left(\frac{\Omega_2}{\Omega_1}\right)^2 J_2 \tag{195-1}$$

(195)

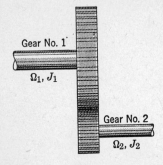

Gear No. 1

Ω_1, J_1

Gear No. 2

Ω_2, J_2

Figure 195a. The effective moment of inertia is proportional to the square of the shaft speeds.

The ratio of speeds is the inverse of the ratio of radii or of the number of teeth. Since the number of teeth can simply be counted it is often the easiest ratio to use for computation, and we may substitute the *number of teeth on gear 1/number of teeth on gear 2* for Ω_2/Ω_1. It will be noticed that when gears are of quite unequal size, the moment of inertia of the faster shaft is more important than that of the slower.

196. Resistance Networks and Transformers

Any network of resistors is a proportional device that is electrical on both sides. The output is a certain fraction of the input at every instant, and the output is always smaller. There is little else to say.

A transformer is also electrical on both sides. In a transformer the voltage can be either increased or decreased, and so can the current. However, if current goes up, voltage goes down, or vice versa, for the output power cannot be greater than the input power. Energy balance is significant in determining the output.

A transformer may be considered a proportional device through a wide band of transmitted frequencies. It fails, however, at both low and high frequencies.

At low frequency the magnetizing current becomes excessive compared to the load current (see Figure 109a). This may happen at 100 cycles per second or at 1 cycle per second, depending on the design of the transformer. Below this frequency the transfer function of the transformer falls off badly, as in the low-frequency range of Figure 109d.

In the high-frequency range, series inductance and distributed capacitance become important, as in Figures 109c and 110a. The result is shown in Figure 109d above 8 or 10 thousand cycles per second. Again, at high frequency, the transfer function falls far below that of the intermediate range.

The transformer is a proportional device in the useful range between two frequencies that may be called $1/\tau_1$ and $1/\tau_2$. Below $1/\tau_1$ the transfer function drops in a manner described by a factor of the form $s\tau_1/(1 + s\tau_1)$. Above $1/\tau_2$ the transfer function drops again, as does a factor of the form $1/(1 + s\tau_2)$. In the intermediate range, the transfer function is the constant $1/a$, where $a = N_1/N_2$. This suggests that a transfer function for the transformer at all frequencies might be

$$\frac{\vartheta_2}{\vartheta_1} = \frac{1}{a} \frac{s\tau_1}{(1 + s\tau_1)(1 + s\tau_2)} \qquad (196\text{-}1)$$

provided τ_2 is many times τ_1, and this function agrees with the experimental evidence.

In the useful intermediate range, when the output signal of the transformer is proportional to the input (Figure 109b), the effective impedance of the output circuit when referred to the input terminals is changed by the square of the turn ratio. That is, as in equation 111-4,

$$Z_{\text{in}} = Z_{\text{primary}} + \left(\frac{N_1}{N_2}\right)^2 Z_{\text{sec. and load}} \qquad (196\text{-}2)$$

where N_1 and N_2 are the number of turns in the primary and secondary windings of the transformer, respectively, and $Z_{\text{sec. and load}}$ is the impedance of the secondary circuit, including load impedance (see Figure 109b).

It is interesting to consider that in some ways a transformer is the electrical analog of gears, but that in other ways it is not.

Although neither gears, transformers, nor resistance networks are electromechanical elements they are useful auxiliaries in electromechanical systems. It should be noticed that for each of them the output energy is supplied entirely by the input signal. There is no additional source of energy as, in the next few examples, there will be.

197. Potentiometers

For proportional transmittance that is electromechanical, with electrical output proportional to mechanical input, the potentiometer circuit of Figure 197a can be used. With v_{in} constant v_{out} is determined by the position of the movable contact on the long, uniform resistor.

(197)

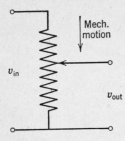

Figure 197a. A potentiometer with sliding contact gives electrical output proportional to mechanical input.

For convenience in mounting, the uniform resistor is usually not straight, but is wound about a toroidal form so that the mechanical motion is circular or helical. This, however, is a detail of minor importance. As implied by its name, the potentiometer gives a potential difference at the output terminals that is accurately proportional to position provided no output current is permitted. The device is used quite commonly with small output currents, but the assumption that the output current is zero is permissible if the output current is a sufficiently small fraction of the input current.

It is important to notice that a potentiometer supplied with constant voltage or constant current, and used to give an electrical output proportional to a mechanical input, is a unilateral device. That is, the mechanical motion of the sliding contact affects the output voltage, but voltage (or current) at the output terminals does not at all affect the mechanical position of the sliding contact. Also, the potentiometer does not convert mechanical energy into electrical energy, but the mechanical motion regulates the amount of energy from another source (from v_{in}) that is allowed to produce an output signal. The potentiometer is therefore not an electromechanical energy converter but a power modulator.

198. Strain Gauges

A resistance strain gauge is a means of changing a very small mechanical displacement into an electrical signal. It is named from its use in measuring such quantities as the slight stretch of a member of a bridge truss when the bridge is loaded, or the bending of a beam, or the elastic deformation of part of a machine. A fine wire, often of nichrome, is bonded in a zigzag pattern (Figure 198a) to a piece of paper or plastic material. A typical gauge might be as

(198)

large as a postage stamp, but some are much smaller. The gauge is used by bonding the paper and wire firmly to the member to be strained so that when strain occurs (vertically in Figure 198a) the nichrome wire is stretched, increasing its resistance.

An electric signal is most commonly derived by using the strain gauge in a bridge circuit, as in Figure 198b, one arm of which is the strain gauge. Greater output signal can be obtained by having two identical strain gauges in diagonally opposite arms of the bridge. To measure the bending of a beam, all four arms may be strain gauges, two being stretched as the other two relax. The input to the bridge is a voltage of constant magnitude; it is usually alternating rather than direct voltage to make amplification of the output signal easier. The bridge is balanced to give no output when strain is zero. The output is then proportional to strain for small strains.

A strain gauge can be used to measure any quantity that produces a small displacement. Pressure is an obvious example; a strain gauge can be attached to an elastic vessel that is deformed by the pressure.

Like a potentiometer, a strain gauge is unilateral, or practically so. Voltage applied to the output terminals will not cause the strain gauge to change in length (assuming that temperature changes are negligible). It is a power modulator, not an electromechanical energy converter; if there is no electrical power supply to a strain gauge, there is no electrical output from it.

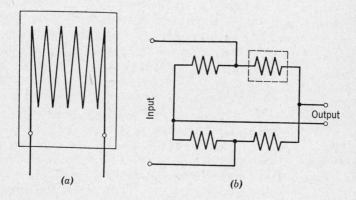

(a)   (b)

Figure 198. (a) A resistance strain gauge. (b) A bridge circuit containing a resistance strain gauge.

(198)

199. Telephone Transmitters

All ordinary telephones use carbon microphones that produce an electric signal from the variable pressure of sound waves in air. A "button" consists of a shallow carbon cup (Figure 199a) containing carbon granules, finer than common salt grains. A lid presses the granules more firmly into the cup when the diaphragm of the microphone presses against the lid. The electrical resistance of the device, from lid to cup, is dependent on the pressure; resistance is lower when pressure is increased. In use, a small direct current flows through the button. Applied voltage is constant. When the resistance of the path through the carbon granules is reduced by pressure the current increases. To a first approximation, the increase of current is proportional to the displacement resulting from pressure.

Thus the carbon-granule device is inherently a proportional device. It has upper and lower limits of useful frequency response, but these are dictated rather by the diaphragm and other associated parts of the device than by the carbon granules. There is appreciable non-linearity of response in a carbon-granule resistance unit, and it is rather unsuitable for quantitative measurement of displacement or pressure. On the other hand, a small amount of acoustical power can control a relatively large amount of electrical signal power. This makes the carbon microphone particularly suitable for telephone work. The microphone itself is an amplifier.

There are a number of types of carbon microphones. Some employ just one "button" of the type shown in Figure 199a. Others, more nearly linear, have two buttons. By using these buttons in a push-pull arrangement they are able to remove a rather large second-harmonic error in the response. With such refinements the carbon

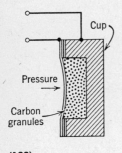

Figure 199a. In the "button" of a carbon microphone, carbon granules are pressed into a cup by motion of the diaphragm.

(199)

microphone is able to have a response of high quality, comparable with other types of microphones. However, a certain amount of noise always results from the presence of the carbon granules in the microphone, and this "carbon noise" cannot be eliminated.

The carbon-granule device is clearly a power modulator and not an electromechanical energy converter. Also, it is strictly unilateral, for a change of current through the device does not cause any mechanical motion; a carbon microphone will not serve as a speaker, as will magnetic types of microphones.

For instance, an office "intercom" system can be made with an element like the dynamic speaker of Figure 13a, and this element will serve as either microphone or speaker. As a transmitter, electromotive force is induced when the coil vibrates, in response to sound waves against the diaphragm, in the magnetic field. This signal is amplified and delivered to another identical unit, which thereupon vibrates and produces a sound wave that is hopefully a replica of the original wave. Clearly the electromechanical devices at each end of this system should be proportional. Actually, as we know from Section 151, there is a time constant above which the transmitter-speaker device is not proportional. Also, if compliance is taken into account, there is a lower limiting time constant as well. Experience with practical "intercom" systems seems to show that the frequency range of proportional response is often somewhat narrow.

Another special case is the dictating machine, which "listens" and "talks back" with the same element. This, again, must have a magnetic, crystal, or other bilateral element that can be used as both microphone and speaker.

The *sound-powered phones* of naval ships give another example. The damage of battle may put phones out of commission if they depend on energy from a battery, while there is a much better chance of leaving unharmed a phone line that draws its energy from sound waves on its own transmitter. Such a sound-powered phone, with a magnetic transmitter at each end (see Problem 14-5), is simpler because it is an energy converter. As long as the instruments are unharmed, and a pair of wires connects them, they will continue to work as well as ever—though their best operation can never have been very sensitive.

200. Piezoelectric Elements

Crystal or ceramic elements used for microphones, phonograph pickups, and similar purposes are electromechanical devices with response proportional to input. Certain crystalline materials, semiconductors, have the property of developing what is called *piezoelectric* electromotive force when they are subjected to mechanical stress. In the simplest possible configuration, voltage appears along one axis of a crystal when another axis is stretched or compressed. In practical devices, bending and torsion are used rather than simple compression, for they give much greater output.

Piezo electromotive force is proportional to strain. Hence, for applications at frequencies well below the natural resonant frequency, a piezoelectric element can properly be considered a proportional device.

It differs from other proportional devices that we have considered in being suitable for practical use at quite high frequencies. But when the frequency is high the mass and mechanical elasticity of the crystal material become significant. In so high a frequency range the piezoelectric device is oscillatory (Type IV of Section 173) rather than proportional (Type I). This property is used, in fact, to control radio frequencies with great precision.

The piezoelectric element is an energy converter, for part of the mechanical energy supplied to strain the crystal is changed into electrical energy. This implies that the crystal cannot be an amplifier, for conservation of energy prevents our getting out more than is put in. It also implies that the crystal is bilateral, and this is true, for the crystal can transmit energy in either direction. When carrying energy from the mechanical to the electrical side, electromotive force is produced by strain; and when converting electrical energy into mechanical energy, voltage applied between the electrodes of a piezoelectric element causes it to move mechanically. Alternating voltage applied to a piezoelectric crystal causes it to vibrate, and sound can be produced by such action (as in "sonar" *hydrophones* for instance).

A number of crystals show an appreciable piezoelectric effect. The effect is very marked in Rochelle salt. Quartz is a particularly interesting example because it is quite insensitive to temperature changes and is therefore conveniently used as a frequency standard. The normal quartz crystal has a hexagonal cross section, as in Figure 200a, and its ends are pointed. If it is cut at right angles to the *x*

(200)

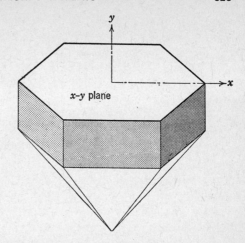

Figure 200a. The z axis of a quartz crystal, the optical axis, is perpendicular to the x-y plane.

and y axes of the figure, an electric field along the x axis (the electrical axis) produces an expansion or contraction of the crystal along the y axis (the mechanical axis). Conversely, a mechanical strain along the y axis results in an electromotive force on the x axis. Because of symmetry there are three electrical axes and three mechanical axes about the optical axis, the z axis of the crystal.

Voltage is usually applied to the crystal, after it is cut to a convenient shape, by sputtering metallic electrodes onto the proper surfaces.

When the crystal is acting as a frequency standard there is no mechanical load and it oscillates freely. The mechanical mass of the crystal and its mechanical elasticity act as a resonant circuit, damped by mechanical loss in the crystal. Since the loss is small the range of resonant frequency is extremely narrow (Q of a crystal may be several thousand to several hundred thousand). The resonant frequency and the nature of distortion in the crystal depend on the dimensions and on the manner in which the crystal is cut; practical values of frequency at resonance vary from a few tens of kilocycles to a few megacycles per second.

An equivalent circuit, an electrical analog of the crystal, is shown in Figure 200b. C_1 is the capacitance between electrodes, and the mechanical system is represented by the series branch of the equivalent circuit. C_1 is characteristically very much larger than C. Normally the low resistance of mechanical series resonance can be observed in the crystal, and then at a very slightly higher frequency

(200)

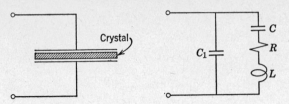

Figure 200b. The actual crystal circuit, and its electrical analog.

there occurs the exceedingly high resistance of parallel resonance between the electrical capacitance C_1 and the mechanical system. These are the useful points of operation of the crystal as a frequency standard.

It will be noticed that this is one of the few electromechanical energy conversion devices we have mentioned that does not work by magnetic action. Its electromotive force results from piezoelectric action in the crystal, not from electromagnetic induction. The small number of non-magnetic examples emphasizes the convenience and practicality of magnetic induction for converting energy.

201. An Integrating Circuit

A mass is an integrating element because its speed is the time integral of applied force. Inductance is an integrating element because its current is the time integral of applied voltage. The water level in a tank is the integral of the flow of water into the tank; voltage across a capacitance is the integral of the electric current into the capacitor.

In Section 176 a frictionless flywheel was shown to be an integrating element. If a system contains a heavy rotating element with negligible friction it will certainly have an integrating action (corresponding to a "free" s in the denominator of the transfer function). However, a flywheel is not usually a convenient device to use in a system for the purpose of integrating a signal. It is heavy, awkward, expensive, and difficult. A gyroscope gives integration with far less weight and size for the same characteristics, and is often used when a mechanical output is to be the integral of a mechanical input. (See Section 204.)

For electrical input and output, a resistance-capacitance circuit is convenient. Figure 201a shows such a circuit. As we shall see, the output voltage is very nearly the integral of the input voltage if R and C are both large.

We begin investigating this circuit by writing the output voltage in terms of the input voltage under steady-state a-c conditions. Assuming that no current is permitted at the output terminals, the input current is

$$I_1 = \frac{V_1}{R + 1/j\omega C} \qquad (201\text{-}1)$$

The output voltage, which is voltage across the capacitor, is

$$V_2 = \frac{I_1}{j\omega C} \qquad (201\text{-}2)$$

Combining these, we find the transfer function to be

$$\frac{V_2}{V_1} = \frac{1}{1 + j\omega RC} = \frac{1}{1 + j\omega\tau} \quad \text{if} \quad \tau = RC \qquad (201\text{-}3)$$

The transfer function as a Laplace transform is correspondingly

$$\frac{\hat{V}_2}{\hat{V}_1} = \frac{1}{1 + s\tau} \qquad (201\text{-}4)$$

Remembering Section 181, we see that this transfer function leads to an exponential time function with a time constant τ. The typical asymptotic approximation of its frequency response is shown in Figure 201b. But if $\omega\tau$ is very large compared with 1 we can write as an approximation of equation 201-4:

$$\frac{\hat{V}_2}{\hat{V}_1} \approx \frac{1}{s\tau} \qquad (201\text{-}5)$$

or

$$\left|\frac{V_2}{V_1}\right| \approx \frac{1}{\omega\tau} \qquad (201\text{-}6)$$

These are good approximations if $\omega\tau$ is much larger than 1, which means that ω is much larger than $1/\tau$; hence they are good for the part of Figure 201b that lies well to the right of the break point.

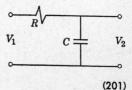

Figure 201a. An RC circuit used for integration.

(201)

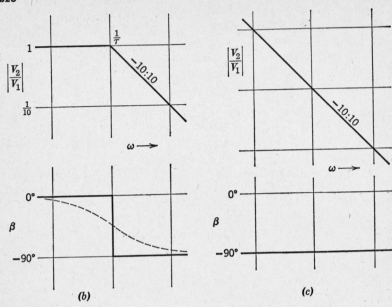

Figure 201. (*b*) The frequency response of the *RC* circuit of Figure 201*a*, and (*c*) the part of the frequency-response curve that applies at high frequency, for which $\omega \gg 1/\tau$.

This part of Figure 201*b* is shown in Figure 201*c*, which will be recognized (compare Figure 177*b*) as characteristic of integration.

There is another way of thinking of the integrating circuit. In Figure 201*a* it may be considered that the capacitor is an ideal integrator of current, and therefore the output voltage is exactly the integral of input current. But the requirement is for the output voltage to be the integral of input voltage, and to meet this requirement the input current must be proportional to input voltage. To have the input current proportional to input voltage, the input impedance must be mainly resistance. Hence the impedance of *R* must be much greater than the impedance of *C*, and for frequencies that are high enough for this condition to be met the device is an accurate integrator of input voltage.

It may be remarked that the transfer function of equation 201-5 is not $1/s$, which would be purely integration, but $1/s\tau$, which corresponds to integration *and* multiplication by $1/\tau$. That is, the output is scaled down by τ. Moreover, we know that τ must be large for the approximation to be serviceable. Hence it follows that the output,

(201)

to be accurately proportional to the integral of the input, must be small in magnitude. Both R and C must be large, and these tend to make the voltage across C small. In practice, the output voltage V_2 will probably need to be amplified. An amplifier with high input impedance is needed, for the integrating circuit should have no appreciable output current. If an amplifier is provided with amplification equal to τ at all the frequencies with which we are concerned (such an amplifier would be a proportional device), the overall transfer function from amplifier output to V_1 would then be $1/s$. In this way, pure integration is obtained.

Note that the resistance-capacitance circuit (like all passive electrical networks) is bilateral. The connection made at the output terminals affects what happens at the input terminals. An amplifier following the circuit must therefore have high input impedance so that it will draw negligible current. The amplifier, however, may be unilateral, and hence may supply a reasonable amount of output current without disturbing the integrating characteristic of the RC circuit.

202. A Differentiating Circuit Using Capacitance

It is remarkable that a resistance-capacitance circuit is also used as a convenient differentiating device. However, the arrangement of the parts, and their magnitudes, are quite different.

Figure 202a shows the circuit. Writing (as in the previous section) the steady-state current and voltages,

$$I_1 = \frac{V_1}{R + 1/j\omega C} \tag{202-1}$$

$$V_2 = RI_1 \tag{202-2}$$

the steady-state transfer function is found to be

$$\frac{V_2}{V_1} = \frac{j\omega RC}{1 + j\omega RC} = \frac{j\omega\tau}{1 + j\omega\tau} \quad \text{if} \quad \tau = RC \tag{202-3}$$

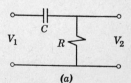

Figure 202a. An RC circuit used for differentiation.

(a)

(202)

This assumes negligible output current. As a Laplace transform,

$$\frac{\hat{V}_2}{\hat{V}_1} = \frac{s\tau}{1 + s\tau} \qquad (202\text{-}4)$$

From this transfer function we should expect an exponential response, as in Figure 148d. But if we limit our consideration to values of $\omega\tau$ much less than 1, we can write

$$\left|\frac{V_2}{V_1}\right| \approx \omega\tau \qquad (202\text{-}5)$$

and

$$\frac{\hat{V}_2}{\hat{V}_1} \approx s\tau \qquad (202\text{-}6)$$

These approximations, good if ω is much smaller than $1/\tau$, apply at frequencies well below the break point of Figure 202b. Figure 202c shows a section of the diagram below the break point, and this line (like Figure 180b) is characteristic of differentiation.

It is again unfortunate that the output signal must be small. Accurate differentiation requires a small value of τ, and hence small

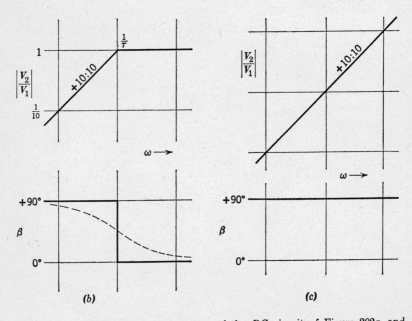

Figure 202. (b) The frequency response of the RC circuit of Figure 202a, and (c) the part of the frequency-response curve that applies at low frequency, for which $\omega \ll 1/\tau$.

(202)

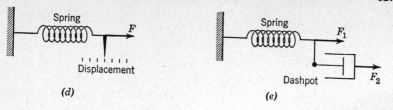

Figure 202. (d) The displacement of the pointer is proportional to force F, and (e) the dashpot makes F_2 approximately the derivative of F_1.

C and small R, both of which result in small voltage across the resistor and small output. Again an amplifier with high input impedance is needed, and for pure differentiation the amplification should equal $1/\tau$. The resistance-capacitance circuit is *bilateral*, but with a vacuum-tube amplifier the combination can be unilateral.

It may be considered in connection with Figure 202a that the capacitor alone is an ideal differentiating element. Current to C is the derivative of the voltage across C. The practical problem, then, is how to observe such a current. If the current could be measured without introducing resistance into the circuit, differentiation would be accurate for all frequencies. However, the easiest way to measure current is to insert a small resistance into the circuit and measure the voltage across it, using a vacuum-tube amplifier. When this is done, the practical requirement is to keep the voltage drop across the resistance from being more than a small part of the input voltage—a conclusion to which we had already come.

A mechanical analog of this differentiating circuit is a spring to which force is applied. In Figure 202d the displacement of the pointer is proportional to the force, so velocity of the pointer is proportional to the rate of change of force, the time derivative. Here the practical problem is to measure the velocity. This can be done with a dashpot as in Figure 202e, linking the pointer to the plunger and taking from the pot a force F_2 proportional to the pointer velocity, and hence to the derivative of the input force F_1. It must not be overlooked that the damping of the dashpot gives this mechanical system the same characteristics that are given to the circuit of Figure 202a by the resistance R, so Figure 202b applies as well to the spring-and-dashpot as to the capacitor-and-resistor system. Various other means of measuring velocity, some of them electromechanical, might be suggested to replace the dashpot. If the means of measurement introduces neither mass nor damping in significant amount, the characteristic of the device can quite accurately be differentiation.

(202)

203. A Differentiating Circuit Using Inductance

Section 148 treats an entirely different electrical differentiating circuit, one having large resistance and small inductance in series. Output voltage is proportional to the rate of change of current in the inductance, and current is proportional to input voltage if R is very large compared to ωL. However, it is impossible to provide a coil to have inductance without resistance, so the physical realization of this inductive differentiating circuit is not very satisfactory. (Note that v_2 in Figure 148c is proportional to the derivative of v_1 provided R is large and L is small.)

The flywheel of Figure 140a could be developed into an analog of this inductive differentiating circuit if damping were very great and the torque exerted by the shaft on the flywheel were used as the output signal, T being the input signal. However, if an all-mechanical differentiator is desired the most satisfactory device is often a gyroscope, for here again (as in integration) the lighter weight makes up for mechanical complication. The "rate gyro" is a usual means of obtaining differentiation, particularly in aircraft and missile control systems. A light high-speed gyro will give a large output torque in response to quite a small input velocity.

204. A Differentiating Gyroscope

Figure 204a shows a differentiating gyroscope. The wheel is kept turning at high speed, usually by electrical or pneumatic means; this gives a large spin to the wheel, a large angular velocity Ω_x to J_x. When there is motion of the device about the y axis the gyroscope tends to precess about the z axis. But the rate gyro is restrained from precessing about the z axis by springs shown in the figure (stiff springs are used, so the cosine of the angular precession is negligible), and the torque exerted by the springs, which is about the z axis, results in precession about the y axis.

Thus a velocity Ω_y about the y axis results in a small motion θ_z against the springs in the z axis. This angle θ_z can be measured; it is proportional to velocity about the y axis and is the output of the device. The gyroscope is a *differentiating* device because θ_z is a measure of Ω_y; that is, the output angle is proportional to the derivative of the input angle.

The transfer function between output angle θ_z and input angle θ_y

(204)

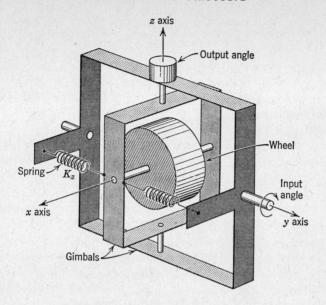

Figure 204a. A differentiating gyroscope.

is given by the following equation * in which each term is a torque about the z axis. (This is one of three equations when three-dimensional motion is considered.)

$$J_z s^2 \hat{\theta}_z + D_z s \hat{\theta}_z + K_z \hat{\theta}_z = J_x \Omega_x s \hat{\theta}_y \qquad (204\text{-}1)$$

Solving for output angle, we obtain

$$\hat{\theta}_z = \frac{J_x \Omega_x}{J_z s^2 + D_z s + K_z} s \hat{\theta}_y \qquad (204\text{-}2)$$

where θ_y and θ_z are angles of motion about the y and z axes, respectively
  Ω_x is angular velocity about the x axis, the spin
  J_x is moment of inertia about the x axis, the spin axis
  J_z is moment of inertia about the z axis
  D_z is the frictional coefficient about the z axis
  K_z is the spring constant relating spring torque to angular displacement of the spring (all measured in mks units and radians of angle)

Our interest lies in interpretation of this function.

---

* A more complete discussion is given by Gibson and Tuteur, Reference 83, in their Chapter 9.

The terms of equation 204-1 may be identified, with each term a torque about the z axis. The first term is the ordinary torque due to moment of inertia when there is acceleration about the z axis. The second term results from friction or damping about this axis. The third term is the torque about this axis exerted by the spring. These three terms are set equal to the z-axis torque that is provided by the gyroscope when there is motion about the y axis.

If D_z represented only the friction that is unavoidable in a good gyroscope it would be very small. If D_z were small the natural response of the gyroscope would be highly oscillatory, for the denominator of equation 204-2 would have complex roots (Type IV). To prevent oscillations (Type III), damping about the z axis is increased, perhaps by immersion in a viscous fluid; damping about the other axes, however, need not be increased.

With a stiff spring, K_z is large. If K_z is very large compared to other terms in the denominator, the other terms can be neglected and, approximately,

$$\hat{\theta}_z \approx \frac{J_x \Omega_x}{K_z} s \hat{\theta}_y \qquad (204\text{-}3)$$

This will be recognized as a purely differentiating relation. It is described by Figure 202c if the vertical scale of amplitude is correctly arranged.

Equation 204-3 gives normal operation of the rate gyro. It will be seen to have an upper frequency limit, for if s becomes too large in equation 204-2 the differentiating action is lost. It would be helpful to decrease J_z, but J_z cannot be decreased indefinitely without decreasing J_x. The useful frequency can also be increased by increasing K_z, the spring stiffness, and here the limit is set by the sensitivity of the output device. The means of measuring θ_z is probably a synchro pickoff, although it could be a potentiometer, and the delicacy with which it measures angle is a limit of operation of the whole device.

It is worth noticing that if the springs are removed, so $K_z = 0$, and the damping D_z is so small as to be negligible, the same gyroscope is an integrating device. In such a case equation 204-2 becomes approximately

$$\hat{\theta}_z \approx \frac{J_x \Omega_x}{J_z s} \hat{\theta}_y \qquad (204\text{-}4)$$

and this, because of the s in the denominator, is a purely integrating

(204)

action. That is, the output angle is then proportional to the integral of the input angle. This integral is of obvious importance in inertial navigation. For practical use, however, the details of operation have to be somewhat modified from Figure 204a.

205. Capacitor Microphone

There are a number of different types and styles of microphones for converting sound energy into electrical energy.* In general these have a diaphragm or crystal or ceramic surface that moves, however slightly, in response to pressure change. A stiffness or restoring force returns the moving part to a neutral position when there is no pressure, a restoring force that is large in pressure-type microphones and small in velocity-type microphones. An arrangement of cavities or passages for air absorbs energy and provides damping.

The essential parts of a capacitor microphone are shown in Figure 205a. The diaphragm moves in response to the pressure waves of impinging sound. The diaphragm is typically of thin aluminum, quite tightly stretched, so a considerable elastic force tends to restore it to its central position. The small natural damping provided by the diaphragm and the entrapped air is commonly increased by cutting small holes or slots in the back plate. Air in the space behind the diaphragm can leak into these small openings as the diaphragm moves, thereby dissipating energy.

Fairly high voltage is applied (from the source E) between the diaphragm and the back plate from which the diaphragm is insulated. Sound waves vibrate the diaphragm, changing the spacing and hence the capacitance between diaphragm and back plate.

If W is spacing, diaphragm to back plate (meters)
  W_0 is spacing when pressure is zero
  C is capacitance (farads)
  C_0 is capacitance when pressure is zero

then, since capacitance is inversely proportional to spacing,

$$\frac{W}{W_0} = \frac{C_0}{C} \qquad (205\text{-}1)$$

As the diaphragm vibrates, the terminal voltage V of the capacitance

---

* A carbon-grain microphone was described in Section 199.

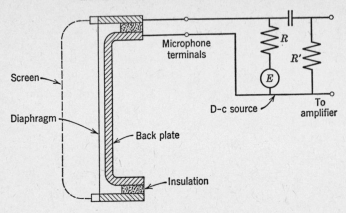

Figure 205a. A capacitor microphone; the diaphragm is stretched tightly.

varies, but is always equal to

$$V = \frac{q}{C} \tag{205-2}$$

The charge placed on the diaphragm in its neutral position by the source E is

$$q_0 = C_0 E \tag{205-3}$$

If R (and R') are such high resistances that the electric charge q on the diaphragm is substantially constant, so $q = q_0$ at all times, the terminal voltage is

$$V = \frac{C_0 E}{C} \tag{205-4}$$

Equation 205-1 is now introduced into this relation to give

$$V = E \frac{W}{W_0} \tag{205-5}$$

That is, the terminal voltage is proportional to the spacing.

If the motion of the diaphragm from its rest position is called w, so that $W = W_0 + w$, and the change of voltage is called v so that $V = E + v$, then the variation of voltage is related to the variation of position by

$$v = E \frac{w}{W_0} \tag{205-6}$$

Sound waves impinging on the diaphragm produce sinusoidal pressure, and w varies sinusoidally. The resulting voltage variation v is correspondingly sinusoidal, and this is the useful output of the microphone. This a-c component of voltage goes to an amplifier, as in-

(205)

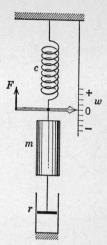

Figure 205b. An analog of a vibrating diaphragm.

dicated in Figure 205a, with an input resistance R' and a blocking capacitor to protect the amplifier from the large d-c component.

The amount of motion produced by a sound wave of known pressure must be determined. The diaphragm is a mechanical system of mass, elasticity, and damping, to which force is applied. It is complicated by having the mass distributed over all the diaphragm, and the force produced by a pressure on the whole surface, while the diaphragm does not move uniformly but vibrates most freely in the center and not at all at the edges. (Higher modes of vibration are usually ignored.) A mechanical vibrating system with lumped elements that is easier to visualize is shown in Figure 205b. The following equations apply (with good approximation at least) to either system.

Let us measure positive force and positive displacement in the same direction (both upward in Figure 205b). If c is the compliance of the spring, the force exerted against the spring is w/c. Force to overcome damping (indicated by a dashpot in Figure 205b) is equal to $r \, dw/dt$, where r is a coefficient of mechanical resistance and dw/dt is the velocity. Force exerted on the mass is the product of mass and acceleration, $m \, d^2w/dt^2$.

The applied force F must provide these three components,* so we write

$$F = \frac{w}{c} + r \frac{dw}{dt} + m \frac{d^2w}{dt^2} \qquad (205\text{-}7)$$

---

* It is classical to assume that the device of Figure 205b is so mounted that its motion is horizontal, with the weight supported on a frictionless plane.

This equation applies as a reasonable approximation to motion of the microphone diaphragm (as well as to the mass and spring) if m represents an effective mass and F an effective force, considering the whole diaphragm.†

To solve this equation of motion we transform it to

$$\hat{F} = \frac{\hat{w}}{c} + rs\hat{w} + ms^2\hat{w} = \left(\frac{1}{c} + rs + ms^2\right)\hat{w} \qquad (205\text{-}8)$$

Then the transfer function between displacement and force is

$$\frac{\hat{w}}{\hat{F}} = \frac{c}{1 + rcs + mcs^2} \qquad (205\text{-}9)$$

If R and R' are so large that the charge q on the diaphragm is substantially constant, we can use equation 205-6 to relate displacement to voltage, and obtain a transfer function for voltage:

$$\frac{\hat{v}}{\hat{F}} = \frac{Ec}{W_0} \frac{1}{1 + rcs + mcs^2} \qquad (205\text{-}10)$$

where v is the time-varying component of terminal voltage (volts)
      F is effective force of air pressure on the diaphragm (newtons)
      E is source electromotive force (volts)
      c is mechanical compliance (meters/newton)
     W_0 is spacing, diaphragm to back plate, at rest (meters)
      r is mechanical resistance (kilograms/sec)
     m is effective mass of the diaphragm (kilograms)

Finally, the interpretation of equation 205-10 is that the microphone will respond in an oscillatory manner if lightly damped, or with

---

It is more imaginative to suppose the device to be carried in a ballistic missile or space ship where gravitational force would not appear. In either case there is no gravitational force that we need consider. When there is a positive displacement the spring is compressed, and the force w/c must be exerted upon the spring to compress it.

In the microphone there is also an electrostatic force between the back plate and the diaphragm. This force should theoretically be included in equation 205-7, but since charge on the diaphragm is not varying this force is nearly constant and is omitted.

† Motion of a diaphragm is treated in many physics books on sound or mechanics. "The effective mass or effective area for this condition is ⅓ of the total mass or total area of the diaphragm." Olson, Reference 146, Chapter III.

(205)

a two-time-constant response if heavily damped. In fact, a good microphone has oscillatory response, but with enough damping to prevent any marked rise of response at resonant frequency. Referring to Figure 187a, ζ should be of the order of magnitude of 0.5.

This provides highly satisfactory "flat" response at all frequencies below $\omega = \omega_0$. It will be recalled that $\omega_0 = 1/\sqrt{mc}$. The corresponding resonant frequency ($= \omega_0/2\pi$) of a good capacitor microphone can be, in fact, higher than 10,000 cycles per second. An extremely thin aluminum alloy diaphragm is used, perhaps 0.001-inch thick, of high tensile strength, tightly stretched. Both m, the mass, and c, the compliance, are thereby made as low as possible. At frequencies higher than $\omega = \omega_0$ the response diminishes quite rapidly; as shown in Figure 187a, it diminishes to about $\frac{1}{100}$ with each decade of increasing frequency.

It is interesting to notice that the capacitor microphone is an electromechanical device that is not magnetic. Energy conversion takes place in the *electric* field. Reference is made in Chapter 1 to such devices, and this is an example.

206. Galvanometers and Other Instruments

Any voltmeter or ammeter, or a sensitive galvanometer, is an electromechanical energy converter in the sense that it receives electrical energy, which it converts to mechanical energy by moving. The mechanical system is inherently oscillatory, for it balances the kinetic energy of motion against the potential energy of a calibrating spring.

Damping is important in determining the response of the instrument. As mentioned in Section 190, the "best" damping for an instrument is slightly less than the critical value for an oscillatory system. A small amount of damping, nonlinear and irregular, comes from pivot friction. Voltmeters are further damped by light vanes that swing in the air. Ammeters and galvanometers have inherent electrical damping.

One of the classic problems of electromechanics is the damping of a galvanometer. This is an important practical problem when sensitive galvanometers are used; they move slowly at best and take many seconds or even minutes to come to rest. The galvanometer coil moving in a magnetic field is essentially the d'Arsonval movement described in Section 14. Electromotive force is induced in the coil as it swings. If the galvanometer is disconnected there is no electrical

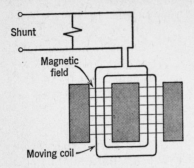

Figure 206a. A d'Arsonval movement is electrically damped as its coil turns in the magnetic field.

damping; if it is connected to a high-resistance circuit there is slight damping. It is desirable to have across the galvanometer terminals, as shown in Figure 206a, a shunt of such resistance that damping of the galvanometer oscillations is approximately critical (Section 190). Such a shunt will, of course, affect the sensitivity of the instrument and is not always possible, but an unshunted galvanometer is extremely tiresome.

The resistance needed to produce critical damping in a sensitive galvanometer, often called the CDRX (critical damping resistance, external), is usually stated by the maker. The CDRX may vary from 10 or 20 times the coil resistance for coils of many turns and high current sensitivity to once or twice the coil resistance if the coil resistance is small. The value may be anything from 10 to 10,000 ohms.

The best amount of damping to use is not exactly the CDRX, but depends on the accuracy of reading desired. (See Section 190.) For instance, an instrument will arrive and remain within 10 per cent of its final value in the quickest time if $\zeta = 0.6$. The time required is then 37 per cent of the undamped period of the instrument. If the need for accuracy is more rigorous, the best damping will be greater and the time will be longer: *

To get a reading within this fraction of final	Best value of ζ (Figure 187a)	Time in fraction of undamped period
10 per cent	0.6	0.37
1 per cent	0.83	0.67
0.1 per cent	0.91	1.0

*A full study of instruments and galvanometers is given by Harris in Reference 40. The values given here are taken from that book.

(206)

It will be recognized that the galvanometer as discussed here is merely a typical example of any device with a quadratic denominator in its frequency-response function. What is said of its deflection and its "best" damping might also be said of a servomechanism or an electric circuit or any other device with a similar mathematical description.

Ordinary d-c ammeters and voltmeters are often damped electrically by having the moving coil wound on a conducting frame of metal. The frame acts as a damper by carrying current as it moves in the magnetic field of the instrument. The dimensions and the material of the metal frame are designed to give the proper damping to the ammeters and voltmeters.

Damping slightly less than critical not only gives the quickest time of reading but also, and perhaps even more important, gives a slight overswing of the instrument. This overswing is easily seen and carries assurance that the instrument is turning freely in its bearings.

207. Summary

Idealization of an actual device retains its essential behavior while discarding extraneous matters. The mathematical model that results can be analyzed conveniently, or combined in designs. After design, ideal models must be realized, as nearly as possible, in practical devices. A number of practical devices and the essential factors to be retained in their mathematical models are considered in this chapter.

Gears are proportional devices, mechanical on both sides. The moment of inertia is important.

Resistance networks are proportional devices, electrical on both sides. They reduce energy.

Transformers are proportional through a limited frequency range. In some ways they are analogous to gears.

A *potentiometer* gives an electrical signal that is proportional to mechanical input. It is not an energy converter, for the source of output energy is not the mechanical motion.

A *strain gauge* indicates deflection by changing resistance. It is conveniently used in a bridge circuit.

Telephone transmitters convert mechanical signals in the form of sound waves to electrical signals on the telephone line. Ideally, they are proportional devices. The carbon microphone modulates energy;

dynamic and magnetic microphones convert energy. Crystal or ceramic microphones convert energy by piezoelectric action.

A *piezoelectric* element is an energy converter that is not magnetic. The principle is widely used in microphones, speakers, and pickups to give approximately proportional response (Type I). At high frequency the mass and elasticity of the crystal make response exceedingly oscillatory (Type IV) and therefore very frequency-selective. In this range, crystals are used as frequency standards.

Voltage across a capacitor is the integral of current. Current entering an *integrating circuit* is made approximately proportional to applied voltage. The output voltage of the circuit is then proportional to the integral of the input voltage.

Current to a capacitor is the derivative of voltage. Output voltage from a *differentiating circuit* is made approximately proportional to current. The output voltage of the circuit is then proportional to the derivative of the input voltage.

Voltage across an inductance is the derivative of current. A differentiating circuit could use this principle if an inductor could have negligible resistance.

Precessional torque of a *gyroscope* is proportional to the derivative of input angle. A differentiating device uses this principle by measuring the torque of precession of a gyroscope. Input is usually mechanical, output electrical.

With certain modifications a gyroscope can be an integrating device.

A *capacitor microphone* is usually oscillatory (Type IV) with rather highly damped oscillation. It is an example of energy conversion in the electric rather than the magnetic field.

Instruments, including ammeters, voltmeters, and galvanometers, are inherently oscillatory. "Best" damping is slightly less than critical. The same considerations apply to rapid response of many other inherently oscillatory (Type IV) devices.

Commutator devices are considered in the next chapter.

PROBLEMS

14-1. An airplane starter motor with moment of inertia J_m exerts torque T_m on a shaft to which is geared a flywheel with a moment of inertia J_f. The gear on the motor shaft has 200 teeth, that on the flywheel shaft has 20 teeth. (a) What is the angular acceleration of the motor, neglecting friction? (b) Replace the gear-connected flywheel by a flywheel on the motor shaft; find what its moment of inertia would have to be to allow the same angular acceleration of the motor with the same motor torque. **(Sec. 195)**

14-2. Figure 109d shows the transfer function of a transformer; the vertical scale is linear with zero at the bottom of the chart. Redraw this curve with a logarithmic vertical scale. Then draw the straight lines that are the asymptotic approximations of this curve. Find $1/\tau_1$ and $1/\tau_2$ (give both cycles/second and radians/second). Compare with the asymptotic approximation of equation 196-1; does this equation fit the curve reasonably well? **(Sec. 196)**

14-3. Section 196 says that "in some ways a transformer is the electric analog of gears." Discuss in what ways they are analogous, and in what ways not. **(Sec. 196)**

14-4. A cantilever beam is loaded at the free end by a force f, as suggested in the figure. Resistance strain gauges are used to measure the bending of the beam at the support. Four gauges are to be

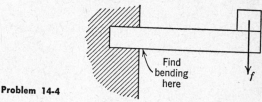

Problem 14-4

used in a Wheatstone bridge circuit to give high sensitivity. (a) Show where these gauges are to be fastened to the beam, and how they are to be connected together electrically to form a bridge circuit. What is to be connected to the input and output terminals? (b) If the resistance of each gauge changes by 1 part in 1,000, owing to strain, how much output can be expected (what fraction of input)?

(Sec. 198)

14-5. An ordinary telephone receiver is shown in the figure. Coils of wire are wound on a permanent magnet. Write an equation for magnetic force on the steel diaphragm (it acts the same as soft iron, magnetically) in terms of A, effective area of one pole; N, total turns in both coils; $\mathfrak{R}$, reluctance of the magnetic circuit; $\mathfrak{F}_0$, magnetomotive force of the permanent magnet; i, the coil current. $\mathfrak{R}$ and $\mathfrak{F}_0$ may be considered constant.

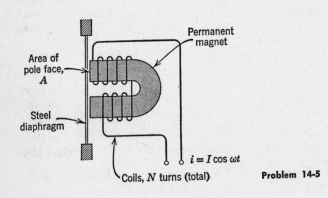

Problem 14-5

Show from your answer that the following results appear if $\mathfrak{F}_0$ is much greater than Ni: (a) The component of force proportional to i is greatly increased by the permanent magnetization. (b) The component of force proportional to i^2 is not increased by the permanent magnetization. (c) Explain these results and tell why they are desirable in a telephone receiver.

(Sec. 199)

14-6. In Figure 200b, assume that the resistance of R is 1 per cent of the reactance of C and of L when C and L are resonant. (a) Plot input admittance to the RLC branch as a function of frequency (in the neighborhood of resonance). (b) Let C_1 be $20C$, and plot input admittance to the parallel-series arrangement of C_1 and RLC as a function of frequency. In both parts, indicate points at which the input impedance is purely resistive. (*Hint.* Consider, first, the curves if $R = 0$, and then modify.)

(Sec. 200)

14-7. An integrating circuit is shown in Figure 201a. What range of frequencies can be used if, in amplitude, the output must be within 1 per cent of a true integral of the input? (Express in terms of R and C. Consider that the output may be amplified as much as needed, but must be proportional to the integral of input.)
(Sec. 201)

14-8. Voltage output from a circuit of L and R is to be the integral of voltage input (or very nearly so). The coil to be used has 3.6 henrys inductance and 0.54 ohm resistance. What is the lowest frequency at which the output will be within 10 per cent (in amplitude) of a true integral of input? What factor do you think would, in actual practice, set the upper limit of useful frequency?
(Sec. 201)

14-9. The output signal of a device is to be the integral of the input signal over a broad frequency range. The integrating elements are to be mechanical (rather than electrical), but a gyroscope is not to be used. Input and output signals are mechanical. Design such a device. (Sec. 201)

14-10. By what percentage (of amplitude) does a device of the type shown in Figure 201 fail to give true integration if the minimum value of ω is 10 times $1/\tau$? What is the error in angle of a sinusoidal frequency? (Sec. 201)

14-11. Relating to the next to last paragraph of Section 201, discuss the nature and amount of error in an integrating circuit if the output delivers appreciable load. (Sec. 201)

14-12. By what percentage (of amplitude) does a device of the type shown in Figure 202 fail to give true differentiation if the maximum frequency is one-fifth of $1/\tau$? What is the error in angle of a sinusoidal frequency? (Sec. 202)

14-13. In reference to Figure 202e it is said that "various other means of measuring velocity might be suggested." Devise two others, at least one of which introduces no appreciable damping or mass. (Sec. 202)

14-14. The last paragraph of Section 203 suggests a mechanical differentiating device employing a flywheel. Invent such a device, showing how an output signal proportional to the derivative of an input torque can be obtained. (Sec. 203)

14-15. If a gyroscope spins at 10,000 rpm, and the moment of inertia about the axis of spin is twice what it is about a central axis at right angles to the axis of spin, and the gyroscope follows equation 204-4 precisely, what is the output if the input is a step function of $\theta_y = 1$ degree? Qualitatively, how would the rate gyro of equation 204-3 respond to the same input? **(Sec. 204)**

14-16. Repeat Problem 14-15, assuming the input to be a ramp function of 1 degree per second. **(Sec. 204)**

14-17. A rate gyro is critically damped. Its speed of spin is 15,000 rpm. Its spring constant is not yet determined. What is its time constant? As a differentiating device, what is its transfer function $\hat{\theta}_z/\hat{\theta}_y$? **(Sec. 204)**

14-18. "A light high-speed gyro will give a large output torque in response to quite a small input velocity." Explain this statement in terms of equation 204-1. **(Sec. 204)**

14-19. Find ζ for the microphone of Section 205, giving it in terms of microphone constants and dimensions. **(Sec. 205)**

14-20. A footnote of Section 205 states that there is an electrostatic force between the back plate and the diaphragm. Revise equation 205-7 to include this electrostatic force. Find a transfer function such as equation 205-10 for the microphone including the electrostatic force; make any reasonable approximations. **(Sec. 205)**

14-21. A capacitor microphone is connected as in Figure 205a, except that the output is across R only, and R is so small a resistance that V (at the microphone terminals) is essentially constant. (a) Find the transfer function of output voltage over input force with this low value of R. (b) Note and discuss any assumption that you now make in computing the transfer function that was not made in Section 205. (c) Sketch and discuss the approximate frequency-response diagram. **(Sec. 205)**

14-22. In the capacitor microphone of Section 205, compliance is made to be great, so w/c is a negligibly small force at normal frequency. Other assumptions made in Section 205, including large R and R', remain. (a) Find the transfer function $\hat{v}/\hat{F}$. (b) What is the nature of the frequency response? (c) Consider whether, under these conditions, the electrostatic force between diaphragm and back plate becomes significant. **(Sec. 205)**

14-23. An ammeter is to arrive and remain within 3 per cent of its final reading as quickly as possible. What is the best value of ζ to use (in the sense of Section 206), and how long will it take to reach this value?

(Sec. 206)

14-24. If the damping of a servo system of Type IV is such that $\zeta = 0.79$, how long will it take (what fraction of an undamped period) for the device to arrive and remain within 1.0 per cent of its final position?

(Sec. 206)

14-25. Referring to Figure 206a, what resistance connected to the terminals of the galvanometer (total, input circuit in parallel with shunt) will make it critically damped? Give the answer in terms of the constants and dimensions of the galvanometer; L of the galvanometer coil may probably be neglected, but resistance of the coil may not. If the galvanometer is available, how can the essential parameters be found experimentally?

(Sec. 206)

FURTHER EXAMPLES: COMMUTATOR DEVICES

chapter 15

208. The Motor with Field Control

Microphones, speakers, relays, and potentiometers are among devices that provide for back-and-forth operation, with limited motion. Unlimited motion is often wanted, however, either for signals or for power, and an obvious means of attaining unlimited motion is by rotation.

One way to achieve rotation is by commutation. In Chapter 6 we considered commutator machines running at steady speed. Other interesting problems can now be considered that arise when commutator machines, transmitting control signals, operate at varying speed.

As with any other link in a system, the transfer function is a useful description. A commutator motor with field control was taken as an example in Chapter 12. A transfer function for this motor was found in equation 161-9, relating output shaft velocity to input voltage in the field circuit:

$$\frac{\hat{\Omega}}{\hat{V}_f} = \frac{k}{R_f D} \frac{1}{(1 + s\tau_m)(1 + s\tau_f)} \tag{208-1}$$

where

$$\tau_m = \frac{J}{D} \quad \text{and} \quad \tau_f = \frac{L_f}{R_f} \tag{208-2}$$

There is one electrical time constant (L_f and R_f are inductance and resistance of the field circuit) and one mechanical time constant (J and D are moment of inertia and rotational damping coefficient).

(208)

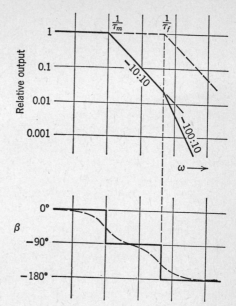

Figure 208a. Frequency response of a field-controlled motor. [By equation 208-1, the vertical scale of amplitude is $(R_f D/k)\,|\Omega/V_f|$.]

We have considered several of the implications of this transfer function, which has two linear factors in its denominator, and a curve of velocity was drawn in Figure 166a to show natural and forced responses to a step function of applied voltage. We can now continue this discussion by finding the frequency response; we shall find that it helps to visualize the behavior of the motor.

In Figure 208a the asymptotic approximation is shown as a function of frequency. One pair of asymptotes (corresponding to the first parentheses of equation 208-1) has its break point at $1/\tau_m$ and the other at $1/\tau_f$; the latter is shown in dashed lines. These two are then added to obtain the three-segment line that approximates the overall transfer function of equation 208-1. It is to be expected that τ_f is a shorter time constant than τ_m, and the diagram is drawn with this supposition.

The phase shift β is shown in the diagram also. As explained in Section 191, β approaches zero at very low frequency. There are two factors in the transfer function that provide 90 degrees of lag each, so at very high frequency β approaches −180 degrees. The two steps give a rough approximation, and the curved line (dashed) gives a better approximation, of phase shift through the intermediate region. The curved line is sketched freehand, guided by symmetry

(208)

at the break frequencies and by the general form pictured in Figure 191b.

The main lesson to be learned from Figure 208a is that the motor acts differently in three ranges of signal frequency. If the input voltage changes are sufficiently slow the motor acts as a proportional device, giving output speed proportional to applied field voltage. To be transmitted in true proportion, voltage changes cannot be faster than would be approximated by a signal frequency of $\omega = 1/\tau_m$.

Then there is an intermediate range of frequencies in which the motor acts as an integrating device. The output is more or less proportional to the integral of the applied signal. Amplitude of response is less at higher frequencies, and there is a 90-degree phase lag.

Finally, there is a high-frequency range, in which the field circuit acts as one integrating element and the mechanical system as another. In this range the overall action approximates double integration. Response falls off very rapidly, and there is a phase reversal between input and output.

209. The Motor with Armature Control

A motor can have *field* control, as in the foregoing example, with electrical signals sent into the field circuit of the machine while the armature carries constant current, and mechanical signals come out at the shaft. Alternatively, a motor can have *armature* control, with signals sent into the armature circuit while field current is constant. Field control provides greater amplification, greater mechanical power output for a given electrical input, because the field circuit usually has more turns than the armature circuit. However, armature control has electrical damping and so has faster response; armature control has the shorter time constant. Sometimes the advantage is with one, sometimes with the other. Both are used.

In Figure 209a the moment of inertia of the motor, shaft, and any attached load is J. We shall at first assume that there is no mechanical damping, no friction, no output of mechanical power, and that the motor does nothing but overcome the inertia of rotating parts. This is a good approximation for many control devices, and it will help to emphasize a point of great importance: although there is no friction, this device (like the galvanometer of Section 206) has inherent *electrical* damping.

The equation of motion of the motor is merely

(209)

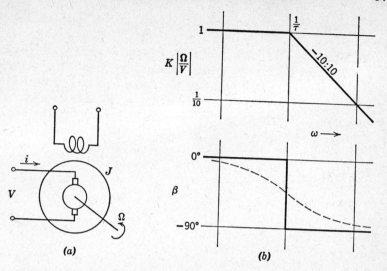

Figure 209a, b. An armature-controlled commutator motor has a time constant $\tau = JR/K^2$.

$$T = J\frac{d\Omega}{dt} \quad \text{(mechanical)} \tag{209-1}$$

(Compare equation 176-1.) T is torque applied magnetically to the motor armature (newton-meters) and Ω the angular velocity (radians/second).

The torque is proportional to armature current. As in equation 80-1,

$$T = \frac{N_s p\Phi}{\pi}i = Ki \quad \text{(electromechanical)} \tag{209-2}$$

where Φ, and hence K, are, for this type of operation, constants.

The amount of armature current is determined by the applied voltage V, the generated counterelectromotive force e, and the resistance R of the armature circuit. (Armature inductance is usually negligible.) As in equation 73-1,

$$i = \frac{V - e}{R} \quad \text{(electrical)} \tag{209-3}$$

By equation 79-2, the generated electromotive force is

$$e = \frac{p N_s \Phi}{\pi}\Omega = K\Omega \quad \text{(electromechanical)} \tag{209-4}$$

and K has the same value as in equation 209-2.

$$\tag{209}$$

We now substitute equation 209-4 into 3, 3 into 2, and 2 into 1, to obtain

$$J \frac{d\Omega}{dt} = K \frac{V - K\Omega}{R} \qquad (209\text{-}5)$$

This is transformed (Laplace transformation) to the algebraic equation

$$Js\hat{\Omega} = K \frac{\hat{V} - K\hat{\Omega}}{R} \qquad (209\text{-}6)$$

and solution for the transfer function relating output speed to input voltage gives

$$\frac{\hat{\Omega}}{\hat{V}} = \frac{1}{K} \frac{1}{1 + s\tau} \quad \text{where} \quad \tau = \frac{JR}{K^2} \qquad (209\text{-}7)$$

We recognize this as a transfer function involving one time constant, and we know the asymptotic approximation of its frequency response is as shown in Figure 209b.

The most interesting aspect of the transfer function is the nature of the time constant. Like other time constants, it involves an energy-storage parameter and a damping parameter. The energy-storage parameter is moment of inertia J, and this is a mechanical quantity. Damping R, on the other hand, is purely electrical and results from resistance in the armature circuit. (Mechanical friction, it will be remembered, is being neglected.) K is the electromechanical coupling between the two sides, between the J and the R. It is not uncommon to find the parameters of a time constant or a natural frequency on opposite sides of an electromechanical device, as they are here with mechanical energy storage and electrical damping.*

210. Electrical Damping

Suppose a motor, as in Figure 209a, but open-circuited at the armature terminals, were given a spin. It would continue to turn indefinitely, for friction is taken to be zero and there is no electrical energy output. No current flows, although electromotive force is generated.

---

*The numerical value of this *motor-inertia time constant*, for a control motor driven from a low-impedance source, typically is in the range between 0.01 and 0.1 second.

In most motors the electrical damping is very much larger than the mechanical friction; K^2/R is typically 100 times D. (Gibson and Tuteur, *Control System Components*, Reference 83.)

But if the armature terminals were short-circuited, the generated electromotive force would produce current through the resistance of the armature circuit; mechanical energy of rotation would be converted into electrical energy, and this would become heat in the resistance. This process results in a damping effect on motion that is entirely similar to the damping effect of friction (to what we have been calling linear or viscous friction). In many electromechanical devices, including an armature-controlled motor, for instance, and also some of the galvanometers of Section 206, electrical damping is far greater than the actual frictional damping. This is one reason why mechanical friction can often be assumed to be linear, although we know it is not truly so. Its effect is minor in any case.

Section 209 deals with the damping of a commutator motor with armature control. Note that a commutator motor with field control, as in Figure 161a, has no electrical damping. This assumes that armature current is truly held constant, as is assumed in deriving equation 161-8. If, however, the armature *voltage* were held constant the equation would become non-linear, and the best solution would then be by approximation. (See Section 4.20 of Reference 83.)

Electrical damping results whenever motion of a device induces electromotive force in a circuit in which current can flow, and this includes a large proportion of electromechanical devices. If resistance is high, damping is slight; if resistance is low, damping is most effective, for the I^2R loss of energy is rapid.

211. The Generator as a Tachometer

In Section 79 it is explained that a commutator generator can be used as a tachometer. (So can an a-c generator, if desired, but this is less common.) As a tachometer, the generator is a proportional device. The output voltage, equal to e of equation 79-2, is proportional to input speed, excitation being held constant.

212. The Generator as an Amplifier

In Section 81 it is suggested that a generator can be used as an amplifier. In this application the generator is driven by a constant-speed motor. An input signal is applied at the field-circuit terminals, and the output signal comes from the armature-circuit terminals.

The generator is an amplifier when operated in this way because

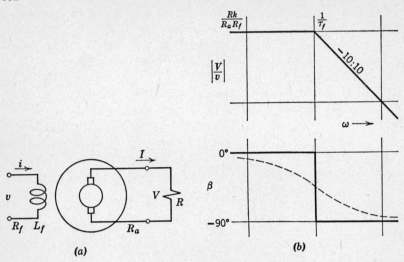

Figure 212a, b. A generator amplifier has a time constant $\tau_f = L_f/R_f$.

the output power may be many times as great as the input power.
A fraction of an ampere of field current may cause several amperes
to flow in the armature winding and the load circuit. The power
gain can be 10 or 20 in a small generator, and 100 or more in a large
machine. If positive feedback is used, so that a fraction of the
output power is added to the input signal, the gain may be made
very great. Output power is then limited only by saturation of the
magnetic circuit of the device. However, great amplification is
produced at the expense of a long time constant, so high gain is realized only with low-frequency input signals (see Section 214).

The simple generator, without feedback, has a transfer function
relating output current to input current that is merely a constant,
as in equation 81-3. We write the transfer function in terms of the
Laplace transforms:

$$\frac{\hat{I}}{\hat{i}} = \frac{k}{R_a} \qquad\qquad (212\text{-}1)$$

where, as in Figure 212a, I is armature current, i is field current, R_a
is the total resistance of the armature circuit including the load
resistance R (it is assumed that inductance of this circuit is negligible), and k is the constant of equation 81-2 having to do with speed,
number of conductors, number of poles, and so on.

(212)

This transfer function, being a constant, indicates that the generator is a proportional device in its relation of output current to input *current*. More commonly, however, the output voltage is to be related to the input *voltage*, and time delay is introduced by the inductance of the field circuit.

This relation is found by recognizing that the output voltage is $V = RI$, and by writing an equation for field current i in terms of the voltage in the field circuit v. The latter relation involves the resistance R_f and inductance L_f of the field circuit (including the field winding itself and any external resistance and inductance to which the voltage v is applied). Written as a differential equation,

$$v = R_f i + L_f \frac{di}{dt} \tag{212-2}$$

Transformed,

$$\hat{v} = R_f \hat{\imath} + L_f s \hat{\imath} = (R_f + L_f s)\hat{\imath} \tag{212-3}$$

Combining expressions for V and v, and then introducing equation 212-1, we obtain the desired transfer function

$$\frac{\hat{V}}{\hat{v}} = \frac{R\hat{I}}{(R_f + L_f s)\hat{\imath}} = \frac{R}{(R_f + L_f s)} \frac{k}{R_a}$$

$$= \frac{Rk}{R_a R_f} \frac{1}{1 + s\tau_f} \quad \text{where} \quad \tau_f = \frac{L_f}{R_f} \tag{212-4}$$

We see that this transfer function is approximated by the constant $Rk/R_a R_f$ at frequencies well below that for which $\omega = 1/\tau_f = R_f/L_f$. This is shown in Figure 212b. At higher frequencies the response will drop off to approximately $\frac{1}{10}$ in each decade. The phase shift β will be negligible at low frequencies, and above the break frequency, $1/\tau_f$, it will approach -90 degrees.

The practical interpretation is that the generator can be used as an amplifier in a system that will not be called upon to handle signals with important frequency components for which ω is greater than one-half, or one-fourth, perhaps, of $1/\tau_f$. This may, for a small generator, be a frequency of the order of a few cycles per second.

213. Two Generators Cascaded

If an electromechanical amplifier is needed, and the power gain given by a single generator is not enough, two possibilities should be considered. Feedback may be used but, as will be seen, this results

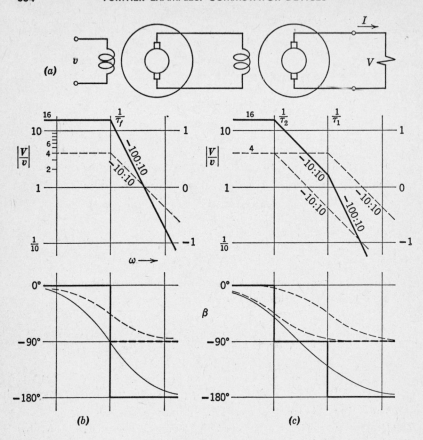

Figure 213. (a) Two generators cascaded, and their frequency-response diagrams (b) with equal time constants and (c) with different time constant.

in a slower time constant. Alternatively, a two-stage amplifier can be used. The output from the armature of one generator is fed into the field circuit of another (Figure 213a), and the output of the second generator is used as the amplified signal.

This connection of two generators in cascade is a practical solution of many problems. The power gain is nearly the square of the single-stage gain (in decibels, twice as much). If the two machines have the same field-circuit time constant, the time constant of the cascaded pair is the same also. Figure 213b shows, as a dash line, the approximate frequency response of a generator with a voltage gain of 4. When two generators are cascaded, two such dash lines

(213)

are added and the solid line is obtained as the approximate response of the two machines.* The approximate voltage gain in two stages is the product of the gains in the two stages individually; at very low frequency it is (in this example) about 16.

If the machines have different time constants, two asymptotic characteristics with different break points are added. In Figure 213c the two generators have the same voltage gain, but the second machine has a time constant 10 times that of the first. The total characteristic, then, has two break points: the solid line is the sum of the two dash lines.

This same relation can be seen, perhaps more fully, from the transfer function. In Figure 213a, call the midpoint voltage, between the first and second machines, v_m. The time constants of the first and second machines are τ_1 and τ_2 respectively, and the respective gains are G_1 and G_2. Then the transfer function relating the output voltage of the device to the midpoint voltage is

$$\frac{\hat{V}}{\hat{v}_m} = G_2 \frac{1}{1 + s\tau_2} \qquad (213\text{-}1)$$

and the transfer function relating the midpoint voltage to the input voltage is

$$\frac{\hat{v}_m}{\hat{v}} = G_1 \frac{1}{1 + s\tau_1} \qquad (213\text{-}2)$$

Combining these, the overall transfer function is

$$\frac{\hat{V}}{\hat{v}} = G_1 G_2 \frac{1}{(1 + s\tau_1)(1 + s\tau_2)} \qquad (213\text{-}3)$$

where τ_1, τ_2, G_1, and G_2 can be evaluated from equations 212-4. Equation 213-3 describes either Figure 213b or c and also allows different gains in the two machines.

214. Rototrol or Regulex

The use of two cascaded commutator generators as a two-stage amplifier was discussed in Section 213. When the first stage is pro-

---

* Adding the two response curves means adding linear distances as measured on the right-hand scales of Figures 213b or c. Linear distances are proportional to the logarithms of the voltage ratio $|V/v|$, and hence their addition is equivalent to multiplying voltage ratios (as read on the left-hand scale).

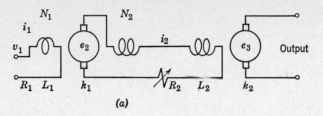

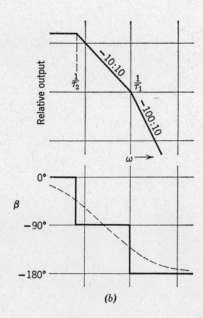

Figure 214a, b. In its useful range, between $1/\tau_1$ and $1/\tau_2$, the Rototrol is an integrating device. (See equation 214-7 for the vertical scale of amplitude.)

vided with feedback the combination has the essential properties of devices known by the trade names of Rototrol or Regulex. Steady d-c operation is described in Section 82. We are now prepared to extend the discussion to include alternating or other time-varying input.

Figure 82a is repeated, as Figure 214a. N_1 and N_2 are the numbers of turns in the control-field and series-field windings respectively.* R_2 is the total resistance and L_2 is the total inductance of

---

*In Section 82, N_2/N_1 is called β. In this chapter the symbol β is used for phase angle, which is an entirely unrelated meaning.

(214)

the circuit containing the armature and series windings of the first machine and the field winding of the second machine.

Generated electromotive forces of the two machines are from equations 82-2 and 81-2, respectively:

$$e_2 = k_1(i_1 + \frac{N_2}{N_1} i_2) \tag{214-1}$$

$$e_3 = k_2 i_2 \tag{214-2}$$

In the field circuit of the first machine

$$v_1 = R_1 i_1 + L_1 \frac{di_1}{dt} \tag{214-3}$$

In the circuit containing the armature winding of the first machine and the field winding of the second,

$$e_2 = R_2 i_2 + L_2 \frac{di_2}{dt} \tag{214-4}$$

These four equations are transformed by Laplace methods. The variables $\hat{i}_1$, $\hat{i}_2$, and $\hat{e}_2$ are then eliminated, leaving one equation that relates the output electromotive force $\hat{e}_3$ to the input voltage $\hat{v}_1$:

$$\frac{\hat{e}_3}{\hat{v}_1} = \frac{k_1 k_2}{R_1} \frac{1}{[1 + s\tau_1][R_2 - k_1(N_2/N_1) + L_2 s]} \tag{214-5}$$

where $\tau_1 = L_1/R_1$.

Note that R_2 is adjustable. It will be recalled from Section 82 that making R_2 equal $k_1(N_2/N_1)$ gives a critical condition. This is clear from equation 214-5 also. If R_2 is greater than the critical value the Rototrol is a two-time-constant device (Figure 214b), one of the time constants being τ_1 and the other being

$$\tau_2 = \frac{L_2}{R_2 - k_1(N_2/N_1)} \tag{214-6}$$

Voltage amplification at frequencies well below the lower break point (below $\omega = 1/\tau_2$) is approximately

$$\frac{\hat{e}_3}{\hat{v}_1} \approx \frac{k_1 k_2}{R_1[R_2 - k_1(N_2/N_1)]} \tag{214-7}$$

As R_2 approaches the critical value, this zero-frequency amplification becomes very great. The time constant τ_2 also becomes very great.

(214)

At the critical value the transfer function of equation 214-5 becomes

$$\frac{\hat{e}_3}{\hat{v}_1} = \frac{k_1 k_2}{R_1 L_2} \frac{1}{(1 + s\tau_1)s} \tag{214-8}$$

At this setting the Rototrol is a one-time-constant-and-integration device, the lower break point having vanished. A free s is left in the denominator, indicating integration. As mentioned in Secton 82, the steady d-c response, the response to zero frequency, is theoretically infinite (this neglects saturation). The response to any finite frequency, however, is finite.

In actual use the critical value of resistance is approached more or less closely, and the useful range of frequencies lies between $\omega = 1/\tau_1$ and $1/\tau_2$. The latter is very low, approaching zero. Thus through the useful range, as shown by the middle section of Figure 214b, the Rototrol (or Regulex) is an amplifying and integrating device. Both high amplification and a high value of τ_2 result if R_2 approaches the critical value. Hence a Rototrol cannot have both a proportional response and high amplification.

215. Amplidyne

A two-stage rotating amplifier with the trade name Amplidyne (a related term *metadyne* is also used, as in Reference 215) was described in Section 83. This device is relatively light and compact because, to put it in somewhat oversimplified terms, the same iron and copper are used twice, once in the direct axis and once in the quadrature axis, to provide the two stages of amplification. Correspondingly, there are unavoidable interrelations within the machine that make for complicated behavior and inflexibility of operation. A change of one element may affect several relations.

Figure 215a (similar to Figure 83c) represents the Amplidyne diagrammatically. Current i_f in the control-field winding causes e_q to be generated in the quadrature winding. Because this winding is

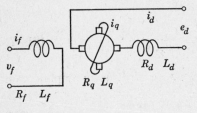

Figure 215a. The Amplidyne is a two-stage amplifier in one frame; its frequency response is similar to Figure 214b.

(215)

short-circuited, i_q results. Assuming linearity, and assuming that the compensating winding prevents any armature reaction from i_d, we write (using transforms from the outset)

$$\hat{e}_q = k_q \hat{\imath}_f \qquad (215\text{-}1)$$

Current i_q in the short-circuited quadrature circuit causes e_d to be generated in the direct-axis circuit of the armature. This is the output voltage if the Amplidyne is unloaded or if R_d and L_d are negligible. Again assuming linearity, we have

$$\hat{e}_d = k_d \hat{\imath}_q \qquad (215\text{-}2)$$

Current in the control circuit is related to applied voltage by the familiar equation based on Kirchhoff's law:

$$\hat{v}_f = (R_f + sL_f)\hat{\imath}_f \qquad (215\text{-}3)$$

and current in the quadrature circuit is related to e_q:

$$\hat{e}_q = (R_q + sL_q)\hat{\imath}_q \qquad (215\text{-}4)$$

Combining these relations gives

$$\hat{e}_d = k_d \frac{\hat{e}_q}{R_q + sL_q} = k_d \frac{k_q \hat{\imath}_f}{R_q + sL_q}$$

$$= k_d \frac{k_q \hat{v}_f}{(R_q + sL_q)(R_f + sL_f)} \qquad (215\text{-}5)$$

whence we find the transfer function

$$\frac{\hat{e}_d}{\hat{v}_f} = \frac{k_d k_q}{R_q R_f} \frac{1}{(1 + s\tau_q)(1 + s\tau_f)} \qquad (215\text{-}6)$$

where

$$\tau_q = \frac{L_q}{R_q} \qquad \tau_f = \frac{L_f}{R_f} \qquad (215\text{-}7)$$

This is a highly simplified result that does not take into account either non-linearities, inaccuracies of adjustment, or the refinements that can be introduced by using additional windings and circuits.

Equation 215-6 implies that the Amplidyne is a two-time-constant device. Its similarity to equation 214-5 for the Rototrol is obvious.

Amplification can be increased, the time constant τ_q being effectively increased also, by means of positive feedback. Current in the quadrature circuit can be used to strengthen the control field in the direct axis (the similarity to a compound-wound generator is evi-

(215)

dent). If a feedback winding of N_2 turns carries current i_q, arranged to strengthen the field of current i_f in a field winding of N_1 turns, equation 215-1 becomes

$$\hat{e}_q = k_q \left(\hat{i}_f + \frac{N_2}{N_1} \hat{i}_q \right) \tag{215-8}$$

From equation 215-4,

$$\hat{e}_q = (R_q + sL_q)\hat{i}_q \tag{215-9}$$

Equating these, we obtain

$$\hat{i}_q \left(R_q + sL_q - \frac{N_2}{N_1} \right) = k_q \hat{i}_f \tag{215-10}$$

Then if

$$R_q = \frac{N_2}{N_1} \tag{215-11}$$

we find that

$$\hat{i}_q = \frac{k_q \hat{i}_f}{sL_q} \tag{215-12}$$

Now from equation 215-2,

$$\hat{e}_d = k_d \hat{i}_q = k_d k_q \frac{\hat{i}_f}{sL_q} \tag{215-13}$$

Finally, with $\hat{i}_f$ from equation 215-3,

$$\hat{e}_d = \frac{k_d k_q \hat{v}_f}{sL_q(R_f + sL_f)} \tag{215-14}$$

or

$$\frac{\hat{e}_d}{\hat{v}_f} = \frac{k_d k_q}{R_f L_q} \frac{1}{s(1 + s\tau_f)} \tag{215-15}$$

Thus the feedback of equation 215-11 gives the Amplidyne a transfer function very like equation 214-8 for the critically adjusted Rototrol. It operates as a one-time-constant-and-integration device, with the same inherent advantages and disadvantages. Figure 214*b* illustrates this type of operation.

216. Summary

This chapter, a continuation of the previous chapter on examples, considers commutator devices.

The *motor* is discussed, first with field control and then with armature control. The motor with field control has greater amplification but a longer time constant. The motor with field control has no feedback from output to input. With armature control, on the other hand, the output speed affects the input current through the counter electromotive force of the machine.

The armature-controlled motor gives an example of *electrical damping* of energy that is stored in mechanical motion. Another example is found in the galvanometer, and another in a speaker circuit.

The *generator* is a proportional device when used as a tachometer. It is also used as an electromechanical amplifier. As an amplifier its transfer function has a linear factor in the denominator, corresponding to low response at high frequency.

If a single stage of amplification is inadequate, two such amplifiers can be *cascaded*.

A variation is to use feedback in the first amplifier (essentially *Rototrol* or *Regulex*). This variation increases amplification but also increases one time constant so much that the machine is no longer proportional but becomes an integrating device, even at low frequencies.

Another variation uses two magnetic fields in the same machine (essentially the *Amplidyne*). Again feedback increases both the amplification and one time constant of the device.

The next chapter considers dynamic operation of induction motors.

P R O B L E M S

15-1. Equation 209-7 is determined with mechanical friction neglected. Revise this equation to include mechanical friction and show that the time constant is then $J/(D + K^2/R)$. **(Sec. 209)**

15-2. In a commutator motor with field control the armature voltage, rather than the armature current, is held constant. Write the differential equation of torque of such a machine. (Neglect armature inductance.) Can Laplace transformation be used? Can a transfer function be found? Why, or why not? Discuss the possibility of solving the differential equation (but do not solve it). **(Sec. 210)**

15-3. A tachometer is a 2-pole permanent-magnet d-c generator with a d-c voltmeter attached. The generator has 1,000 conductors (coil sides) connected in 2 parallel circuits between brushes. Generator resistance, brush to brush, is 500 ohms; resistance of the voltmeter is 2,500 ohms. Air-gap flux is $2.88 \cdot 10^{-4}$ weber per pole. What speed in revolutions per minute will be indicated by each volt on the voltmeter?   **(Sec. 211)**

15-4. The generator and motor in the figure are identical machines, having the same electrical characteristics including the same armature inductance and resistance. On open circuit, each generates 1 volt at 1 radian/sec for a field current of 1 amp. (*a*) Derive a transfer function from i_{f1} to Ω_2. (*b*) Let i_{f1} be a unit step. Find Ω_2. Neglect R_a and L_a for this calculation.   **(Sec. 212)**

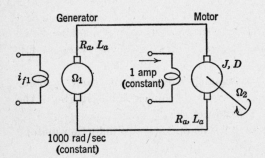

Problem 15-4

15-5. In equation 212-1 find k in terms of physical quantities that can be determined from the generator. Check the units of this equation to show that the two sides agree.   **(Sec. 212)**

15-6. The speed of the generator in the figure is constant at a value that makes the open-circuit voltage = 100 volts. The main field

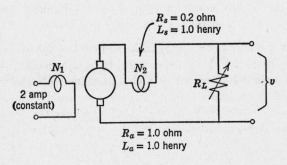

Problem 15-6

has 50 times as many turns as the series field; that is, $N_1 = 50N_2$.
(a) With the series field disconnected (with R_L connected directly
to the brushes), find the steady-state value of v as a function of R_L.
(b) With the compound generator connected as shown in the figure,
find the steady-state value of v as a function of R_L. Draw sketches
showing this voltage as a function of load conductance, $(1/R_L)$ from
0 to 1 mho, with and without the series field. (c) Assume that the
compound generator is unloaded. At $t = 0$, a load of 1 ohm is suddenly connected, as in the figure. Find the voltage across the load
as a function of time. **(Sec. 212)**

15-7. Derive equation 214-8 for the Rototrol. **(Sec. 214)**

15-8. A commutator generator is driven at constant speed to
operate as an electromechanical amplifier. Field current i is the in-

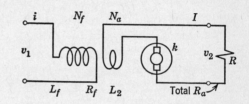

Problem 15-8

put signal; armature current I is the output. Armature current is fed
back into a coil on the field poles, as shown in the diagram, to
strengthen the field. (a) Under what conditions will there be instability, with I continuing to increase though i is reduced to zero?
(b) As a d-c amplifier, find the time constant relating output I to
applied voltage v_1. Discuss the delay of a signal. (c) As an a-c
amplifier, show response as a function of frequency (approximately).
In each part of this problem, assume all relations to be linear. Neglect inductance in the armature circuit, including the series field coil
and the load. **(Sec. 214)**

15-9. Repeat (b) and (c) of Problem 15-8 if inductance L_2 of the
series field coil is *not* negligible. (Continue to neglect mutual inductance between the two field coils.) **(Sec. 214)**

INDUCTION DEVICES
chapter 16

217. Types of Control Motors

There are a number of uses for induction motors in control systems, and the more interesting are the more unusual. A three-phase motor that turns most of the time at a little less than synchronous speed may be similar in all but size to the larger motors used for other steady-state purposes, and it introduces no new ideas. For special purposes, however, the induction motor is adapted in a number of rather surprising ways.

Small control motors, rated in watts, may be constructed with squirrel-cage rotors, as are larger motors, but there are also two other designs. The *solid-iron-rotor* type has a cylindrical rotor of iron with reasonably high electrical conductivity. The iron is not laminated, and circulating currents in the iron itself, instead of currents in a copper squirrel cage, produce the torque of the motor. The

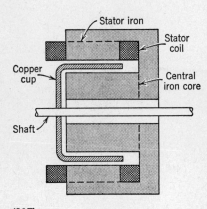

Figure 217a. A drag-cup motor. (Bearings, etc., are not shown.)

(217)

torque is somewhat less than it would be in a similar motor having a copper squirrel cage.

The *drag-cup motor* is essentially an induction motor in which the rotor is a copper cylinder surrounding a central iron core. See Figure 217a. It is somewhat as if the iron of a squirrel-cage rotor were held stationary while the copper squirrel cage, removed from its slots (and in fact extended to be a smooth cylinder instead of just a squirrel cage) were allowed to turn in the air gap between the iron of the stator and the iron of the central core. The outstanding feature of the drag-cup motor is the low moment of inertia of its rotor. This gives it rapid mechanical response. On the other hand, its torque is lower than that of a squirrel-cage motor because of the wide gap of air and copper in which the drag cup turns, and this tends to reduce its advantage over heavier types.

218. Torque Motors

An interesting application is to use a two-phase induction motor to produce torque on a shaft that is not allowed to rotate at any considerable speed. Such a device, called a torque motor, provides an output torque that is proportional to the amplitude of an input signal.

To operate in this way (see Figure 218a), a two-phase motor (usually of small size, rated a few watts) has one of its two stator coils supplied with alternating current of constant amplitude. The frequency may be 60 cycles per second, but 400 cycles is more often used in control systems. An incoming signal current of the same frequency is supplied to the other of the two stator coils. This incoming signal is of variable magnitude. It might be received, for example,

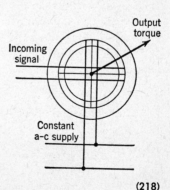

Figure 218a. A two-phase induction type torque motor.

(218)

from an a-c tachometer (see Section 230). The phase relations of the control current (the incoming signal) and the reference current (from the supply line) are so adjusted that the currents are in quadrature.

If there is no signal current, the reference current alone produces no torque in the motor for, as in any single-phase induction motor, there is no standstill torque. When signal current is received the motor becomes a two-phase motor. Although the two phases do not in general have balanced currents, the resultant magnetic field in the motor has some similarity to a rotating field, and it produces a torque on the rotor. At zero speed (or very low speed) this torque is proportional to the magnitude of the signal current. The output torque can then be used to operate any kind of control device, giving output torque proportional to input current.

It has been mentioned that a motor of this kind usually does not turn at an appreciable fraction of synchronous speed. Indeed, it may be so restrained that although it changes position with a change of torque it turns through only a fraction of a revolution, or perhaps a few revolutions, and then is stopped.

One of the requirements of this kind of operation is that the motor should not be able to run on the reference phase alone after having been given a start in one direction or the other by the control current. Ordinary motors that are intended to run near synchronous speed on a single-phase supply are started in just such a manner, but a torque motor must be incapable of *single phasing*, as it is called, after the control current has been stopped. A short study of Figure 128a shows that the necessary condition to avoid single phasing is for negative-sequence torque to exceed positive-sequence torque at all operating speeds. Negative-sequence torque must exceed positive-sequence torque when the control winding of the motor is short-circuited, as is usual with motors of the type shown in Figure 218a, and negative-sequence torque must still be the greater if the control winding has any passive impedance connected across it. The latter is the more difficult, but in both cases single phasing is prevented by high rotor resistance. This situation is suggested by Figure 119a and will now be studied further.

219. Symmetrical Components

Voltages applied to the two-phase induction motor of a control system, being in general unbalanced, are conveniently studied by analyz-

(219)

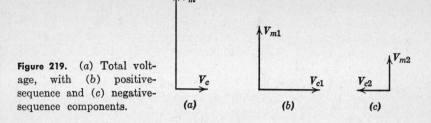

Figure 219. (*a*) Total voltage, with (*b*) positive-sequence and (*c*) negative-sequence components.

(*a*)   (*b*)   (*c*)

ing into symmetrical components. In Section 126 a pulsing field was considered to be the sum of two rotating fields. This is a simple example, and the method of symmetrical components is a more refined means of analyzing any unbalanced condition into the sum of balanced conditions.

The two-phase motor of Figure 218*a* has alternating voltage of constant value steadily applied to the main winding. This we call V_m. Another alternating voltage is applied to the control winding. This we call V_c. V_c is usually smaller than V_m, although it is not necessarily so. The control voltage V_c may be of either polarity.

We now analyze the two applied voltages V_m and V_c into symmetrical components. To do this, we find a balanced pair of two-phase voltages with a phase sequence that we call positive, and another balanced pair with the opposite phase sequence that we call negative; these must add to equal the unbalanced applied voltages.

If the relation between currents, fields, and electromotive forces is linear, the principle of superposition permits us to consider these symmetrical components of voltage separately and to add their effects—which means, in this case, to find the torque produced by each symmetrical component of voltage and then to add the resulting torques.

The applied voltages, unbalanced, are V_m and V_c as in Figure 219*a*. The positive-sequence pair are V_{m1} and V_{c1} as in Figure 219*b*, and the negative-sequence pair are V_{m2} and V_{c2} as in Figure 219*c*. In each of these pairs the symmetrical systems are balanced, that is,

$$V_{c1} = -jV_{m1} \quad \text{and} \quad V_{c2} = +jV_{m2} \qquad (219\text{-}1)$$

The necessary conditions are that

$$V_m = V_{m1} + V_{m2} \qquad (219\text{-}2)$$

$$V_c = V_{c1} + V_{c2} \qquad (219\text{-}3)$$

$$(219)$$

These conditions are met by letting

$$V_{m1} = \tfrac{1}{2}(V_m + jV_c) \tag{219-4}$$

$$V_{m2} = \tfrac{1}{2}(V_m - jV_c) \tag{219-5}$$

To this point our analysis is quite general. We now assume that the control voltage V_c is accurately in quadrature with the main field voltage V_m. Whatever the source of V_c we expect that adjustments of the apparatus are correct and V_c is one-quarter cycle behind or ahead of V_m. It is because of this assumption that Figures 219a, b, and c show V_m, V_{m1}, and V_{m2} in phase with each other; this would not otherwise be true.

220. Torque from Components

Average torque on the induction motor, by the method of symmetrical components, is the sum of that produced by the positive-sequence voltage and that produced by the negative-sequence voltage. We compute the torque produced by each of these balanced systems as if they acted separately. This is permitted by the principle of superposition if linearity can be assumed.* The total average torque is then the sum of these two (Figure 220a).

Torque is expressed in terms of slip, and the symbol S will now be the positive-sequence slip, the fractional difference between the speed of the rotor of the machine and the synchronous speed of the positive sequence field. The negative-sequence slip, the rotor speed relative to the negative-sequence field, is $(2 - S)$. For positive rotation of the rotor, from standstill to synchronous speed, S is between 1 and 0, and negative-sequence slip $(2 - S)$ is between 1 and 2.

Torque that would be produced by the motor at slip S if the applied voltages were balanced, each applied voltage being equal to V_b, we call $T_b(S)$. Torque produced by positive-sequence voltage we shall call T_1. Since torque is proportional to the square of the balanced applied voltages (equation 122-4), we then have

$$T_1 = T_b(S) \left| \frac{V_{m1}}{V_b} \right|^2 \tag{220-1}$$

---

* Some authors go to the extent of saying that the balanced voltages of opposite phase sequence act as if they were applied to separate induction motors mechanically coupled on a common shaft. This may help visualization and is true for average torque, but it omits interaction.

(220)

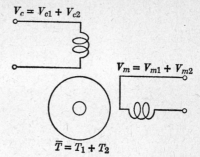

$V_c = V_{c1} + V_{c2}$

$V_m = V_{m1} + V_{m2}$

Figure 220a. Average torque is the sum of the torques of the components.

$\overline{T} = T_1 + T_2$

Similarly, negative-sequence torque with balanced voltages of magnitude V_b is found from the same function T_b, but it is a function of the negative-sequence slip $(2 - S)$ and so will be denoted $T_b(2 - S)$. It is proportional to the square of the negative-sequence voltage and is exerted in the negative direction, so

$$T_2 = -T_b(2 - S) \left| \frac{V_{m2}}{V_b} \right|^2 \qquad (220\text{-}2)$$

Finally, the average total torque for any amounts of positive-sequence and negative-sequence voltage, acting together, is

$$\overline{T} = T_b(S) \left| \frac{V_{m1}}{V_b} \right|^2 - T_b(2 - S) \left| \frac{V_{m2}}{V_b} \right|^2 \qquad (220\text{-}3)$$

In summary, then, the unbalanced two-phase applied voltages are taken to be the sum of two balanced systems of voltages of opposite phase rotation. Each of these balanced systems produces its own magnetic field. Each magnetic field produces a torque on the rotor of the machine. The average total torque is the sum of these two torques and may be so computed.

221. Total Torque

Thus far there are no approximations (except linearity), but the function T_b has not yet been expressed. It is possible to write T_b with various degrees of precision. We have derived an expression for torque from balanced voltages in equation 122-4 and, although it neglects magnetizing current, it will be precise enough for use here. Equation 122-4 is therefore repeated here with the subscript b to indicate that this is torque for balanced voltage:

(221)

$$T_b = \frac{gR_2'}{\Omega_s} \frac{S|V_b|^2}{(R_1 S + R_2')^2 + X^2 S^2} \tag{221-1}$$

It will be remembered that

    g is the number of phases
    V_b is the applied balanced voltage, rms volts
    Ω_s is synchronous speed, radians/second
    S is slip (positive phase sequence)
    R_2' is rotor resistance referred to the stator, ohms
    R_1 is stator resistance, ohms
    X is reactance of stator plus rotor reactance referred to stator, ohms

Equation 221-1 is now entered into equation 220-3, to obtain

$$\overline{T} = \frac{2R_2'}{\Omega_s} \left[\frac{S|V_{m1}|^2}{(R_1 S + R_2')^2 + X^2 S^2} - \frac{(2-S)|V_{m2}|^2}{[R_1(2-S)+R_2']^2 + X^2(2-S)^2} \right] \tag{221-2}$$

This is the torque of a control motor in terms of positive-sequence and negative-sequence voltages applied.

However, since the main voltage is usually constant while the control voltage varies, it is more convenient to express torque in terms of V_m and a factor k that is proportional (for a given V_m) to V_c. By definition,

$$k = \frac{|V_c|}{|V_m|} \tag{221-3}$$

Combining equation 221-3 with equations 219-4 and 5, and the fact that V_m leads V_c by 90 degrees, we obtain

$$\frac{|V_{m1}|}{|V_m|} = \tfrac{1}{2}(1 + k) \tag{221-4}$$

and

$$\frac{|V_{m2}|}{|V_m|} = \tfrac{1}{2}(1 - k) \tag{221-5}$$

Using k in equation 221-2, and eliminating V_{m1} and V_{m2}, we have

$$\overline{T} = \frac{|V_m|^2 R_2'}{2\Omega_s} \left[\frac{S(1 + k)^2}{(R_1 S + R_2')^2 + X^2 S^2} - \frac{(2-S)(1-k)^2}{[R_1(2-S)+R_2']^2 + X^2(2-S)^2} \right] \tag{221-6}$$

This is perhaps the more useful form. Torque can be found as a function of signal voltage, speed being constant, by letting k vary, or as a function of speed, signal being constant, by letting slip vary.

(221)

The latter relation is commonly and conveniently shown by a family of curves as in Figure 224b.

222. Signal Voltage Time Constant

It will be noted that this discussion of torque is for steady operation of the motor. When the signal voltage V_c is suddenly applied, should the transient effect be taken into account? In general the answer is no; it need not be.* When alternating V_c is suddenly applied to the motor there will be the forced component of current that has been considered and also a natural component that dies away exponentially. The natural component, unidirectional, acts to reduce the developed torque, but its duration is short, being determined by the time constant of the control circuit. The time constant of the control circuit depends on the inductance of the stator and rotor circuits and is so much shorter than the mechanical time constant, which is, as we shall see, determined by the moment of inertia of motor and load, that torque due to the natural component can be neglected.

223. Single Phasing

As was mentioned in Section 218, a control motor of this kind must not run on the single-phase voltage of the main field after control voltage is removed. To prevent this *single phasing*, torque must be zero or negative when V_c is zero, regardless of speed. Hence the negative-sequence torque must be equal to or greater than the positive-sequence torque at all positive speeds. Figure 128a shows that this will result if positive-sequence torque at positive speed is of lesser magnitude than positive-sequence torque at equal negative speed. The shape of the speed-torque curve being what it is, this will follow if the rate of change of torque with respect to speed is negative when speed is zero; that is, if the slope of the speed-torque curve is negative at the vertical axis.

Figure 119a shows that this negative slope at the vertical axis corresponds to high rotor resistance compared with rotor reactance, higher than is shown in the figure. Induction motors for control are therefore designed with a high rotor resistance. (This is one of

* References 83, 222A, 222B.

the reasons for the low efficiency of control motors.) To see that a high rotor resistance gives a negative derivative, we may differentiate torque of a control motor with respect to speed.

We could differentiate torque in equation 221-6, but this step can be simplified by neglecting the terms containing R_1 in each denominator. There are two justifications for doing so. The first is the fact that rotor resistance of a control-type motor is intentionally high, and hence it is probably true that R_1 is much less than R_2'. The second is that the *form* of the equation that we differentiate can be extended to include R_1, and thus the following conclusions and methods can be shown to be correct,* although the constants of the torque equation are not, in that case, related accurately to the letters we use.

Let us, then, differentiate equation 221-6 after letting R_1 be zero. It is convenient to differentiate with respect to slip. The result is

$$\frac{\partial \overline{T}}{\partial S} = \frac{R_2' |V_m|^2}{2\Omega_s} \left\{ \frac{(R_2'^2 + S^2 X^2)(1 + k)^2 - S(1 + k)^2(2SX^2)}{(R_2'^2 + S^2 X^2)^2} \right.$$

$$\left. + \frac{[R_2'^2 + (2 - S)^2 X^2](1 - k)^2 - (2 - S)(1 - k)^2 2(2 - S)X^2}{(R_2'^2 + (2 - S)^2 X^2)^2} \right\}$$

$$(223-1)$$

We are interested in this derivative when speed is zero (on the vertical axis of Figure 119a), and that is when slip is one. We shall therefore let $S = 1$ in the above derivative, and

$$\left. \frac{\partial \overline{T}}{\partial S} \right|_{S=1} = \frac{R_2' |V_m|^2}{\Omega_s} \frac{(R_2'^2 - X^2)(1 + k^2)}{(R_2'^2 + X^2)^2} \qquad (223-2)$$

Our criterion is that the derivative with respect to *speed* should be negative. This derivative with respect to *slip* should therefore be positive, and it is evident that the necessary condition to avoid single phasing is therefore that $R_2'^2 > X^2$.

It is interesting that this necessary condition gives negative slope with respect to speed for all values of k, although to prevent single phasing we are concerned only with the slope when no signal is

---

*When $R_1 S \ll R_2'$, equation 221-1 becomes of the form $T = S/(C_a + C_b S^2)$, where C_a and C_b are not functions of slip. Gibson and Tuteur (Reference 83) obtain this same form without neglecting either stator resistance or magnetizing current. They have less restrictive assumptions but more complicated algebra.

(223)

arriving and $k = 0.$. The slope at other values of k will be used in Section 225; it will then help to determine the torque of a motor at low speed.

224. Practical Speed-Torque Data

A manufacturer often gives the speed-torque curve of a motor with balanced rated voltages applied, or corresponding data. These data are obtained experimentally and are equivalent to a graph of equation 221-1. The general appearance of such a curve is shown in Figure 224a. Torque, as a fraction of the torque at zero speed, is plotted against motor speed as a fraction of synchronous speed; voltages are balanced and have rated value.

We wish to write the dynamic equations of motion of the motor, relating acceleration, speed, and load torque to developed torque, and developed torque to control voltage. Our problem is to find from the given information how much torque is developed by the motor for any amount of signal voltage on the control winding, and for any speed of the motor.

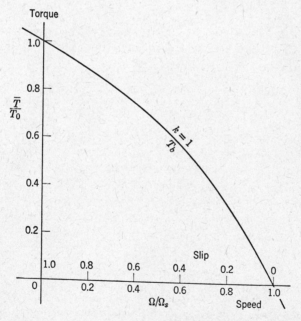

Figure 224a. Data on the balanced running of an induction motor.

(224)

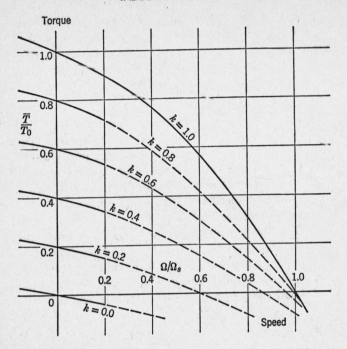

Figure 224b. The data are extended to give torque at low speed for any signal by using equation 225-8.

Most of the information that we need could easily be read from a family of curves like the ones suggested in Figure 224b, in which a curve shows torque as a function of speed for each value of k. Such a family could presumably be developed from the curve of Figure 224a with the aid of equation 221-6. The work would be considerable, however, and a short cut can be used.

225. Taylor Approximation

Let us suppose that we are given the curve of Figure 224a, for $k = 1$, and that we wish to find torque as a function of speed. As an approximation, however, we shall limit our attention to low speeds. This limit may mean speeds up to 10 per cent of synchronous, or 30 or 50 per cent, depending on the accuracy required.

The approximation will represent torque by only the first two terms of a Taylor expansion. Torque and its first derivative are used;

higher derivatives are neglected. (Also, as in Section 223, R_1 is assumed negligible compared to R_2'.)

Torque and its derivative are to be found at the vertical axis where $S = 1$. Letting $S = 1$ in equation 221-6 (and also $R_1 = 0$),

$$\bar{T}\big|_{S=1} = \frac{|V_m|^2 R_2'}{\Omega_s} \frac{2k}{R_2'^2 + X^2} \tag{225-1}$$

By definition, T_0 is the value of this expression when $k = 1$ (as well as $S = 1$). Then

$$T_0 = \bar{T}\big|_{S=1,k=1} = \frac{|V_m|^2 R_2'}{\Omega_s} \frac{2}{R_2'^2 + X^2} \tag{225-2}$$

and in equation 225-1,

$$\bar{T}\big|_{S=1} = T_0 k \tag{225-3}$$

This is the height at which each curve of Figure 224b crosses the vertical axis, and T_0 is the height of intersection of the curve for which $k = 1$ (the curve of Figure 224a), a value supplied by the manufacturer of the motor.

The derivative of torque is found by differentiating equation 221-6; the result is equation 223-1. At the vertical axis, with $S = 1$, the derivative is equation 223-2. By definition, T_b is the value of torque when $k = 1$ (balanced voltages, the curve of Figure 224a); that is

$$T_b = \bar{T}\big|_{k=1} \tag{225-4}$$

Now letting $k = 1$ (as well as $S = 1$) in equation 223-2, we find the derivative of T_b:

$$\frac{\partial T_b}{\partial S}\bigg|_{S=1} = \frac{\partial \bar{T}}{\partial S}\bigg|_{S=1,k=1} = \frac{R_2' |V_m|^2}{\Omega_s} \frac{2(R_2'^2 - X^2)}{(R_2'^2 + X^2)^2} \tag{225-5}$$

and in equation 223-2,

$$\frac{\partial \bar{T}}{\partial S}\bigg|_{S=1} = \frac{\partial T_b}{\partial S}\bigg|_{S=1} \frac{1 + k^2}{2} \tag{225-6}$$

Since $\Omega = 0$ when $S = 1$, and the derivative with respect to Ω is the negative of the derivative with respect to S,

$$\frac{\partial \bar{T}}{\partial \Omega}\bigg|_{\Omega=0} = \frac{\partial T_b}{\partial \Omega}\bigg|_{\Omega=0} \frac{1 + k^2}{2} \tag{225-7}$$

This is the slope at which each curve of Figure 224b crosses the vertical axis, and $\partial T_b / \partial \Omega$ at $\Omega = 0$ is the slope at which the curve of Figure 224a

crosses the vertical axis, a value easily obtained from the manufacturer's data.

Now to find the approximate torque at any speed and signal voltage, the values of $\overline{T}$ at the axis and its slope at the axis are used as the first two terms of a Taylor approximation. We combine equations 225-3 and 225-7 to write

$$\overline{T} \approx k T_0 + \Omega \frac{1 + k^2}{2} \frac{\partial T_b}{\partial \Omega}\bigg|_{\Omega = 0} \qquad (225\text{-}8)$$

where T is average torque developed

   Ω is speed

   k is a measure of the signal voltage (see equation 221-3)

   T_0 is torque with balanced voltage at zero speed (This is the *value* at which the curve of Figure 224a, obtained from the manufacturer's data, crosses the vertical axis.)

$\dfrac{\partial T_b}{\partial \Omega}\bigg|_{\Omega = 0}$ is the slope of the curve for T_0 at zero speed (This is the *slope* of this same curve at the vertical axis.)

(Note that the unit of Ω is to be the same as the unit of speed in $\partial T_b / \partial \Omega$.)

Equation 225-8 is an approximation of torque at low motor speed. Its limited range is indicated by the shortness of the solid lines through the axis of Figure 224b. Equation 225-8 describes these as straight lines, and when their curvature is considerable the approximation is no longer satisfactory. The family of curves is continued beyond the straight-line region by dash lines in Figure 224b, and these dash lines are not exact but are fairly typical. Torque might be computed more precisely from equation 221-6 if labor were no object, but the simple equation 225-8 includes many practical situations.*

226. A Dynamic System

To illustrate the use of relations that have been derived, let voltage V_c be applied to the control winding of a two-phase induction motor. Voltage on its main winding is V_m. All the torque developed by the

---

* Gibson and Tuteur, Reference 83, give a much more detailed consideration of the induction motor. In particular, they include impedance of the signal source, which reduces the slope of the curves in Figure 224b without greatly changing their shape. "Both the gain and damping for the operating point $k = 0$, $S = 1$ will be reduced by the presence of Z_c in the control circuit" (page 294). See also Koopman, Reference 225.

(226)

motor is used to accelerate the motor and load, moment of inertia being J. If T is the developed torque, the mechanical equation is simply

$$T = J \frac{d\Omega}{dt} \qquad (226\text{-}1)$$

The torque developed is given by equation 225-8. The latter equation is a little simplified if we write $-G$ for the slope of the balanced-voltage curve at the vertical axis. By definition, then,

$$-G = \frac{1 + k^2}{2} \frac{\partial T_b}{\partial \Omega} \bigg|_{\Omega=0} \qquad (226\text{-}2)$$

With this symbol, equation 225-8, the electromechanical equation, becomes

$$\overline{T} = kT_0 - G\Omega \qquad (226\text{-}3)$$

This is the equation for the straight-line part of the family of curves in Figure 224b. It will be noticed that G is in fact a function of k, although as an approximation it is sometimes taken as a constant with $k = 1$ or with $k = 0$. If the incoming signal is small, $k = 0$ is a good approximation, and this is usual.

An interesting aspect of equation 226-3 is its similarity in form to the equation for a commutator motor with armature control. An analogous equation can be written for such a motor by combining equations 209-2, 3, and 4 to give

$$T = \frac{K}{R} V - \frac{K^2}{R} \Omega \qquad (226\text{-}4)$$

The first term gives the motor torque at zero speed, and the second term gives the damping as a result of speed. Analogy of G to the *electrical damping* constant is more than superficial; G is a measure of electromotive force induced in the stator by rotation, as is the analogous K^2/R.

To return to our problem, equations 226-1 and 3 can be equated (the average torque is used) to give

$$kT_0 = J \frac{d\Omega}{dt} + G\Omega \qquad (226\text{-}5)$$

Laplace transformation is permissible if G is constant. Transforming, and substituting $|V_c|/|V_m|$ for k, we have

$$\frac{|\hat{V}_c|}{|V_m|} T_0 = Js\hat{\Omega} + G\hat{\Omega} \qquad (226\text{-}6)$$

A transfer function relating speed to signal voltage can now be found:

$$\frac{\hat{\Omega}}{|\hat{V}_c|} = \frac{T_0}{|V_m| G} \frac{1}{1 + \tau s} \tag{226-7}$$

where $\tau = J/G$. Note that the time constant is the ratio of the moment of inertia to the electrical damping.

This is a simple example of a dynamic system, but it illustrates the use of such an equation as 226-3 for the torque developed by an induction motor. The various approximations must be remembered.

227. Unbalanced Operation

The general idea of dividing unbalanced voltages into symmetrical components was considered in Section 219, and that idea can now be carried somewhat further in discussing operation of the induction motor on unbalanced voltage.

In Figure 121a, one phase of a balanced induction motor is represented by a short-circuited transformer. If positive-sequence voltage is applied to a motor this equivalent circuit can be used to give the positive-sequence current, positive torque, and other positive-sequence quantities. If negative-sequence voltage is applied, the diagram gives negative-sequence quantities. If both sequences are applied simultaneously, the diagram is used twice, once for each sequence, and total voltage, current, torque, and so on, are found by adding.

Figure 227a does just this: it gives the equivalent diagram twice. (For simplicity in this diagram, the ideal transformer of Figure 121a is omitted, and it is understood that R_2 and X_2 are the rotor resistance and reactance referred to the stator winding.) Voltage applied to the upper part of the diagram is V_{m1}, and voltage on the lower part is V_{m2}. The appropriate slip is shown in each part of the diagram. Current in the upper part is I_{m1}; in the lower part I_{m2}.

In Figure 227a the two diagrams, one for positive sequence and one for negative sequence, are put together back to back in such a way that the total voltage at the extreme left is V_m, in accordance with equation 219-2, which shows that

$$V_m = V_{m1} + V_{m2} \tag{227-1}$$

This is a general equation that must always be satisfied, and the diagram is arranged so that it is satisfied automatically.

(227)

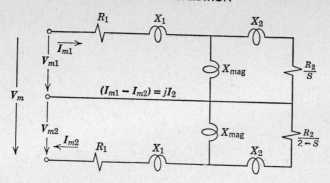

Figure 227a. An equivalent diagram for a two-phase induction motor running on unbalanced voltage.

If the proper sequence voltages were applied to the equivalent circuit of Figure 227a, I_{m1} could be measured (or computed) in the upper wire, and I_{m2} in the lower wire. I_m, the current in the main winding, is then the sum of these, as

$$I_m = I_{m1} + I_{m2} \qquad (227\text{-}2)$$

(This is the same equation as 219-2, with a different symbol.) Thus I_m can be obtained, and V_m can be measured between upper and lower terminals.

Other equations that apply by definition of sequence quantities are

$$I_c = I_{c1} + I_{c2} \qquad (227\text{-}3)$$

where

$$I_{c1} = -jI_{m1} \quad \text{and} \quad I_{c2} = +jI_{m2} \qquad (227\text{-}4)$$

Figures 219a, b, and c can be used for currents as well as voltages with a mere change of symbol from V to I.

Now, putting equations 227-4 into 227-3, we find that

$$I_{m1} - I_{m2} = jI_c \qquad (227\text{-}5)$$

and this gives an easy way of measuring (or computing) the current I_c in Figure 227a.

Torque in the total motor is the difference between positive-sequence and negative-sequence torques. Each of these can be found from the diagram by remembering that the power per phase producing average torque in the motor is equal to that consumed by $R_2/S - R_2$ in the positive-sequence system and $R_2/(2 - S) - R_2$ in the negative.

(227)

It is of course obvious that this diagram for the induction motor *
on unbalanced voltages or currents reduces to Figure 121a for the
motor on balanced voltages if the voltages are indeed balanced, in
which case $V_m = V_{m1}$ and $V_{m2} = 0$. The lower part of Figure 227a
then ceases to exist.

228. The Single-Phase Motor

A most interesting arrangement, because of its practical importance,
is the single-phase induction motor of the kind discussed in Section
128. Many millions of such motors, usually in fractional horsepower
sizes, are used to operate a multitude of household, office, and factory
devices.

The operation of such a motor is defined by the statement:

$$I_c = 0 \qquad (228\text{-}1)$$

This says that the second winding carries no current; the equation is
satisfied if the second winding is open-circuited, which is the condition
we wish to study. (The equation might equally well mean that the
second winding does not exist at all, and indeed it might not, except
for starting.)

Since the statement that $I_c = 0$ defines this kind of operation, it is all
that is needed, besides the general equation already listed, to describe
the operation of the single-phase motor. Perhaps the idea that it con-
veys can be combined into our equivalent circuit. We shall find, as a
matter of fact, that it can.

With the aid of equations 227-3 and 227-4, 228-1 expands to

$$I_c = I_{c1} + I_{c2} = -jI_{m1} + jI_{m2} = 0 \qquad (228\text{-}2)$$

whence

$$I_{m1} = I_{m2} \qquad (228\text{-}3)$$

To make the equivalent diagram necessarily agree with equation 228-3,
the central connection is omitted from Figure 227a. Figure 228a then
results.

Thus Figure 228a accounts for the operation of a single-phase motor
when the inoperative coil is open-circuited.† Certain interesting rela-

---

* This discussion assumes that the two stator coils of the two-phase motor
are alike. If they are not, a minor modification of the diagram of Figure
227a is needed. See Fitzgerald and Kingsley, Reference 78F.

† This is a familiar diagram except that some authors show each impedance
divided by 2; the total current, correspondingly multiplied by 2, is then I_m.

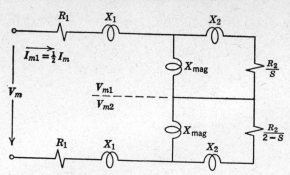

Figure 228a. An equivalent diagram for a single-phase induction motor.

tions in such a motor are seen almost by inspection of Figure 228a.

First, if a single-phase motor is stationary the two loops of Figure 228a are identical. For the stationary motor, $V_{m1} = V_{m2} = \frac{1}{2}V_m$. The two symmetrical components of applied voltage are equal, and the two symmetrical components of current are equal. The two rotating magnetic fields are equal; each is half of the total pulsing field, and Figure 126a applies. Positive torque is equal to negative torque, and there is no net torque; the motor does not start.

Second, if the motor is running near synchronous speed the slip S is much smaller than 1. The upper loop of Figure 228a then has much higher impedance than the lower loop. The positive-sequence voltage is therefore higher than the negative, and the positive-sequence magnetic field is correspondingly stronger than the negative-sequence field. The positive torque is also greater than the negative torque unless, to prevent single phasing, R_2 has been made very large.

In the limit, the motor may approach nearly synchronous speed. Then the positive-sequence field in the machine is almost what it would be in a polyphase motor, because of polyphase rotor current, while the negative-sequence field is almost negligibly small. The rotating magnetic field is now almost uniform in magnitude, as in a polyphase machine, of such magnitude that the electromotive force it induces in the stator winding is nearly equal to the applied voltage V_m. This almost-uniform magnetic field induces electromotive force not only in the stator winding on which voltage is applied, but also in any other windings there may be on the stator.

It is of practical importance that if only single-phase power is available, a three-phase induction motor can be run (without load) from that single-phase line; and three-phase power, almost balanced,

(228)

can then be drawn from the three terminals of the motor. This is a simple form of *phase balancer*.

Note that positive-sequence voltage V_{m1} will be nearly as large as V_m when the motor is running at full speed, whereas V_{m1} is only one-half of V_m at standstill. It follows that the positive-sequence torque at standstill is of the order of one-fourth of what it would be if V_{m1} then equaled V_m. This fact must be taken into account in the curves of Figure 128*a*, as is stated in the footnote to Section 128.

It may again be mentioned that this Section 228 pertains more particularly to the single-phase motor designed for power than to one intended for control work. From that point of view, this section is a continuation of Section 128, made possible by introduction of the theory of symmetrical components.

229. The Induction Motor as a Tachometer

In another interesting application, a two-phase induction motor of small size serves as a tachometer or speed-measuring device. One of its windings is excited from a constant a-c supply line, as in Figure 229*a*. When the motor is standing still there is no electromotive force induced in the unexcited coil of the motor, for it is at right angles to the excited coil and hence is not linked by any of the magnetic flux. But when the rotor turns, motion of the rotor produces a magnetic field that *does* link with the unexcited coil of the stator, and this *does* induce electromotive force in the unexcited coil. Hence when the motor is turning there is a terminal voltage (of the same frequency as the exciting current) between the terminals of the unexcited winding, which can be measured by a voltmeter. At low speed the voltage is very nearly proportional to speed. At higher speed the voltage fails to increase in proportion.

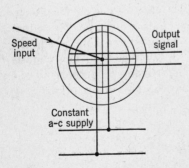

Figure 229*a*. A two-phase induction motor used as an a-c tachometer.

(229)

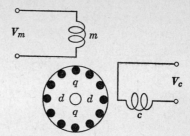

Figure 229b. Circuits of the induction tachometer.

Such operation of an induction motor as a tachometer is essentially the same whether the motor has a squirrel-cage, solid-iron, or drag-cup rotor. The simple drag-cup type is often used for this purpose, for it is very light and adds little to the moment of inertia of the system in which speed is to be measured.

Quantitatively, the tachometer can be considered from the point of view of symmetrical components. (In Reference 229, Frazier does so in detail.) If the tachometer is stationary there is a pulsing magnetic field produced by current in the coil marked m in Figure 229b; in the diagram the axis of this field is shown as vertical. This vertical field can be divided into two rotating fields with positive and negative rotation, as in Figure 126a. It may be considered that each of these rotating fields induces an electromotive force in the second coil on the stator, marked c, but since the axis of c is at right angles to the axis of m the electromotive forces induced in c are in opposition to each other and add to zero. This results from the fact that the two rotating fields have equal magnitude.

If, now, the tachometer is not stationary but moving slowly in the positive direction the positive-sequence magnetic field becomes slightly stronger and the negative-sequence field slightly weaker than before. The positive-sequence field, being stronger than the negative-sequence field, now induces a greater electromotive force in coil c. Since the increase of one field, and the decrease of the other, are very nearly proportional (at low speeds) to the speed, the terminal voltage V_c is also proportional to the speed. It is thus that the device acts as a tachometer.

Figure 228a suggests that the change of strength of the magnetic fields is not accurately proportional to speed. Output of the tachometer is therefore *proportional* to speed only at low speeds, but it is still an accurate measure of higher speeds if properly calibrated.

(229)

230. The Cross-Field Theory

An entirely different point of view of single-phase operation, known as the cross-field theory, does not use the symmetrical-component theory at all. It will be introduced for the tachometer, although not elaborated, because it gives an excellent mental picture of operation.

Again in Figure 229b, current in coil m produces a pulsing vertical field, inducing current in the rotor conductors by transformer action even though the machine is stationary. Current induced by transformer action is maximum in the rotor bars marked d–d, and current in these bars produces an opposing magnetic field, also vertical. Neither of these magnetic fields has any horizontal component, and no electromotive force is induced in coil c. The voltage V_c is zero.

Now the rotor begins to turn. The vertical magnetic field, the *transformer field*, is hardly affected by the motion; there is still current in whichever rotor bars are in the position marked d–d. But now the rotor bars in the other axis, the bars marked q–q, are cutting mechanically through the vertical flux because of rotation. Electromotive force is induced in these bars in proportion to speed, current flows in response, and this current produces a *velocity field* that is mainly in the horizontal axis and therefore induces electromotive force in coil c. Hence the voltage V_c appears, proportional to speed if the speed is fairly low.

Whether the cross-field theory or the theory of symmetrical components is used the result is of course the same. It is interesting and important that the output of this *a-c tachometer* is an alternating voltage of the same frequency as that of V_m, with magnitude a measure of speed, proportional to speed at low values. In Section 218 it was mentioned that an a-c tachometer might supply (through an amplifier) an induction type of torque motor. It will now be seen that an input speed might give, by this means, an output signal of torque, or (with a spring) of angular position, at some fairly remote location.

The practical advantages of the a-c tachometer are two. First, its output signal is alternating at a given frequency and can be amplified easily; a d-c amplifier is not needed. Second, there are no slip rings and no commutator; hence there are no sparking and no wear. As a disadvantage, however, constant V_m must be supplied.

(230)

231. Summary

Types of control motors are *squirrel-cage, solid-iron rotor*, and *drag-cup*.

Torque motors may have two coils, with constant reference voltage applied to one and signal to the other. The method of *symmetrical components* is convenient. Total torque is the sum of the torques of the two components (average over a cycle).

Torque of such a motor is conveniently shown as a function of speed by the family of curves in Figure 224b. The spacing of the family of curves and their slope at low speeds is readily found from motor data. Such information regarding developed torque is used in *system equations* describing dynamic behavior, as shown by a simple example.

The electrical input time constant of an induction motor is usually negligible compared to the mechanical *time constant*, in which damping is electrical.

When the received signal is zero there must be no torque in a control motor. *Single phasing* is prevented by having high enough resistance in the rotor.

An equivalent diagram for *unbalanced* operation of a two-phase motor makes use of the relation that $V_m = V_{m1} + V_{m2}$.

By adding the relation that $I_c = 0$, this becomes the diagram of a *single-phase* motor. The single-phase motor produces, when running, a polyphase field and polyphase voltages.

The induction motor is used as a *tachometer*. The output is of the same frequency as the reference voltage, and its magnitude is a measure of speed. The *cross-field theory* is suggested, as well as the theory of symmetrical components.

PROBLEMS

16-1. Verify equations 219-4 and 5. **(Sec. 219)**

16-2. $V_m = 115$ volts, $V_c = -j25.4$ volts. Find V_{m1}, V_{m2}, V_{c1}, and V_{c2}. Show them in diagrams. Check your results in equations 219-2 and 3. **(Sec. 219)**

16-3. $V_m = 110$ volts, $V_c = j13.6$ volts. Find V_{m1}, V_{m2}, V_{c1}, and V_{c2}. Show them in diagrams. Check your results in equations 219-2 and 3.   **(Sec. 219)**

16-4. $V_m = 120 \underline{/90°}$, $V_c = 19.6 \underline{/18°}$. Find V_{m1}, V_{m2}, V_{c1}, and V_{c2}. Show them in diagrams. Check your results in equations 219-2 and 3.
                                                                    (Sec. 219)

16-5. The three voltages of a 3-phase system are V_a, V_b, and V_c. These voltages, in general unbalanced, are to be analyzed into three symmetrical systems. In the positive sequence system, $V_{a1} = V_{b1} \underline{/120°} = V_{c1} \underline{/240°}$; in the negative sequence system, $V_{a2} = V_{b2} \underline{/-120°} = V_{c2} \underline{/-240°}$; in the zero sequence system the three components are equal and are called V_0. These yield equations similar to 219-1. Write them, and also the summation equations similar to equations 219-2 and 3. Then derive equations (similar to equations 219-4 and 5) by which the three 3-phase components can be computed.   **(Sec. 219)**

16-6. If V_c is less than V_m, is the torque of the motor that they operate uniform in magnitude throughout a cycle? (This question relates, of course, to instantaneous torque, not average.) Show definitely whether it will be, or not. Linearity of response may be assumed.   **(Sec. 221)**

16-7. Experimental data on an induction motor are given as a curve in Figure 224a. (This same curve is repeated in Figure 224b, where it is perhaps easier to read.) From this experimental curve, evaluate design parameters in equation 221-6 and use the resulting numbers to extend the curve for $k = 0$ of Figure 224b. Extend this curve for $k = 0$ from zero speed to synchronous speed.   **(Sec. 221)**

16-8. Verify the units of equations 221-6, as in Appendix 4.
                                                                    (Sec. 221)

16-9. Derive equation 223-2 from 221-6.   **(Sec. 223)**

16-10. Using the method of equation 225-8 and the data of Figure 224a, compute torque (as a fraction of T_0) when $k = 0.20$ and speed $= 0.20$ of synchronous. Compare this with the corresponding curve of Figure 224b.   **(Sec. 225)**

16-11. Using the method of equation 225-8 and the data of Figure 224a, compute torque (as a fraction of T_0) when $k = 0.80$ and speed is one-tenth of synchronous. Compare this with the corresponding curve of Figure 224b. **(Sec. 225)**

16-12. It is common practice to give a speed-torque characteristic of an armature-controlled motor, showing steady speed as a function of steady load torque. The result is a family of lines, each for a different value of armature voltage, somewhat similar to Figure 224b. Draw such lines for the motor of Figure 209a, using any of the assumptions of Section 209 that may be applicable. Draw a line for armature voltage at rated value ($V = V_0$), a line for half rated value ($V = \frac{1}{2}V_0$), and a line for $V = 0$, all for the same constant field current. Measure T on the horizontal axis and Ω on the vertical axis, and give values of all intersections with axes in terms of design constants and V_0. **(Sec. 225)**

16-13. In a load driven by an induction servomotor, an appreciable part of the developed torque is used in overcoming friction. Change equation 226-1 accordingly, and compute a transfer function and time constant to take this friction into account. **(Sec. 226)**

16-14. A certain drag-cup induction motor gives the data of Figure 224b and also the following (from the dealer's catalog), of which any that are pertinent may be used: primary 115 volt, 60 cycles, 2 poles, 1,600 ohms resistance, 4,500 ohms impedance, 14 gram-cm^2 moment of inertia, $T_0 = 230$ gram-cm. It drives a load with an equal moment of inertia (14 gram-cm^2) and no appreciable friction. For a small incoming signal find the transfer function (as in equation 226-7), including the time constant. **(Sec. 226)**

16-15. An induction servomotor has the following characteristics: reference volts, 115; control volts, 115; poles, 2; frequency, 60 cycles/ sec; locked torque, 275 gram-cm; moment of inertia, 10 gram-cm^2; output, 5 watts. Find the transfer function of output speed over control voltage if the load is negligible. What steady speed can be expected when the control voltage is 10 volts? About how long will it take for the speed to come within 14 per cent of this value? **(Sec. 226)**

16-16. A figure of merit sometimes used to judge a servomotor is the *torque-to-inertia ratio*, which, in our symbols, is T_0/J. Is this a suitable figure of merit for a motor to be used as in Section 226? Why or why not? For commercial motors this figure may range from 15 to 45 cm^{-1}. What is its value for the motor of Problems 16-14 or 16-15 (as assigned)? Is a high or low value usually desirable? Why? **(Sec. 226)**

16-17. In a two-phase induction motor for control purposes, one coil is short-circuited so that $V_c = 0$. In terms of V_m (which is not zero) find positive and negative sequence components of main and control voltages and draw phasor diagrams to show the derivation. Show an equivalent network diagram that could replace Figure 228a for such a motor.   **(Sec. 228)**

16-18. Prove that if magnetizing current is neglected an induction motor with only one phase winding carrying current will be able to develop positive torque in some speed range by "single-phasing" on its one winding. Or, if this is not true, prove that it will not.

(Sec. 228)

16-19. When the following motor is used as an induction tachometer, with 115 volts on the main field winding, what is its output, at low speed, in volts per hundred rpm? What is its output at 2,160 rpm? (Use of Figure 228a is suggested.) Parameters of the equivalent circuit are: $R_1 = 50$ ohms, $X_1 = 125$ ohms, R_2 (referred to stator) $= 110$ ohms, $X_2 = 0$, $X_{mag} = 160$ ohms; poles, 2; frequency, 60 cycles/sec.   **(Sec. 229)**

16-20. Repeat Problem 16-19 when a motor with the following parameters (115 volts being used on the main winding) is used as an induction tachometer: $R_1 = 90$ ohms, $X_1 = 240$ ohms, R_2 (referred to stator) $= 200$ ohms, X_2 is negligible, $X_{mag} = 300$ ohms; poles, 4; frequency, 60 cycles/sec.   **(Sec. 229)**

16-21. The third paragraph of Section 230 says that in the induction tachometer the voltage V_c is "proportional to speed if the speed is fairly low." Explain why this is not true at higher speeds; why must the speed be fairly low?   **(Sec. 230)**

ELECTROMECHANICAL SYSTEMS
chapter 17

232. Systems

The word *system* is used with various meanings by different people, usually reflecting their personal interests, but the essential idea common to them all, and broad enough to include all, is that a system is an organization of interacting components.*

The behavior of every device is affected by the circuits and other devices to which it is connected. Every device is part of a system, and (as discussed in Section 3) the system must be considered as a whole.

Most devices of a system are *two-port* devices in which the signal or transmitted energy enters at one port and leaves at another. A two-winding transformer, for instance, is a two-port device; energy goes in at one pair of terminals and comes out at the other. An induction motor is a two-port device; electrical energy goes in at the electrical terminals and mechanical energy comes out at the shaft. Electro-mechanical two-port devices in information systems are commonly called *transducers*.

Transfer functions that relate a condition at one port of a device to a condition at the other have been computed in previous chapters.

Some transfer functions are zero, and in that case the output signal does not affect the input signal. Thus (as in Section 159) some relations are unilateral. There is no channel for feedback, and a device

---

* "The first essential aspect of a system is that it represents a network of interacting components. . . . One might say that the problem of system analysis is a problem of handling simultaneous equations because one must handle the component interrelationships simultaneously. This description is certainly valid but incomplete. . . ." (William K. Linvill, Reference 232.)

(232)

with no feedback gives an obvious place at which to divide a system into the blocks of a block diagram.

233. Cascaded Blocks

Historically, each block originally represented a device. Thus Figure 233a shows an electrical input signal, amplified, applied to the field circuit of a motor, with the mechanical output of the motor turning a load (a gun turret, perhaps) that has inertia and friction. This concept has been replaced for mathematical purposes by the idea that each block represents an equation. There is an input function and an output function, and the operation of the block is characterized by the transfer function that relates them.

Thus Figure 233b represents the same system as Figure 233a. Input is the same. The first block represents the amplifier, and its gain—that is, the ratio of V_f to the input voltage—is G_A. Over the practical range of operation G_A may well be a constant, although in general it might be a function of frequency. The transfer function is conveniently written within the block.

The next two blocks are taken from Figure 161b for a field-controlled motor. The first block represents equation 161-2, which is

$$\frac{\hat{I}_f}{\hat{V}_f} = \frac{1}{R_f}\frac{1}{1+s\tau_f} \qquad \tau_f = \frac{L_f}{R_f} \qquad\qquad (233\text{-}1)$$

In this block, R_f must include the plate resistance of the amplifier, and the voltage V_f is a hypothetical voltage within the amplifier that is as-

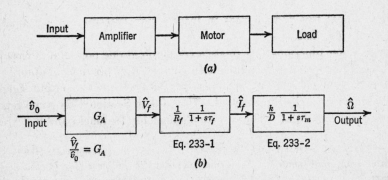

Figure 233. (a) A block diagram with blocks representing devices. (b) A block diagram with blocks representing equations.

(233)

sumed to drive the current I_f through the plate resistance as well as through the motor field winding.

The last block represents equation 161-8:

$$\frac{\hat{\Omega}}{\hat{I}_f} = \frac{k}{D} \frac{1}{1 + s\tau_m} \qquad \tau_m = \frac{J}{D} \qquad (233\text{-}2)$$

Mechanical properties of the motor and of the load are represented by equation 161-8 and hence by this block.

Note that the transfer function of the first block, the amplifier, is (or is assumed to be) independent of input to the second block. Also, the field-current output of the second block is independent of the behavior of the third block.

When two (or more) blocks are cascaded, as in this diagram, the transfer function for the two (or more) blocks is the product of the transfer functions of the individual blocks. If transfer functions can be computed for each block independently, it is then easy to multiply them together. Equation 161-9 is an example, being the product of equations 233-1 and 233-2.

Analysis of a system is much easier if it can be broken down into a large number of blocks. For that reason it is usual to assume unilateral behavior wherever possible. In fact, a relation that is truly bilateral is often considered to be unilateral, for convenience in analysis, even if this is not a very close approximation.

For instance, the potentiometer of Figure 233c would commonly be considered unilateral if the output current were much smaller than the input current. The amount of output current would then make little difference to the output voltage, and it would be a reasonably good

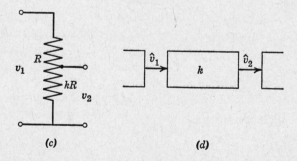

(c)   *(d)*

Figure 233c, d. A potentiometer circuit, and its representation by a block in a block diagram if output is small.

(233)

approximation to write

$$\frac{\vartheta_2}{\vartheta_1} = k \qquad (233\text{-}3)$$

and to represent this equation by the block marked k in Figure 233d. The output current is small if the input impedance to the next block of Figure 233d is much greater than the resistance R of the potentiometer itself.

A more general expression of this requirement is that the impedance level of the succeeding block must be much higher than the impedance level of the block in question. When this is true the succeeding block will not be a heavy load on the block in question and will not greatly affect its output value.

How much difference there must be in the impedance levels of two blocks to consider that the second one does not appreciably load the first is dependent on how good an approximation is required, and perhaps on how much labor can be saved. An impedance-level ratio of ten to one might be enough in a typical problem; a ratio of one-hundred to one would almost always be satisfactory.

234. Feedback

When the approximation of Figure 233d is not satisfactory, and the operation of the potentiometer must be computed with greater precision, there are two ways of advancing. One is to alter the transfer function of the potentiometer from $\vartheta_2/\vartheta_1 = k$, which is inexact, to

$$\frac{\vartheta_2}{\vartheta_1} = \frac{k}{1 + \dfrac{R}{R_0} k(1 - k)} \qquad (234\text{-}1)$$

which is exact, R_0 being the input impedance (resistance, in this case) of the device represented by the next block of the diagram. It is awkward, of course, to have the input impedance of the next block appearing in the transfer function of the potentiometer.

An alternative procedure is to represent the potentiometer by two blocks in a diagram as in Figure 234a. In one block the transfer function is k, as in Figure 233d. But this simple transfer function is now modified, for greater precision, by a correction supplied by the feedback block in which the transfer function is $(R/R_0)(1 - k)$. This block carries a signal only from right to left, and its output

(234)

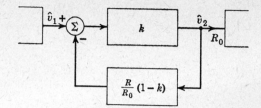

Figure 234a. An exact representation of the potentiometer circuit, using feedback.

feeds into the summing device marked Σ. The meaning of this summing device is that the input to the block marked k is the sum or difference of v_1, which comes from the left, and the output from the feedback block. Connections to the summing device are such (as indicated by the plus sign from the left and the minus sign from below) that in this example the input to the block marked k is the algebraic *difference* of the two incoming signals.

We do not yet have to consider the physical nature of this summing device for in this example it is physically non-existent. All that we really mean to say is that *if* there were such an arrangement as that of Figure 234a in a circuit, it would have exactly the same result as would the potentiometer represented by equation 234-1. In other words, Figure 234a shows a model of a potentiometer.

That the model of Figure 234a is correct can be shown by considering that its output v_2 is

$$\hat{v}_2 = k\,[\hat{v}_1 - \frac{R}{R_0}(1-k)\hat{v}_2] \qquad (234\text{-}2)$$

Since this yields the exact transfer function of the potentiometer, the model is a true one. It is of interest to notice that in Figure 234a, as well as in equation 234-2, if R_0 is very much larger than R the correction vanishes and the transfer function is then approximately k.

It may be mentioned that a convenient and powerful algebra of block diagrams has been devised. The analysis of *signal-flow graphs* is a highly developed means of computation based on graphical representation of equations. We are content, in this chapter, however, with the simplest of concepts.

235. A Closed-Loop System

We have seen in Figure 234a that a mathematical model can include feedback to represent the effect that the output of a device has

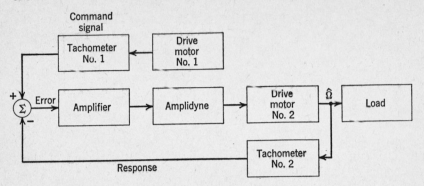

Figure 235a. A servomechanism to maintain motor No. 2 at the speed of motor No. 1.

on its input. This happens in any bilateral device, in which output unavoidably influences input and the feedback takes place through the device itself.

Feedback may also be provided intentionally in a system, through an external circuit. Such feedback is for the purpose of conveying part of the output function back to the input side of the device. Feedback may serve a number of purposes, such as increasing or decreasing amplification, but the ability to compare is one of the most important.

Control systems are often arranged so that the output is compared with the input. By this means it is possible to determine whether the output is exactly what it should be and, if not, to correct it. Suppose, in a steel mill, the speed of one roll is to be exactly equal to the speed of another roll. If the speed of the first changes, the speed of the second must change equally. To maintain control, it is obviously necessary to compare the two speeds.

Figure 235a shows a system in which tachometer No. 1 produces a voltage proportional to the speed of the controlling roll. Tachometer No. 2 produces a voltage proportional to the speed Ω of the controlled roll. These two voltages are compared in the summing device Σ, which may be two high resistances in series. As indicated by + and −, the tachometer signals are combined with reversed polarities, so the output of the summing device is equal to their difference. This output, called the error signal, is then amplified by an amplifier and an Amplidyne to control the speed of drive motor No. 2. If there is no error, drive motor No. 2 continues at the speed for which it was

(235)

adjusted. If there is an error in speed, the error signal acts to change the motor speed until the error is eliminated and the error signal becomes zero. If drive motor No. 1 changes speed for any reason, drive motor No. 2 will change speed equally as soon as the control system can be effective.

Without yet attempting any analysis, it is evident that effective operation of this control system is dependent on certain characteristics. Large amplification is needed to permit a tachometer signal of milliwatts to control a motor power of kilowatts. Rapid response is required to bring motor No. 2 quickly to the speed of motor No. 1 after a disturbance. Rapid action results from short time-constants, and corresponds to a frequency-response characteristic that remains "flat" to sufficiently high frequencies.

The possible instability of such a closed-loop system or servomechanism must always be considered. Suppose motor No. 1 has some kind of periodic fluctuation of speed, which might result from rolling a bumpy piece of iron. Suppose the motor gains speed for half a second, then slows for half a second, and so on. If motor No. 2 continued to run at constant speed, there would be an alternating error signal.

However, because of the control system, motor No. 2 will not run at constant speed. If the control were ideal, motor No. 2 should have the same speed changes as motor No. 1, at the same time. But there is certain to be a delay in the response of motor No. 2, a delay approximated by the time constant of the control devices. If, as the worst possible example, the time delay is half a second (equal to half a cycle of the input fluctuation), the fluctuations of motor No. 2 will be exactly out of phase with those of motor No. 1, instead of being exactly in phase. Motor No. 2 will be running slow when motor No. 1 is running fast, and vice versa.

With this amount of delay the attempts of motor No. 2 to follow the speed fluctuations of motor No. 1 will not decrease the error signal, but will increase it. The output of tachometer No. 2, when reversed in polarity in the summing device, will add to the output of tachometer No. 1, making the error signal larger than the signal from tachometer No. 1 alone. The larger error signal will then produce larger fluctuations of speed in motor No. 2, which will cause the error signal to be still larger; the fluctuations will increase still further, giving a yet larger error signal, and the system speed will fluctuate more and more wildly until some protective device operates to stop it. The system is unstable.

If a system is unstable it is not, in fact, necessary for tachometer

No. 1 to introduce a periodically fluctuating command signal to cause trouble. The system will go into oscillation spontaneously as a result of any kind of minor disturbance. An unstable system is good for nothing. Instability must be prevented in the design of the system.

236. Instability

Stability is so essential, and so easily lost, that it will be worth while to define the situation more exactly.

Let tachometer No. 2 be disconnected from the summing device Σ in Figure 235a. The closed loop is thereby broken, leaving what is called an open-loop system. The characteristics of this open-loop system can be found by feeding in an error signal and measuring (or computing) the response that results at the open-circuited output terminals of tachometer No. 2. If an alternating signal is fed in, an alternating response comes out, and the two are related by the *open-loop transfer function* of the system.

To avoid being specific about the components, let us refer to the representation in Figure 236a of a closed-loop system in which no detail is shown. G is the *forward* transfer function, H is the *feedback* transfer function. The open-loop transfer function is GH. If, with the loop open, a signal ϑ is fed in, the response at the end of the open loop is $GH\vartheta$.

Let us now close the loop, and immediately cease feeding in any signal from an external source. Output of the feedback loop, $GH\vartheta$, is now being fed into the summing device and hence, taking into account the reversal of polarity in the summing device, the signal fed to the block G from the summing device is $-GH\vartheta$. If this fed-back signal $-GH\vartheta$ is equal to the external signal ϑ that started the action, but that has now been disconnected, the signal fed into G will be the same as before (though it now comes from feedback instead of from an external source), and the action will continue by itself; that is, if $GH = -1$ the feedback will be enough to keep the signal going around the closed loop.

If the fed-back signal $-GH\vartheta$ is greater than ϑ it will be more than enough to maintain the signal. The oscillation will increase, and will continue to increase without limit. This is instability, and it results when GH is a larger negative number than -1. (It is evident that this can happen only if there is an increase of signal strength in either G or H, and it is usually from amplification in G.)

If, on the other hand, the fed-back signal is smaller than the initial disturbance ϑ it will not maintain the oscillation. After the external

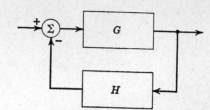

Figure 236a. A general closed loop.

signal ceases the oscillation will die away. Thus the system is stable if GH is between -1 and 0. It is stable also if GH has any positive value, for then, after reversal of polarity in the summing device, feedback will oppose rather than aid the oscillation, and action will cease.

To summarize, if GH is more negative than -1 the system, when closed, will be unstable.

237. Phase Reversal

In this criterion of stability, the negative sign is to be interpreted as meaning reversal of phase of a signal while passing through G and H. We have considered (Section 191) that there is ordinarily a difference in phase angle between the input and output signals of a device or system. The shift of phase is a function of frequency, and we are giving attention to the frequency at which the phase shift in G and H is 180 degrees. To restate the foregoing paragraph in other words:

If, at the frequency that gives phase reversal, the signal output from H is greater than the signal input to G, the system of Figure 236a, when closed, cannot be stable.

It does not matter whether the frequency at which the phase shift is 180 degrees lies within the useful range of the system. It is necessary for the system to be stable at all frequencies. If the system is unstable at any frequency it will go into spontaneous oscillation and be useless. Hence *there must be no frequency* at which GH is a real number more negative than -1.

238. A Test for Instability

To make practical application of this criterion, we draw a frequency-response diagram for G and H as members of an open loop. The phase shift in G and H is a function of frequency; it is usually

(238)

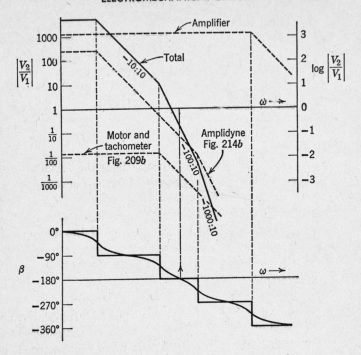

Figure 238a. Stability of the system is precarious.

negative, and usually less for low frequencies than for high frequencies. Locate the frequency at which the phase shift is −180 degrees (or, if it goes the other way, +180 degrees) and see if the magnitude of the transfer function at that frequency is greater or less than 1. If it is greater than 1, the system is not stable.

Figure 238a gives an example. It shows the frequency response of the network of Figure 235a for one particular set of adjustments of amplifier gain, of Amplidyne feedback, and so on. A dash line shows the amplifier response; gain is high, and flat to a relatively high frequency. Another dash line shows the Amplidyne response which, with feedback, is similar to Figure 214b. A third dash line is shown for motor No. 2 and its tachometer combined. Response of the tachometer is proportional (through all this frequency range) to speed, so the shape of the combined characteristic is determined by the motor response (Section 209). These three dash lines are then added * to

---

* Linear distances on the diagram are added, using the scale at the right-hand margin.

obtain the solid line marked "Total." This is the response of the system as an open loop.

The lower part of the diagram shows the phase angle between output and input voltages of the open loop. First we draw the vertical steps, which are mentioned in Section 191 as being a very rough approximation of phase angle. These are determined from the slope of the amplitude characteristic according to the table in Section 192. Then the curve, which is also an approximation, but a better one, is sketched in.

Finally we note the frequency at which this curve for phase angle crosses the horizontal line at −180 degrees. The point of intersection is marked in the diagram with a vertical arrow; the vertical line is followed upward to discover whether the amplitude indicated by the "Total" characteristic is greater or less than 1 at this frequency.

In this example it turns out to be slightly less than 1, but not much. In view of the approximations that have been made, this indicates that the system will probably, or at least possibly, be stable. It can be expected to have "absolute" stability, meaning that it will not oscillate by itself. But its "relative" stability will be poor, meaning that the damped oscillations of the system that follow any disturbance will die away slowly. As a closed-loop servomechanism the system will overshoot, and the speed of the controlled motor will not come quickly to the speed of the controlling motor, but will oscillate about the desired speed.

Such poor relative stability is not satisfactory. The most obvious means of improving operation is to reduce the gain of the amplifier. Lower gain tends to reduce accuracy of response of the servo system, and this is undesirable. However, Figure 238a shows that reducing gain will lower the "Total" characteristic without changing the phase angle response and will therefore provide the required stability.

There are other ways to provide stability, by changing the design of the system, without having to accept lower amplification. These are explained in books on control systems.*

---

* Figure 238a presents a simplified version of the Bode diagram. The Bode diagram gives the simplest and most direct criterion of system stability. Other tests for stability, employing the Nyquist, Hurwitz and Routh criteria, the root locus method, etc., have a greater range of applicability, but are less simple. References 173, 187A, B, C, D, and 238A, B, and C may well be studied with this chapter as background.

(238)

239. Summary

A system is an organization of interacting components.

Behavior of a component is described by a transfer function that relates an output quantity to an input quantity. A transfer function must often be expressed in terms of the termination into which the component feeds: in electrical terms, the terminating impedance.

Devices may be bilateral or unilateral. For a unilateral component, one transfer function is zero.

Block diagrams are used to represent systems. Each block represents an equation (or a group of equations combined). Often each block is assumed to have a unilateral relation to the next block. Blocks connected in cascade comprise a system.

Feedback occurs in any device in which the output affects the input. Feedback may, if desired, be represented by a feedback block in a diagram.

In a closed-loop system, part of the system output is fed back to combine with the input. This is often for comparison. If there is amplification, a closed-loop system may be unstable. If the overall open-loop transfer function has, at any frequency, a real value more negative than -1, instability results when the loop is closed. A simplified form of the Bode diagram illustrates the use of this criterion.

PROBLEMS

17-1. Automobiles are crossing a bridge. One section of the bridge, about 10 feet long, is free from the other sections, and has a strain gauge attached to it. The output of the strain gauge is in a Wheatstone bridge circuit, and the bridge circuit output goes to a pen recorder driven by a d'Arsonval movement. Automobiles enter the bridge section irregularly, but not closer than one-fourth second apart. The pen recorder must distinguish the arrival of each individual automobile. What are the essential requirements of the system (a) assuming the strain-gauge output is a step function when an automobile arrives, and (*b*) considering also the mechanical properties of the bridge section? **(Sec. 233)**

17-2. "Electronic Associates, Inc." give the following problem in their *Application Notes:*

DESIGN OF AN AUTOMOBILE SUSPENSION SYSTEM. To investigate the response of an automobile suspension system for selected disturbances. The system response to these disturbances for various values of the

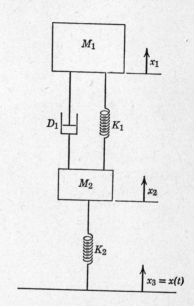

Problem 17-2

system design parameters are obtained. The most suitable values of the system parameters are determined by selecting the desirable response from the solution.

M_1 = one quarter of mass of automobile
    = 25 slugs
M_2 = mass of the wheel and axle = 2 slugs
K_1 = spring constant of main auto spring
    = 1,000 lb/ft
K_2 = spring constant of tire (assumed linear)
    = 4,500 lb/ft
D_1 = shock absorber damping constant
    = 20 lb sec/ft
x_1 = displacement of automobile body

x_2 = displacement of wheel

x_3 = roadway profile displacement

$$x_1 = x_2 = \frac{dx_1}{dt} = \frac{dx_2}{dt} = 0 \qquad \text{at } t = 0$$

$x_3 = x(t)$

Find displacement of automobile body x_1/x_3 and wheel x_2/x_3 for a deflection in road profile (x_3 is a square pulse of 35 milliseconds duration).

[*Note:* Interpret x_3 as an impulse and find transfer functions $\hat{x}_1/\hat{x}_3$ and $\hat{x}_2/\hat{x}_3$. Write numerator and denominator (of each) as a polynominal with *numerical* coefficients of s; these polynominals need not be factored. It is easiest to start by writing differential equations of force on M_1 and M_2. Use 1 slug = 32.2 lb.]   **(Sec. 233)**

17-3. Show that the potentiometer circuit can be represented exactly by a single block if the transfer function, instead of being k, is as given in equation 234-1.   **(Sec. 234)**

17-4. Show that Figure 234a, for the feedback model of the potentiometer, gives the same result as the exact equation 234-1.   **(Sec. 234)**

17-5. The RC circuit of Figure 201a has the transfer function $\hat{v}_2/\hat{v}_1 = 1/(1 + s\tau)$ if output current is zero, with $\tau = RC$. It is

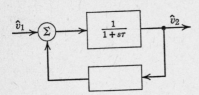

Problem 17-5

desired to represent this circuit *exactly* by a block diagram as shown when its output current is *not* zero, but is v_2/R_0. What must be the transfer function of the feed-back block?   **(Sec. 234)**

17-6. The RC circuit of Figure 202a has the transfer function $s\tau/(1 + s\tau)$ if output current is zero, with $\tau = RC$. It is desired to represent this circuit exactly by a block diagram when the output current is not zero, but is v_2/R_0. Referring to Figure 236a, let G be $s\tau/(1 + s\tau)$. What must H be if the two blocks are to represent the device with output current?   **(Sec. 234)**

17-7. In Figure 236a let forward block G be a potentiometer for which the transfer function is given by equation 234-1. What must be the transfer function H of the feedback block for the overall transfer function of the two blocks together to be exactly $\hat{v}_2 = k\hat{v}_1$? Consider that the output v_2 feeds into a resistance R_0. Would use of a potentiometer with such a feedback circuit be a practical means of obtaining the desired output? Consider whether there are simpler means.   **(Sec. 235)**

17-8. Describe a system that is nonlinear. Write the differential equation for the system to show that the equation is a nonlinear differential equation (see Section 241). Which of the following methods can be used on nonlinear systems: (a) energy balance, (b) minimization of inductance, (c) differential equations, (d) Laplace transformation, (e) transfer functions?   **(Sec. 239)**

BEYOND
chapter 18

240. Further Investigations

Now with this background, this study of magnetic devices and a few devices of other kinds, where do we go? What is beyond?

The next subject depends on one's interest. Up to a certain point we all need to know the basic ideas of electromechanical systems. Beyond that point some of us specialize, perhaps in one of the following areas:

1. There is much more to be known about linear magnetic devices. There are many other such devices, perhaps less common than the examples of this book. There are additional means of control. Transfer functions can be of third degree, fourth degree, and higher. (References 40, 146, 187B.)

2. Rotating machinery can be studied much more fully. Only the most basic ideas of rotating machines have been presented, and this study can become increasingly fascinating as the careful investigations of the last half century are reviewed. Recent discussions are from the point of view of the similarity of various machines. (References 78E, F, G, 215.)

3. The study of systems has barely been introduced. There are other points of view, other and more powerful methods of analysis (of which the root-locus method is outstanding), and interesting means of design. Many systems are electromechanical, particularly for control. Other systems may be mechanical, or electrical, or they may be pneumatic, or hydraulic, or even economic. (References 83, 173, 187A, B, C, D, 232, 238A, B, C.)

4. Nonlinearity is typical of many electromechanical devices, particularly those that develop mechanical translation and those that involve magnetic saturation. (References 78D, 187A.)

(240)

5. Energy can be converted by other than magnetic means. We have spoken, for instance, of the electric field in the capacitor microphone. Also, piezoelectric conversion suggested sonar hydrophones and the quartz-crystal frequency standard. A number of other electromechanical processes are of interest, too, and some of them can be of practical importance.

6. New ideas are coming quickly in this fruitful time. New methods are being applied to devices that did not exist a few years ago. New uses are being planned even now for devices that exist only on the drawing boards.

A few of these topics invite a little more discussion in the following brief sections.

241. Linearity

Many—indeed, most—of the concepts and methods of this book have been limited to linear operations. A device is called linear, and the equation describing it is a linear equation, if the response of the device is proportional to the applied disturbance.*

Thus a spring that obeys Hooke's law is linear; the stretch is proportional to the force. The charge on a linear capacitor is proportional to the applied voltage. The electrokinetic momentum λ (flux linkages) of a linear inductor is proportional to the current.

On the other hand, a spring stretched beyond its elastic limit becomes nonlinear. A coil with an iron core in which there is magnetic saturation is nonlinear; it does not have constant inductance. A transistor is nonlinear; in general, current in a crystalline semiconductor is not proportional to applied voltage.

An elastic spring is linear, and the force required to stretch it is proportional to the displacement. But the force required to pull a piece of iron away from a magnet is not proportional to the displacement; the relation is nonlinear. Indeed, the magnetic force actually grows less as the displacement becomes greater, and in certain extreme but well-known examples the inverse-square law is a good approximation of magnetic force.

Many electromechanical devices are nonlinear. In Section 27 for

---

* The mathematical definition of linearity is more precise. If a disturbance $x_1(t)$ gives a response $y_1(t)$, and a disturbance $x_2(t)$ gives a response $y_2(t)$, then if the system is linear the disturbance $ax_1(t) + bx_2(t)$ gives the response $ay_1(t) + by_2(t)$, where a and b are any finite numbers.

instance, the flux in a phonograph pickup device was expressed by equation 27-1. The relation between Φ and u in this equation is not linear. As a result, the relation between induced electromotive force in the pickup coil and motion of the stylus is nonlinear.

It is regrettable that so many electromechanical relations are non-linear, for nonlinear equations are much harder to solve than linear equations. However, some method of approximation can ordinarily be used.

The usual procedure is to "linearize" a nonlinear equation by neglecting certain terms. The example of Section 27, for instance, was worked in this way.

When the response of a device is small, its deviation from linear behavior is small. This statement merely says, in accord with Taylor's theorem, that a small section of any continuous function may be approximated by a linear function; that a sufficiently short length of any smooth curve is nearly a straight line. If it is not obvious in any particular equation that certain terms are much smaller than other terms (we found it obvious in Section 27), Taylor's series is used to expand nonlinear functions, and higher order terms are then dropped. By this means (as in equation 27-2) a linear relation is obtained.

For problems involving *small signals* this process of linearization is effective. It has been formalized as the method of *small perturbations* (Reference 187A). It can be used when a disturbance and its response are small enough to make the linear approximation acceptable even though the relation involved is truly nonlinear.

242. Methods for Nonlinear Problems

Large-signal problems in nonlinear systems are more difficult. Exact solution of the nonlinear differential equation that describes action of the system is sometimes possible, but Laplace transformation and most of the methods of this book are ruled out because the basic principle of superposition does not apply to nonlinear relations. Usually an approximate solution of some kind is the most suitable.

Linearization implies the acceptance of a straight-line characteristic in place of a curved characteristic to show the relation between two variables. An example is the acceptance of a straight line, which is approximate, instead of a curve, which may be exact, to show the relation between ampere-turns of magnetomotive force in a coil and the resulting magnetic flux in a core of iron.

(242)

However, if the departure from linearity is very marked, it may well be that the assumption of simple linearity is not good enough. In the example of the magnetic core, for instance, the magnetization curve might not satisfactorily be represented by a single straight line. The magnetization curve can then be more closely represented by one straight line in one range of magnetomotive force, joined to another straight line that approximates the curve in another range of magnetomotive force. Different linear approximations are thus used in different ranges. This attack on problems, an improved form of linearization, is called the *piecewise-linear* method.

If a piecewise-linear solution is not suitable, the mathematics of *nonlinear analysis* provides other means of attacking nonlinear differential equations. These are sometimes formal, sometimes numerical, and sometimes graphical, and they can be as nearly exact as one's patience permits. When numerical methods are used the computations are likely to be lengthy and repetitive, and a digital computer will often save time in doing the arithmetic.

Analogy is sometimes helpful in finding solutions to nonlinear problems. An *analog computer* provides a convenient and systematic means of obtaining a solution in the form of a curve that may be drawn on paper or displayed on the screen of a cathode-ray tube.

Finally, there is always available the method of *finite differences*. This, also called the *step-by-step* method, is often the most attractive approach. The solution of a problem begins from the initial conditions, which are known. Relations among the variables are determined from these initial conditions, and are assumed to remain unchanged for the short but finite time of an initial step. At the end of the brief time of this first step the relations are modified to be consistent with new conditions, and these new relations are then applied through the duration of a second step. This process continues, step by step, indefinitely, and if the steps are short enough the accuracy can be high. An electronic digital computer is a great help in obtaining precise results by this method.

The excellence of the method of finite differences is that it can be used to solve any problem whatsoever, provided the essential physical relations are known. It is, indeed, an approximation to the manner in which physical behavior actually takes place.*

---

* A brief presentation of graphical and step-by-step methods is given in Chapter VIII of Reference 145.

The ultimate in the step-by-step method is achieved mechanically by the differential analyzer, as described by V. Bush (Reference 242A).

An example of a nonlinear electromechanical problem solved by graphical

Fortunately, linear approximations are satisfactory for handling a great many of the devices and problems of electromechanics. That is the justification for discussing, in the foregoing chapters, only linear relations and those that can be linearized without difficulty.

243. Criteria

Once in a while, but hardly more than a few times in a century, science is applied in such a new context that previous experience is of little value. The criteria of good engineering are then changed by the new circumstances. A solution of practical problems that was thoroughly poor for one use may be a brilliant success in the new environment.

Even now, in this present decade, we have the necessity and the intriguing opportunity of considering electromechanical problems in two new environments. One is the high temperature and untouchability of nuclear power. The other is the lightweight subminiaturization of space vehicles.

Surely the basic engineering criterion of achieving the best result with the least expenditure remains to guide us. Perhaps the expenditure may still be measured in dollars, or at least in materials and effort. But our evaluation of the best result is utterly changed. Long life is of no value whatever for a device in a rocket that will be blown to its ultimate shreds in 35 seconds. And the weight of iron in an electromagnetic pump, however desirable for a nuclear power plant in a submarine, might be absurd for a vehicle designed to go into orbit about the moon.

244. An Electromagnetic Pump

Let us think of a pump for the liquid that carries useful heat from the reactive core of a nuclear reactor. There are ever so many different kinds of mechanical pumps—piston pumps, centrifugal pumps, gear pumps—but the cooling liquid from a pile is dangerously radioactive. It must not leak. Bearings with stuffing boxes are not entirely dependable in the course of years. And when the liquid that is in fact a melted metal is at the temperature of melted sodium, or

---

means can be found in Reference 242B, and a solution of a nonlinear mechanical problem by electrical analogy in Reference 242C.

(244)

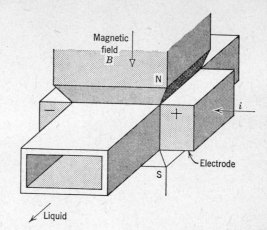

Figure 244a. Pressure in the electromagnetic pump is at right angles to the electric current and magnetic field.

a sodium-potassium alloy, or lead-bismuth eutectic, this dangerous liquid becomes exceedingly difficult to contain with dependability.

Then the electromagnetic pump is used, for it has no moving parts, no stuffing box, no leakage. The Bli law is the principle on which it works.

There are two major types of electromagnetic pumps. The d-c pump passes current through the liquid to be pumped (and since the liquid is a metal it is highly conducting) at right angles to a strong magnetic field, and the result is a pressure in the liquid that is normal to both current and field. Figure 244a shows diagrammatically the essential parts, and the figure on page 30 gives a cross section. The good points of such a pump are obvious; the disadvantages are equally plain. The pressure produced is limited by the possible magnetic field strength B and the possible electric current i. Designers talk about 20,000 amperes at half a volt, from homopolar generators. The limit of current is what the electrodes and the liquid itself will stand without overheating.

The actual configuration need not be much like Figure 244a. The force on a column of liquid is Bli. Useful output of the pump can be increased by using the same magnetic flux several times, and this can be done by having the liquid pass repeatedly through the same magnetic field. Also, output of the pump can be increased by using the same current a number of times, and this also is accomplished by ingenious design of the liquid flow. The length l in which the pump acts can be increased at will, though this increases the expense in proportion. With all the designer can do, electric

(244)

current to operate the pump remains excessive, and electrodes exposed to the hot liquid metal are subject to corrosion. (References 244A and B.)

245. The Induction Pump

Despite these difficulties the d-c pump is used, but both troubles are overcome by the a-c induction pump. The a-c pump works on the same Bli principle, but current is induced in the liquid metal by induction, by changing B, and no electrodes are needed. In fact, the pump is an induction motor in which the squirrel cage is replaced by the liquid that is being pumped.

Figure 245a suggests this device, although hardly in a practical form. As shown, the iron is half of the stator of an induction motor plus a return path for magnetic flux after the flux passes through the pumped liquid. The winding is that of a three-phase induction motor, and it produces a flux pattern that rotates clockwise, from bottom to top. The changing flux induces current in the liquid, and since the conducting liquid under each stator pole is equivalent to one short-circuited turn this current in the liquid may be very large. The magnetic field then exerts a mechanical force on the liquid because of this induced current. In the diagram, force on the liquid is in a clockwise direction, as it would be on the rotor of an induction motor.

Again ingenuity of the designer suggests many better forms for an induction pump. Both iron and copper can be saved by a more symmetrical arrangement (References 245A and B), but the basic

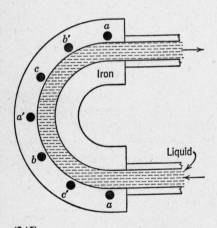

Figure 245a. Half of an induction motor is a pump.

(245)

principle of operation is as shown. Electric current in the stator can be kept to a relatively small value by using a great many stator turns. However, the magnetizing current is large, and unavoidably so as long as the pumped liquid is non-magnetic. It will be seen that this induction pump has the advantage of having no moving parts and no electrodes or other metal parts exposed to the corrosive action of the hot liquid metal. The electromagnetic induction pump is therefore more useful than the d-c style.

246. A Flow Meter

Like other energy converters, the electromagnetic pump can transfer energy in the opposite direction and be a generator. A device almost the same as the d-c pump is used as an indicating instrument. A voltmeter connected to the electrodes will indicate the speed at which liquid passes through the magnetic field (Reference 244B). This method of measurement is used not only for liquid metals but also for any reasonably conducting liquid such as the sea water ballast that is pumped back and forth to prevent rolling of a ship.

An extremely small device that is basically the same is used to measure the flow of blood in an artery. The artery must be exposed so that electrodes can be brought in contact with its wall, between small permanent magnets, but no puncture need be made. (References 246A, B.)

247. Magnetohydrodynamics

The same device is more exciting as a hopeful means of getting energy from a fast-moving stream of gas. The gas must be electrically conducting. It must therefore be highly ionized; it must be what is called a plasma. This seems to mean that it must be very hot, perhaps comparable to an electric arc in temperature. A mere flame is hardly hot enough.

When ionized gas shoots between the poles of Figure 244a, the positive ions are driven by the magnetic field toward one electrode and the negative ions or electrons toward the other. Electric current can then be drawn from the electrodes as the ions raise one to a positive and the other to a negative potential. The force is magnetic, but the source of energy is the fast-moving gas that leaves the generator more slowly than it enters.

Thus mechanical energy of the gas stream becomes electrical

energy for a d-c load. But the gas must be highly ionized. "In order to ionize air to an extent which will make it sufficiently conductive for this purpose, it must be heated to approximately 4,000 K (6,740 F). By 'seeding' with an alkali metal vapor such as potassium, the temperature can be lowered to approximately 2,500 K (4,040 F), but this is still a lot hotter than engineers are accustomed to handle, except in the case of nose cones, rocket engines, and electric arcs, where the duration is very short." (R. W. Porter, Reference 247A.)

Engineers are thinking of MHD power generation (the lovely word *magnetohydrodynamics* refers to the motion of an ionized gas or plasma as determined by the gas laws and by Maxwell's electromagnetic equations at the same time) in terms of hundreds of thousands of kilowatts. On a small scale it is possible but not efficient. Only a few kilowatts are now being generated by this means, and those few for only a few minutes. (References 247A, B, C, E.) But it is "hoped to be operating an MHD generator in a utility's central plant by 1970." (Reference 247C.)

"There is no longer any doubt," says Porter (Reference 247A), "that an MHD converter will work—for a little while at least. The immediate engineering problems are concerned with learning how to make it work for thousands of hours. . . ."

But where is the energy to come from, the high-speed gas? Only a nuclear reactor seems to provide so much power, at so high a temperature. Gas will escape at tremendous speed from the reactor in which it is heated, and if the heat is great enough it will be ionized to a plasma. Thus the conditions for MHD generation are attained.

In fact, fusion power seems more suitable for MHD generation than fission power, when and if the thermonuclear power of fusion becomes available. For fusion power, as for MHD generators, we think in millions of kilowatts, and temperatures incredibly high. Perhaps MHD generation can be used in a "topping" unit, to remove the first energy from gas before it delivers power to a turbine. The gas will exhaust from the MHD unit still at the high temperature required for ionization, and a generator of another type can then be used to recover more energy from the exhaust gas.

It has been proposed that oscillations of the thermonuclear plasma might provide electric power. This suggests an electromagnetic generator of the induction type, with magnetic coils to receive the power, but no electrodes. "In principle . . . this can be done for a fraction of the released energy. . . . However, much of the energy released . . . is in the form of neutrons. This energy can be recovered only by utilizing a neutron absorbing blanket and a heat cycle." (Mills, Reference 247D.)

So here we have interesting possibilities, but no certainty.

248. Ion Propulsion

However, it is really in space vehicles that a totally new environment must be considered. Here heavy things are not pulled down by gravity. Temperatures vary from the extreme cold of shadow to the extreme heat of the sun's radiation, with ultraviolet and perhaps x-ray radiation accompanying visible light from the sun. Space is not air, but vacuum. The mechanical designer must not forget that some metals tend to weld together, even though cold, in vacuum, and the electrical designer must remember that air at low pressure ionizes more readily than air at high pressure. Sparking and corona discharge take place more easily in low-pressure air than at normal pressure, although a complete vacuum is a perfect insulator.

But, above all, the important new factor is the extreme cost of weight, which may run to thousands of dollars per pound. The cost, of course, is not the value of the material, but the expense of launching it into its orbit; the extra cost of vehicle and fuel. Perhaps it is worth spending a thousand dollars to save an ounce of weight, or half an ounce. This new problem may open a radically new field of electromechanics. (Reference 248.)

For instance, the ion engine seems to be a practical electromechanical means of holding a vehicle on its course. It "ionizes propellant atoms by electrical bombardment and derives its thrust by expelling the ionized atoms electrostatically." (Reference 247B.) Is it light and small? The answer is yes. It is, then, a contender for being carried aloft in a vehicle, to help level and steer. The cost of manufacture is of little importance, but the cost of launching is great. Does it need gravity to operate? No. Does temperature matter? No. Will it work in vacuum? Yes, if electricity can be applied without breakdown. Good; it is worth thought and experiment.

An ion engine is an interesting electromechanical device because it uses the electric rather than the magnetic field to acclerate material particles. See Figure 248a. Positive ions, perhaps of cesium, are produced. There are various methods; thermionic ions can be emitted by a hot filament properly coated. Then these ions, because of their positive charge, are greatly accelerated by an electric field. As they gain momentum an equal but opposite momentum is im-

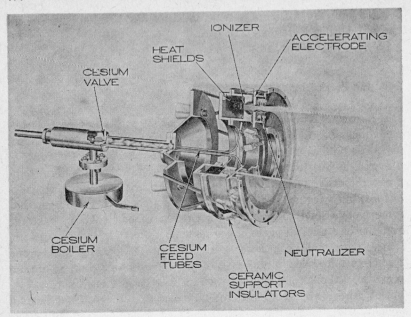

Figure 248a. A device for ion propulsion of a space vehicle; thrust approximately 1.6 millipounds. (Courtesy of Hughes Research Laboratories and of H. S. Seifert.)

parted to the device that drives them. The ions are shot off into space and lost; their momentum does not further affect the space vehicle from which they were sent. But the opposite momentum remains with the vehicle, for changing the speed or the orientation. Thus the momentum of the vehicle is under control as long as the supply of ions lasts.

The ions are very light; indeed, this is their outstanding virtue. They can be given tremendous velocity by the electric field, and so their momentum becomes appreciable though slight. Momentum of a vehicle could be changed by throwing out buckshot, too, but the momentum of buckshot is likely to be more mass (which is expensive) and less velocity, so it follows that under these extraordinary circumstances, ions are cheaper.

If an ion engine is to be used, it requires electric power for operation. Where is the electric power to come from?

249. Like a Teatray in the Sky

Power from a battery? Lead-acid battery? Too heavy. Nickel-cadmium? Not much better. A primary battery with zinc and silver electrodes? Yes. This is several times lighter, and worth consideration if it is needed for only a few hours, to deliver well under a kilowatt. A fuel cell, of the type that combines hydrogen and oxygen in porous membranes to give water and electrical energy? This seems even better. Like everything else, development work is required. (Reference 248.)

Is there some means of getting energy from the radiation of the sun? A hopeful source. A thermoelectric cell? This includes the thermocouple of two metals, and its more modern equivalent of p-type and n-type semiconductors with one hot junction and one cold. No; perhaps it is too heavy, and certainly there is no answer to the problem of how the cool junction is to be kept cool since heat radiators are heavy and occupy too much space. (References 247A, 248, 249A.)

Photovoltaic cells? Yes, these are used. They constitute the "paddles" sometimes thrust out by satellites when they are in orbit, or cells in the surface of other satellites. The photovoltaic cell is of silicon, with a thin p layer on the surface of n material. Something like a hundred watts can be obtained from a square meter of solar cells. (Reference 249B; also 247B, 248.)

Thermionic devices that give energy to ions in the narrow space between electrodes by emitting them from a cathode heated by the sun's rays? Perhaps. The thermionic converter is light and compact. The hot element is very hot, 2,400 C or more, so the cooler element need not be so very cool, perhaps 700 C. "The thermionic converter appears to have a greater growth potential than other methods of generating electrical power for long duration applications. The high temperatures at which the device operates permit the use of small light-weight radiators (. . . a major stumbling block in the design of light-weight thermoelectric converters)." (From Reference 248; see also 247A.) The thermionic converter is improved by choosing cathode and anode materials with appropriate work functions (a high Fermi level for the anode), and the space-charge barrier of high-vacuum devices is kept down by filling the interelectrode space with some such gas as cesium vapor. Perhaps the thermionic converter offers a possible source of energy for vehicles that travel for many days; however there are (as Porter says) imposing problems.

(249)

Can a radioactive source aboard a vehicle be used to give energy? Again the answer is maybe. (References 248, 249A.) A supply of a radioactive isotope is light and small. Polonium or tritium might be suitable, and they, produced by nuclear reactors, are readily available. They give energy as heat, which must then be converted to mechanical or electrical energy, and the devices already mentioned might again be considered. The inevitable decay of radio-active substances threatens to produce too much energy at first and too little later, unless some energy storage is possible.

All these are energy-conversion problems, though not electro-mechanical. Many of them require conversion from heat to elec-tricity. This is not electromechanics; this is another field. Go, and may you fare well.

MAGNETIC CIRCUITS
appendix 1

Electromechanics is presented with the expectation that the reader is acquainted with magnetic circuit ideas and terminology. This appendix is offered as a quick review of the subject, but it may also serve if needs must be as an introduction to the elementary ideas required in this book.

A1-1. The Magnetic Circuit

It is customary to draw an analogy between a magnetic circuit and an electric circuit, between magnetomotive force (mmf) and electromotive force (emf), between flux and current, between reluctance and resistance, permeance and conductance, permeability and conductivity, and so on. This analogy is helpful if it is not pushed too far, in which case it tends to break down.

Figure 1a shows diagrammatically a magnetic circuit. It is drawn with a certain rather obsolete type of electrical machine in mind. The circle might represent a cylindrical iron armature, with the C-shaped field structure, also of iron, providing a path for magnetic flux. A typical flux path is indicated by the dash line. Between armature and field poles there are air gaps; these are necessary to permit rotation of the armature, and they are usually as short (in the dimension parallel to the magnetic field) as practical construction permits.

Magnetomotive force in this magnetic circuit is supplied by coils wound on the field structure. Representing magnetomotive force by $\mathfrak{F}$,

$$\mathfrak{F} = Ni \qquad \text{amperes} \qquad (1\text{-}1)$$

where N is the number of turns of the current-carrying coil
i is current in the coil (amperes)

(A1-1)

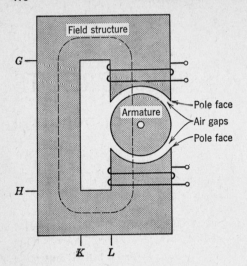

G

H

K L

Figure 1a. A magnetic circuit.

The unit of magnetomotive force is commonly and descriptively called ampere-turns, but for purposes of dimensional analysis it is merely *amperes*, the number of turns being considered a dimensionless number.

Magnetic potential difference (scalar potential difference) is analogous to electric potential difference or voltage. The magnetic potential difference across each element of the magnetic circuit is

$$\text{MPD} = \Phi\mathcal{R} \tag{1-2}$$

where Φ is the magnetic flux in that element (webers)

$\mathcal{R}$ is the reluctance of that element (amperes/weber)

The unit of magnetic potential difference, like the unit of magnetomotive force, is the ampere (or ampere-turn).

This equation 1-2 is analogous to Ohm's law, $v = iR$. It leads to a circuital law analogous to Kirchhoff's voltage law for the electric circuit. In the magnetic circuit a rise of magnetic potential is produced by the magnetomotive force of linking ampere-turns, as a rise of electric potential is produced in an electric circuit by the electromotive force of a generator. Then, as one follows around the magnetic circuit, the magnetic potential falls; there is a drop of potential in each part of the circuit. *The potential rise*, the sum of mmf's in a magnetic circuit, *is equal to the sum of the magnetic potential drops in all the elements* of that circuit. That is,

$$\mathcal{F} = \Sigma(\text{MPD}) \tag{1-3}$$

where Σ indicates summation.

(A1-1)

A1-2. Computation of Reluctance

For any uniform section of the magnetic circuit, as for example from G to H in Figure 1a, the reluctance is

$$\mathfrak{R} = \frac{l}{\mu A} \tag{2-1}$$

where μ is permeability of the section (henrys/meter)

l is the length of the section (meters)

A is the cross-sectional area of the section (meters^2)

The permeability of empty space, or air, usually called μ_0, is $4\pi \cdot 10^{-7}$, or $12.566 \cdot 10^{-7}$. The *permeability* of iron and of useful magnetic alloys may be a few hundred to some thousands of times as great. This ratio, μ/μ_0, is called the *relative* permeability of the iron or other material. Its value is determined, for purposes of analysis or design, from tables, curves, or other experimental data.*

The total reluctance of a magnetic circuit is the sum of the reluctances of the sections that are put together in series. The circuit of Figure 1a has at least four sections: the field structure, the armature, and the two air gaps. Clearly equation 2-1 applies only to a section of unchanging cross section and permeability. If the section K-L of the figure is of different cross-sectional area from the section G-H its reluctance will be computed separately and added. On the other hand, if all the field structure has the same cross section a single computation may be enough, using the average length of flux paths through the structure from pole face to pole face. An accurate computation taking into account the curvature of flux paths around corners is not entirely easy and fortunately is not often necessary.

Reluctance of each air gap is found, using equation 2-1 with $\mu = \mu_0$ as the permeability. The length of the air gap l is the spacing between the armature surface and the pole face. If this spacing is not everywhere uniform but is approximately so, an average may be used for l. The effective length of air gap to a toothed armature is a few per cent greater than the distance from the pole face to the tips of the teeth.

In considering the value to use for A it must be remembered that

---

*For good charts, see Chapter 13 of Attwood, Reference A1-2. Three of Attwood's charts are reproduced here, by permission, as Figures 5a, b, and c.

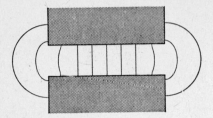

Figure 2a. Fringing of air-gap flux.

magnetic flux spreads out somewhat in a gap between parallel iron surfaces. Thus in Figure 2a the "fringing" effect is shown. The *effective* cross-sectional area of the air gap is a little greater than the area of the iron pole face. An approximation sometimes used in computing A for the air gap is to increase each dimension of a rectangular pole face (or the diameter of a circular pole face) by the length of the air gap. This correction is negligible for short gaps, and inadequate for long gaps, but is useful in an important practical range. However, if moderate accuracy is good enough, the uncorrected area of the pole face may be used as A for the air gap.

Reluctance of a part of the circuit that has non-uniform cross section, such as the armature, can theoretically be found by integration. The section is divided into many slices, the dividing surfaces being magnetic equipotential surfaces. Permitting the number of slices to increase without limit, we find the reluctance as the integral which is the limit of the sum of the reluctances of the slices:

$$\mathcal{R} = \int \frac{dl}{\mu A} \tag{2-2}$$

This is a more general statement than equation 2-1, which it includes.

A1-3. Series and Parallel Relations

As stated by equation 1-3, the total magnetomotive force applied to a magnetic circuit is equal to the sum of the magnetic potential drops in the elements of the circuit. If the flux in the magnetic circuit is Φ and the *total* reluctance of the *closed* circuit is $\mathcal{R}$,

$$\mathcal{F} = Ni = \Phi\mathcal{R} \tag{3-1}$$

Adding reluctances of the elements that are in series to obtain total reluctance is analogous to adding resistances in an electric circuit. A similar analogy applies to elements of a magnetic circuit

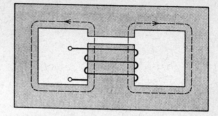

Figure 3a. Parallel elements in a magnetic circuit.

arranged in *parallel*. In Figure 3a, for example, the flux is partly in the right leg of a three-legged magnetic circuit, and partly in the left leg, while all the flux is in the central leg and (ideally) crosses the air gap. The reluctance of the left and right legs may be combined in parallel, and the result added to the reluctance of the central leg (including the air gap) to find the total reluctance of the circuit.

Inductance. An electric circuit that produces flux in a magnetic circuit (as, for instance, the winding about the iron core in Figure 3a) is said to have a certain *inductance*. Inductance is equal to the number of flux linkages produced per ampere of current:

$$L = \frac{N\Phi}{i} \tag{3-2}$$

where L is inductance (henrys)

    i is current in the electric circuit (amperes)

    N is number of times this current encircles the magnetic circuit

    Φ is flux produced in the magnetic circuit (webers)

Combining equations 3-1 and 2, the inductance of a coil is proportional to the square of the number of turns of the coil, and inversely proportional to the reluctance of the magnetic circuit:

$$L = \frac{N^2}{\mathcal{R}} \tag{3-3}$$

A1-4. Circuit and Field Relations

The foregoing discussion has dealt with such magnetic-circuit quantities as flux, reluctance, and magnetic potential difference. Their macroscopic relations can be derived from the familiar microscopic equation of the magnetic field:

(A1-4)

$$B = \mu H \tag{4-1}$$

where B is magnetic flux density (webers/meter^2)
   H is magnetic intensity (amperes/meter)
   μ is permeability (henrys/meter)

B is related to flux, μ to reluctance, and H to magnetic potential difference as follows.

In a uniform magnetic field, total flux is the product of flux density and normal cross-sectional area:

$$\Phi = BA \tag{4-2}$$

Magnetic potential difference is the product of magnetic intensity and length in the direction of the field:

$$\mathrm{MPD} = Hl \tag{4-3}$$

Reluctance is related to permeability by equation 2-1. It is interesting to notice, from this equation, that the reluctance of a unit cube of a homogeneous material is equal to the reciprocal of its permeability.

In a non-uniform magnetic field, the products of the foregoing equations become integrals. Using the dot product of vector notation (Section 10), we obtain

$$\Phi = \int \mathbf{B} \cdot d\mathbf{A} \tag{4-4}$$

$$\mathrm{MPD} = \int \mathbf{H} \cdot d\mathbf{l} \tag{4-5}$$

and reluctance is given by equation 2-2 instead of 2-1.

A1-5. Magnetic Circuit Computations

Magnetic circuit computations are approximate at best. The precision of electric circuit computations cannot be attained, mainly because magnetic flux is not confined to the iron of a magnetic circuit as completely as current is confined to the copper of an electric circuit.

The basic reason is that the permeability of iron is of the order of magnitude of 10^3 or 10^4 times the permeability of space or of any material that may surround the magnetic circuit, whereas the conductivity of copper is of the order of magnitude of 10^{22} or 10^{23} times the conductivity of good insulating material, such as rubber, in which the conductor may be enclosed. This great difference makes leakage

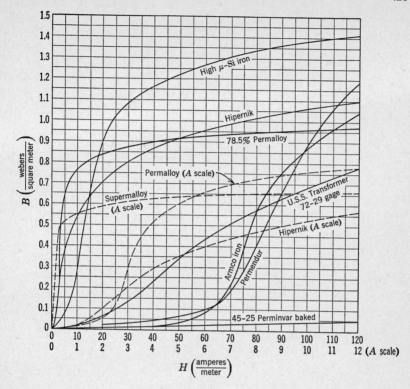

Figure 5a. Magnetization curves. (Courtesy S. S. Attwood.)

flux from a magnetic circuit something like 10^{18} (a million-million-million) times greater than leakage current from a well-insulated electric circuit of the same geometry.

To keep leakage of magnetic flux to a minimum is perhaps the major problem in magnetic circuit design. The iron of magnetic circuits is made as short and thick as possible to keep down reluctance (as suggested in Figure 3a for instance), and it is essential that the coil that produces a *rise* of magnetic potential be located as near as possible to that part of the circuit, usually an air gap, in which the greater part of the *fall* of magnetic potential takes place. Thus in Figures 1a and 3a the coils are located quite close to the air gaps, and not at the other side of the magnetic circuit, which would leave much more opportunity for leakage flux to escape from the circuit.

There are two considerations of great importance in magnetic circuit computations, one fortunate and one unfortunate. The fortunate

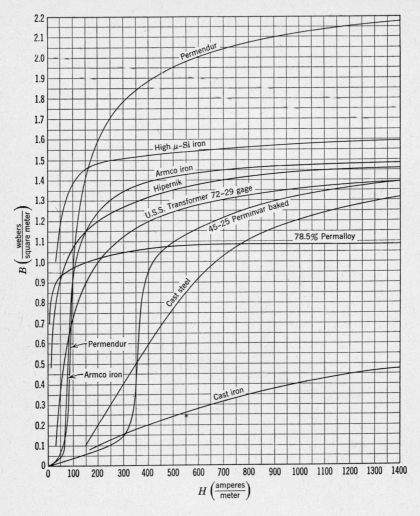

Figure 5b. Magnetization curves. (Courtesy S. S. Attwood.)

consideration is that in any electromechanical device the magnetic circuit must necessarily have an air gap to permit mechanical motion, and the permeability of iron is so much greater than that of air that the reluctance of the air gap is likely to be most of the reluctance of the magnetic circuit—provided the flux density is low enough so that the iron is not saturated. This makes magnetic circuit computations particularly easy. By assuming that all the reluctance

(A1-5)

Relative permeability μ_r

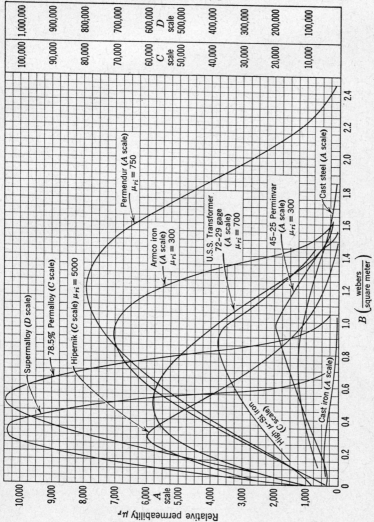

Figure 5c. μ versus B curves. (Courtesy S. S. Attwood.)

425

(A1-5)

is in the air gap it is necessary only to consider that the magnetic potential difference across the gap (or the gaps, if there are more than one in series) is equal to the total magnetomotive force.

If the magnetic field in an air gap is uniform (that is, if B and H are constant throughout the gap or, for practical purposes, approximately so), equation 4-3 gives H in terms of gap length and the magnetic potential difference across the gap. Assuming that the permeability of the iron of the magnetic circuit is so great compared to that of the air gap that reluctance of the iron may be neglected, we equate this magnetic potential difference to the ampere-turns of magnetomotive force:

$$\mathcal{F} = Ni = Hl \tag{5-1}$$

Since B in the air gap is related to H by μ_0 (which is $4\pi \cdot 10^{-7}$ henrys/meter, or $12.566 \cdot 10^{-7}$),

$$B = \mu_0 H = \mu_0 \frac{Ni}{l} \tag{5-2}$$

When the assumptions are justified, this is a convenient equation for computing magnetic flux density in an air gap.

If the magnetic field in an air gap is not uniform, equation 4-3 does not apply. The integral form of equation 4-5 can then be used, but the solution of the integral equation for unknown H is not easy. It is often best to find H or B with the aid of a flux plot.

So much for the fortunate fact that in a magnetic circuit with an air gap the iron can often be considered to have infinite permeability and zero reluctance (compared to the air gap). The unfortunate consideration is that practical design often requires, for economic reasons, so high a value of B that the iron is magnetically saturated. Its permeability then becomes less (see Figures 5a, b, and c, courtesy of S. S. Attwood, Reference A1-2) and the reluctance of saturated iron may be a significant part of the reluctance of the entire magnetic circuit including the air gaps. Since, with saturation, permeability is variable, a function of B, some kind of numerical or graphical solution is then necessary. These we shall not consider here.

A1-6. Amperian Current

Finally, our discussion of magnetic circuits should be related to the concept of Amperian current as discussed in Section 12. From the Amperian-current point of view, the mathematics is not changed, but the concepts are totally different. Now we forget about any analogy between reluctance and electrical resistance. Now we consider that the same magnetic intensity is required to produce a given magnetic flux density in any material, whether air or iron. Now we say that current in a coil produces a stronger field in an iron core than in an air core because there is added to the relatively small magnetomotive force of current in the coil the large magnetomotive force of Amperian current in the iron.

With Amperian current in mind, we write for magnetic flux density

$$B = \mu_0(H + \chi H) \qquad (6\text{-}1)$$

The first term in the parentheses, H, is the magnetic intensity produced by current in the electric circuit. The second term, χH, is the contribution of Amperian current, caused by electron spin in the iron and it is χ times as great as the effect of current in the external circuit. This means that every ampere-turn of current in the coil lines up the electrons enough to produce the equivalent of χ amperes of Amperian current. In iron the numerical value of χ may be several thousand, and in certain alloys (see Figure 5c) it reaches several hundred thousand.

In this concept, permeability has nothing to do with the ease with which magnetic flux passes through a given material; any such idea has been discarded. Permeability is now a measure of the effectiveness of Amperian current in increasing the magnetic intensity. To see this, equation 6-1 can be written as

$$B = \mu_0(1 + \chi)H \qquad (6\text{-}2)$$

and comparison with equation 4-1 shows that

$$\frac{\mu}{\mu_0} = (1 + \chi) \qquad (6\text{-}3)$$

Thus in iron with relative permeability of 1,000, χ is 999. It will be seen that numerical values of χ and of relative permeability μ/μ_0 are practically the same in all good ferromagnetic materials.

It is rather impressive to think of the many thousands of amperes of Amperian current produced by electron spin in quite a small piece of Permalloy when it is working with a relative permeability of a hundred thousand or more.

PROBLEMS

A1-1. Given the magnetic circuit shown with path reluctances (constant, and mostly in the air gaps) as follows:

$$R_a = 1.84 \cdot 10^6 \text{ ampere-turns per weber}$$

$$R_b = 1.58 \cdot 10^6 \text{ ampere-turns per weber}$$

$$R_c = 1.32 \cdot 10^6 \text{ ampere-turns per weber}$$

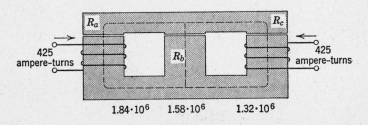

Problem A1-1

Find the flux through the center leg b with 425 ampere-turns applied (in the positive direction) to both paths a and c.   **(Sec. A1-3)**

A1-2. Repeat Problem A1-1 when the magnetomotive force in the left-hand coil is 100 ampere-turns and that in the right-hand coil is 170 ampere-turns.   **(Sec. A1-3)**

A1-3. The electromagnet shown in Figure 37a has the following dimensions: pole face at A, 2 by 2 cm. Same cross section of iron from A to the pivot. Moving armature, pivoted, cross section 2 by 2 cm. Average air gap $w = 0.1$ cm. Other dimensions needed can be scaled from the figure, which is half actual size. (a) Find the reluctance of the air gap. (b) Find the total reluctance of the magnetic circuit. (c) Find the ampere-turns necessary to make B = 0.6 weber/m², average, in the air gap. (d) What is H in the armature? (e) What is H in the air gap? (f) What is the MPD across the air gap?   **(Sec. A1-4)**

A1-4. The core of an audio-frequency transformer is 1.0 cm square and the average length of the magnetic path is 8.0 cm. Average relative permeability of the iron in the core is 4,000. (*a*) If the core is a closed iron path, with well-designed corners at which the laminations overlap, find the ampere-turns necessary to make *B* equal 0.8 weber/m². (*b*) If the core has butt joints (rather than overlapping laminations), which, though well made, are equivalent to an air gap in the core of 0.1 mm, find the ampere-turns necessary to make *B* equal 0.8 weber/m².   **(Sec. A1-4)**

A1-5. The magnetic circuit for an electric generator is shown in Section A1-1 as Figure 1*a*. The distance across each air gap is 1.2 cm. Other dimensions can be scaled from the figure, which is one-fifth actual size. The back of the field structure, from *G* to *H*, is square in cross section, and thickness of the entire magnetic circuit (normal to the page) is uniform. There are 500 turns in each coil. The field structure and armature are of Armco iron. Find the field current necessary to produce 1.0 weber/m² in the part of the field structure from *G* to *H*. What is the flux density in the air gap? (Neglect fringing at the edges of the air gap and consider the flux to be radial.) What percentage of the magnetomotive force is used in the air gap?   **(Sec. A1-5)**

A1-6. It is desired to get more output from the machine of Problem A1-5. Repeat the computation with 1.5 webers/m² in the field structure from *G* to *H*.   **(Sec. A1-5)**

COMPLEX FUNCTIONS

appendix 2

A2-1. An Electric Circuit

Those acquainted with a-c steady-state analysis will find that Appendix 2 leads to a familiar technique. A rapid reading of these sections is nevertheless suggested, to see the steps by which the demonstration proceeds.

Figure 1a shows an electric circuit containing inductance and resistance to which an alternating voltage is to be applied. The applied

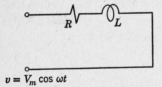

$v = V_m \cos \omega t$

Figure 1a. A circuit with alternating voltage applied.

voltage is equal to the voltage across the resistance R plus the voltage across the inductance L, and we write

$$v = R\,i + L\frac{di}{dt} \tag{1-1}$$

If the problem were reversed, and we knew the current and wanted to find the voltage, it would be quite straightforward. We would say: let i be sinusoidal, as

$$i = I_m \cos \omega t \tag{1-2}$$

and substitute this value into equation 1-1, obtaining

(A2-1)

$$v = RI_m \cos \omega t + L \frac{d}{dt} I_m \cos \omega t$$

$$= RI_m \cos \omega t - \omega L I_m \sin \omega t$$

$$= I_m \sqrt{R^2 + (\omega L)^2} \cos (\omega t + \phi) \tag{1-3}$$

where

$$\phi = \tan^{-1} \frac{\omega L}{R} \tag{1-4}$$

Hence when the current is sinusoidal the voltage is sinusoidal also. Its magnitude is related to the magnitude of the current by a quantity called impedance, Z, which is seen to be

$$Z = \sqrt{R^2 + (\omega L)^2} \tag{1-5}$$

and the voltage wave leads the current wave by a phase angle ϕ.

But clearly this argument can be worked backward, and we can say that if voltage is sinusoidal, current can be sinusoidal also, related in magnitude by Z, and lagging behind voltage by the angle ϕ. This, indeed, is the argument we shall follow, but for convenience we shall use a mathematical formulation that makes computation easier (trigonometric functions being awkward to manipulate).

However, before proceeding, it is necessary to emphasize that the solution we shall obtain for current is not the most general solution. In the previous paragraph we read that current *can be* sinusoidal. In the steady state, current *is* sinusoidal. But equation 1-1 can be satisfied by an expression for current that is the sum of a sinusoidal term *and* an exponential term. This is the general solution, which includes a transient exponential term (the complementary function, the natural response) as well as the steady-state term (the particular integral, the forced response). We shall not compute the transient term at this time, however, for we are at present concerned with steady-state behavior.

A2-2. The Complex Exponential Formulation

To avoid trigonometric functions, let us express current and voltage in the more easily handled exponential functions. By Euler's formula,

$$e^{j\omega t} = \cos \omega t + j \sin \omega t \tag{2-1}$$

The real part of the left-hand member will be written $\mathfrak{Re}\,\{e^{j\omega t}\}$, follow-

$$\tag{A2-2}$$

ing the customary mathematical notation, and the real part of the right-hand member is obviously $\cos \omega t$. Equating these two real components, we obtain

$$\cos \omega t = \mathfrak{Re}\,\{e^{j\omega t}\} \tag{2-2}$$

Similarly, of course,

$$\cos(\omega t + \theta) = \mathfrak{Re}\,\{e^{j(\omega t + \theta)}\} \tag{2-3}$$

This real component of the exponential function can be used to express sinusoidally varying voltages and currents as well as the cosine function, for they are equal. Let us use it to write expressions for the voltage and current of the circuit of Figure 1a. Let us write voltage in a general sinusoidal form as

$$v = V_m \cos(\omega t + \theta_1) = V_m\,\mathfrak{Re}\,\{e^{j(\omega t + \theta_1)}\} \tag{2-4}$$

and current with corresponding generality as

$$i = I_m \cos(\omega t + \theta_2) = I_m\,\mathfrak{Re}\,\{e^{j(\omega t + \theta_2)}\} \tag{2-5}$$

A2-3. Transforms

These expressions could now be substituted into the differential equation 1-1 for v and i, but it is helpful first to rewrite equations 2-4 and 5 as follows:

$$v = \mathfrak{Re}\,\{V_m e^{j\theta_1} e^{j\omega t}\} \tag{3-1}$$

$$i = \mathfrak{Re}\,\{I_m e^{j\theta_2} e^{j\omega t}\} \tag{3-2}$$

Now at any given frequency the complex quantity $V_m e^{j\theta_1}$ tells all there is to know about the voltage: V_m is amplitude of the voltage and θ_1 is its phase angle. The quantity $V_m e^{j\theta_1}$ is going to be so useful that we introduce a new symbol to represent it. The new symbol is V. By definition, we let $\sqrt{2}\,V = V_m e^{j\theta_1}$ (the $\sqrt{2}$ is introduced so that the new symbol will have the rms value of the voltage instead of its maximum value). Our *definition* of V is therefore

$$V = \frac{V_m}{\sqrt{2}}\,e^{j\theta_1} \tag{3-3}$$

Similarly we introduce a new symbol I that is defined as

$$I = \frac{I_m}{\sqrt{2}}\,e^{j\theta_2} \tag{3-4}$$

(A2-3)

and with the aid of these new symbols, which will be called *transforms* of voltage and current, equations 3-1 and 3-2 become

$$v = \Re_e \{\sqrt{2} V e^{j\omega t}\} \tag{3-5}$$

$$i = \Re_e \{\sqrt{2} I e^{j\omega t}\} \tag{3-6}$$

Note that if the instantaneous voltage v is known, the transform of voltage, V, can be written (equation 3-3) simply by inspection; or, vice versa, if V is known (and the frequency), v can be written by inspection (equation 2-4). The voltage v and its transform V are called a transform pair.

A2-4. The Transformed Equation

Now the groundwork has been laid for solution of the differential equation of the inductive and resistive circuit of Figure 1a. To carry out the solution, substitute equations 3-5 and 3-6 for v and i into equation 1-1, to obtain

$$\Re_e \{\sqrt{2} V e^{j\omega t}\} = R \, \Re_e \{\sqrt{2} I e^{j\omega t}\} + L \frac{d}{dt} \Re_e \{\sqrt{2} I e^{j\omega t}\}$$

$$= \Re_e \{\sqrt{2} R I e^{j\omega t}\} + \Re_e \{\sqrt{2} L I \frac{d}{dt} e^{j\omega t}\} \tag{4-1}$$

We now differentiate the exponential function of time, and make algebraic changes in the equation,* to obtain

$$\Re_e \{\sqrt{2} V e^{j\omega t}\} = \Re_e \{\sqrt{2} R I e^{j\omega t}\} + \Re_e \{\sqrt{2} j\omega L I e^{j\omega t}\}$$

$$= \Re_e \{\sqrt{2} R I e^{j\omega t} + \sqrt{2} j\omega L I e^{j\omega t}\} \tag{4-2}$$

Here are equated the real components of two complex quantities. Since these real components must be equal *at all times* (for all values of t), the complex quantities themselves must be equal. Hence

$$\sqrt{2} V e^{j\omega t} = \sqrt{2} R I e^{j\omega t} + \sqrt{2} j\omega L I e^{j\omega t} \tag{4-3}$$

The factor $e^{j\omega t}$ can now be divided out of this equation, leaving a relation among the coefficients that is not a function of time. Also the $\sqrt{2}$ can be divided out, resulting in

$$V = (R + j\omega L)I \tag{4-4}$$

or

$$I = \frac{V}{R + j\omega L} \tag{4-5}$$

---

*These operations are more critically examined in Chapter 3 of *Electrical Engineering Circuits,* reference 7A.

(A2-4)

This completes our solution of the differential equation 1-1 for steady current. An expression for the transform of current has been found. Numerical values of I can be computed if values of voltage, resistance, and inductance are known. We can compute the current that would be produced by voltage at some given frequency, or current can be computed as a function of frequency. Note that the relation between V and I is in general a function of frequency.

Having computed the transform of current I, instantaneous current can be found by inspection. Indeed, finding instantaneous current from the current transform is so obvious that it is usually not done. In solving a problem for current it is customary to find I and stop there. In fact, I is often called "current," though of course it is not. It is a complex quantity, a transform of current.

A2-5. Transformation of Operations

In the foregoing example we have solved the differential equation of a circuit the hard way. Fortunately, there is an easier way, a short cut.

In Section A2-4 the differential equation (equation 1-1)

$$v = Ri + L\frac{di}{dt} \qquad (5\text{-}1)$$

was *transformed* into the algebraic equation (equation 4-4)

$$V = RI + j\omega LI \qquad (5\text{-}2)$$

by substituting into it exponential expressions for voltage and current, and performing the indicated operations of calculus. Any differential equation of this type (linear, with constant coefficients) can be so transformed. However, the transformed equation can be obtained without the labor of going through the transformation by the following simple rule:

1. Write the differential equation.
2. Write another equation, similar except that V replaces v, I replaces i, etc.; also $j\omega$ replaces d/dt, and (if there are integrals in the equation) $1/j\omega$ replaces $\int \ldots dt$.

The resulting transformed equation will, like equation 5-2, be an algebraic equation relating transforms of voltage, current, force, torque, velocity, and so on (represented by symbols such as V, I, F, T, Ω) instead of being a differential equation, like equation 5-1, relating instantaneous values of voltage, current, force, torque, and velocity (represented by v, i, F, T, Ω). The transforms are complex numbers; the actual quantities are real functions of time.

The change from equation 5-1 to 5-2 is an example of the application of this rule. Other examples will be frequent. A general proof of the validity of the rule could be given, but perhaps it will be enough to note that any transformation made by this rule can be verified by following the steps of Section A2-4.

A2-6. Impedance

One of the chief values of the transform method is the concept of complex impedance that it makes possible. By definition, impedance is the ratio of the voltage transform to the current transform. The symbol Z is used, and for the circuit of Figure 1a the impedance is found from equation 4-4 (or 5-2) to be

$$Z = \frac{V}{I} = R + j\omega L \qquad (6\text{-}1)$$

Thus impedance is a complex number. Its magnitude is the ratio of the magnitudes of V and I. Its angle is the difference of angle between V and I. By a trigonometric change in equation 6-1, impedance can also be written in what is called the polar form:

$$Z = R + j\omega L = \sqrt{R^2 + (\omega L)^2}\, e^{j\phi}$$

$$= \sqrt{R^2 + (\omega L)^2}\, \underline{/\phi} \qquad (6\text{-}2)$$

where

$$\phi = \tan^{-1}\frac{\omega L}{R} \qquad (6\text{-}3)$$

(Compare with equations 1-3 and 4.) The symbol $\underline{/\phi}$ has the same meaning as $e^{j\phi}$ and is usually read "at an angle of ϕ."

These expressions for impedance will be recognized as familiar acquaintances by anyone who has studied electric circuits. The impedance of the circuit under consideration can be written $R + j\omega L$ by inspection, without any bother about differential equations and transformation. Electrical students have spent months learning to do just this, and for them electric circuits or networks have no mysteries. But mechanical devices with alternating forces applied may be less familiar, and the concept or formulation of a mechanical impedance would perhaps require some thought. In particular, electromechanical systems, in which the electrical and mechanical parts react on each other, are probably new to the reader. When a situation is unfamiliar the best approach is to write the differential equations that describe its behavior, then to transform them into algebraic equations by the rule of Section A2-5, and to study the relations among the various parts by working with the transformed equations. This approach is illustrated in many examples.

A2-7. Summary

The differential equation of any (linear) circuit or network is solved in the steady state, by a form of transformation using complex quantities.

Current or *voltage* is a function of time, and is always a purely real quantity. It can be written as a trigonometric function (equation 1-2) or as a component of an exponential function (equation 2-4 or 2-5).

The *transform* of current or voltage (equation 3-3 or 3-4) is not a function of time. It is in general a *complex quantity*. It is specified at a particular frequency.

Real currents and voltages, expressed as real components of complex quantities, are written in the differential equations of a circuit or network. Simplification leaves a relation between transforms.

This relation between transforms is extremely useful. It leads to the complex ratio of transforms V/I which is called *impedance*. It also leads to the concepts of admittance and transmittance.

A simple *rule* is given for transforming a differential equation for steady-state solution.

PROBLEMS

A2-1. In equation 1-1 of Section A2-1, each term is a voltage. Keep the form of this equation but change meanings of symbols; by this means find the dual electrical network in which each term is a current. Find a mechanical (translational) device for which each term of the equation is a force, and another in which each term is a velocity; these are analogous devices. Find also two analogous rotational mechanical devices. Can you also find two hydraulic analogs? (See Section 153.) **(Sec. A2-1)**

A2-2. Voltage applied to a circuit is sinusoidal. It has a frequency of 60 cycles/sec, it reaches its maximum value at $t = 0$, and the value of that maximum is 173 volts. Express the value at each instant, as a function of time. Write the transform pair, v and V. **(Sec. A2-3)**

A2-3. Current entering a circuit is sinusoidal. It has a frequency of 60 cycles/sec, it reaches its maximum value one-sixth of a cycle after $t = 0$, and the maximum is 0.735 amp. Write the transform pair i and I. **(Sec. A2-3)**

A2-4. Using information from the two preceding problems for voltage and current, write equation 4-2 of this appendix in numbers. Find the complex impedance of the circuit under consideration. **(Sec. A2-6)**

A2-5. A circuit consists of a resistor and capacitor in series. Write the differential equation of voltage applied as a function of current, transform the equation, and write the complex impedance.

(Sec. A2-6)

A2-6. A circuit consists of resistance, inductance, and capacitance in series. Write the differential equation of voltage applied as a function of current, transform the equation, and write the complex impedance. **(Sec. A2-6)**

LAPLACE FUNCTIONS
appendix 3

A3-1. Times of Change

Transfer functions and impedance functions characterize a device. These functions tell how the device behaves when alternating current of any frequency is steadily applied. Now we shall see that they tell how the device behaves during times of change as well as during steady-state operation.

Use of the same transfer and impedance functions for both transient and steady-state analysis results from the concept that even a sudden disturbance can be analyzed into steady sinusoidal components. The step function, for instance, shown in Figure 1a, in which the voltage

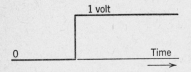

Figure 1a. A unit step function of voltage.

is zero until a switch is closed, and 1 volt thereafter, can be expressed as an integration of steady, sinusoidal components.

A3-2. The Spectrum

Such analysis of a discontinuous voltage (or current, or force, or velocity) is reminiscent of Fourier analysis of an irregular wave into its steady sinusoidal components. The relation is, in fact, very real and close. The Fourier series analysis develops into Fourier integral

(A3-2)

analysis, and this in turn is a close relative of the Laplace integral, which we shall now be using.*

It will be recalled that the coefficients of a Fourier series are found by integration. The function to be analyzed is multiplied by a sine or cosine function of a particular frequency, and when the product is integrated over one complete period the result is a measure of the amount of that particular frequency in the original function. This method works because of what the mathematician calls the orthogonality of functions: if two sine waves of different frequencies are multiplied together, the integral of the product over one period is zero, whereas if they have the same frequency it is not.

So in the Laplace integral, †

$$\hat{f}(s) = \int_0^\infty f(t)\, e^{-st}\, dt \qquad (2\text{-}1)$$

the function to be analyzed is $f(t)$. This is multiplied by an exponential function e^{-st}, in which s corresponds to frequency, and when the product is integrated through all time, the result, $\hat{f}(s)$, is a measure of the exponential component e^{st} in the original function $f(t)$.

The idea of using an exponential function in place of a sinusoidal function is not unfamiliar; we did this in Section A2-2. It need not

---

* Gardner and Barnes, Reference A3-2, *Transient Electric Currents*, Reference 145, and *Electrical Engineering Circuits*, Reference 7A, for instance, develop this idea.

† Regarding notation: The left-hand member of equation 2-1, the Laplace transform of $f(t)$, is more commonly written $F(s)$ than $\hat{f}(s)$. Small and capital letters commonly denote a time function and its transform. Thus in electrical theory a time function of voltage is usually represented by $v(t)$ and its transform by $V(s)$, current by $i(t)$ and its transform by $I(s)$. In electromechanical work, however, there are so many time functions that the use of small and capital letters becomes troublesome, and different authors have adopted various notations. We shall follow the one that seems both clearest and simplest: *the circumflex indicates the transformed function* (Reference 83).

Thus the transform of the voltage $v(t)$ is $\hat{v}(s)$. Note that v and $\hat{v}$ are different functions (as v and V are different functions in the other notation). The transform of current $i(t)$ is $\hat{i}(s)$. The transforms of such other time functions as F, T, Ω, Φ, and θ are $\hat{F}$, $\hat{T}$, $\hat{\Omega}$, $\hat{\Phi}$, and $\hat{\theta}$.

With the circumflex, functional notation is unnecessary, for v is always a function of t, and $\hat{v}$ of s. However, functional notation sometimes improves the clarity or the emphasis, and in some places, as in equation 2-1, it may be found helpful.

(It is customary to let the symbol $\mathcal{L}$ mean "the Laplace transform of." This symbol would save so little time in the present brief discussion that it has not been used.)

trouble us that the letter s is used in Laplace transformation instead of the more familiar $j\omega$. For purposes of visualization it is satisfactory to consider that s is the same as $j\omega$; that is, if we want to find what happens at a frequency of 60 cycles per second, for which $\omega = 377$, we let s equal $j377$, and so on for other frequencies. (We shall later find it necessary to let s have other than purely imaginary values, but at present we may consider that $s = j\omega$.)

The function that we indicate by $\hat{f}(s)$, found from equation 2-1, is our analysis of $f(t)$. That is, $\hat{f}(s)$ tells us how large a component of any frequency is contained in the time function $f(t)$.

For example, to find how large a component of frequency s_1 is in a time function $f(t)$, we find $\hat{f}(s)$ from $f(t)$ (by means of equation 2-1), and then in the expression thus obtained for $\hat{f}(s)$ we let $s = s_1$. The result is a number, and it gives the relative amount of the component of the form $e^{s_1 t}$ that is contained in the time function $f(t)$. Hence the function $\hat{f}(s)$ is called the *spectrum* of $f(t)$, for it shows the strength of the various frequency components of $f(t)$.

This brief statement no doubt leaves the mathematics of the Laplace transformation quite obscure, but one or two examples will readily show how the method is used.

A3-3. Transform Pairs: the Step Function

Perhaps the simplest *discontinuous* time function is the unit *step* function shown in Figures 1a and 3a. This function is zero for all time before a certain instant, which we choose to call $t = 0$, and after that instant it has the value 1. It is sometimes called the switch-closing function, for obvious reasons. It was called the unit function by the mathematician Heaviside, and some authors call it the Heaviside function in his memory.

We shall insert this step function into equation 2-1 as $f(t)$.

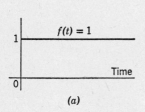
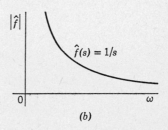

Figure 3. (a) A step time function and (b) its frequency-distribution spectrum.

(A3-3)

Since the range of integration is from $t = 0$ to $t = \infty$, and since through all this time the value of the step function is simply 1, the integral reduces to

$$\hat{f}(s) = \int_0^\infty e^{-st}\, dt \tag{3-1}$$

The integration is easily performed:

$$\hat{f}(s) = \int_0^\infty e^{-st}\, dt = -\frac{1}{s}\left[e^{-st} \right]_0^\infty = -\frac{1}{s}(0 - 1) = \frac{1}{s} \tag{3-2}$$

This tells us that the spectrum of the step function is $1/s$.

The spectrum is shown graphically in Figure 3b. This diagram shows relative amouts of various frequency components by the height of its curve, as the spectrum of the sun shows relative amounts of various frequency components by the brightness of its light. Figure 3b shows that the step function contains a large amount of low-frequency components for which s (and hence ω) is small, and less of higher-frequency components corresponding to large s. It is seen that all frequencies are present in the spectrum of the step function although the higher-frequency components are relatively less intense. To avoid possible misunderstanding it should be stated at once that the amount of any particular frequency is infinitesimal; the step function of Figure 3a is the sum of an infinitely wide range of infinitely small frequency components.

The unit-step time function and its spectrum $1/s$ are called a *transform pair*. They are a Laplace-transform pair. We can use this pair whenever, in the future, we have need for the spectrum of a step function of voltage, or of force, or current, or of any other physical quantity. Also, *inversely*, the pair can be used whenever we know that a spectrum is of the form $1/s$ and we want to know the time function of which this is the spectrum. The answer is: a step function.

A3-4. The Discontinuous Exponential

Another time function that we shall need to use is the discontinuous exponential function shown in Figure 4a. The solution of differential equations in Chapter 10 has shown how often the response of a physical system is described by an exponential function that begins sud-

(A3-4)

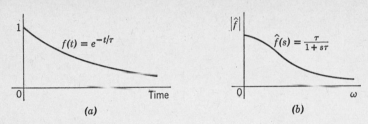

Figure 4. (*a*) A discontinuous exponential function and (*b*) its spectrum.

denly when the disturbance takes place. Let us find the spectrum
of such a function.

This function is zero for all negative time, and through all positive
time it is equal to $e^{-t/\tau}$. The figure, drawn for an exponential with
a positive real value of τ, starts at 1 and diminishes to 0 as time becomes large without limit. This might be the shape of a voltage or
current pulse, or it might be a force or motion occurring in a mechanical system. Indeed, the natural response of all linear (lumped-
parameter) systems is made up of such components, sometimes with
real exponents as shown here, and sometimes with complex exponents.

To analyze this exponential pulse, substitute $e^{-t/\tau}$ for $f(t)$ in
equation 2-1, giving

$$\hat{f}(s) = \int_0^\infty e^{-t/\tau} e^{-st}\, dt = \int_0^\infty e^{-(1/\tau + s)t}\, dt$$

$$= -\frac{\tau}{1 + s\tau}\left[e^{-(1+s\tau)(t/\tau)} \right]_0^\infty = \frac{\tau}{1 + s\tau} \qquad (4\text{-}1)$$

Thus the spectrum of the discontinuous exponential function is
$\tau/(1 + s\tau)$.

This is not greatly different from the spectrum of the step function,
as may be seen by comparing Figure 4*b* with Figure 3*b*. Indeed, the
two may be made as much alike as desired by letting τ be very large.
Also, if τ is very large the discontinuous exponential becomes indis-
tinguishable from the step function. If we had not already computed
the transform of the step function it would now be unnecessary to do
so, for it could merely be considered as the limiting case of the discontinuous exponential.

As a variation of this same transform pair, let us start with $f(t) =$
$(1/\tau)e^{-t/\tau}$. Substituting this for $f(t)$ in equation 2-1, we find its transform to be $1/(1 + s\tau)$. This time function differs from the one used in

(A3-4)

equation 4-1 only in being multiplied by a constant $1/\tau$, and the transform differs from the transform of equation 4-1 by the same factor, $1/\tau$. That is,

The transform of $\dfrac{1}{\tau} e^{-t/\tau}$ is $\dfrac{1}{1 + s\tau}$ $\hspace{2cm}$ (4-2)

Let us list our Laplace-transform pairs. They can be tabulated for later reference (rather like a table of integrals) as pairs 1 and 2 in Table A3-4.

Table A3-4. Laplace-Transform Pairs

Pair No.	$f(t)$, the time function (of voltage, current, etc.) for $t > 0$	$\hat{f}(s)$, the Laplace transform (the spectrum)
1	1 (the unit step function)	$\dfrac{1}{s}$
2	$e^{-t/\tau}$ (the discontinuous exponential)	$\dfrac{\tau}{1 + s\tau}$
3	$1 - e^{-t/\tau}$	$\dfrac{1}{s(1 + s\tau)}$
4	$1 + \dfrac{1}{\tau_1 - \tau_2}(\tau_2 e^{-t/\tau_2} - \tau_1 e^{-t/\tau_1})$	$\dfrac{1}{s(1 + s\tau_1)(1 + s\tau_2)}$
5	δ (the unit impulse)	1
6	t (the unit ramp function)	$\dfrac{1}{s^2}$
7	$\dfrac{1}{\tau_1 - \tau_2}(e^{-t/\tau_1} - e^{-t/\tau_2})$	$\dfrac{1}{(1 + s\tau_1)(1 + s\tau_2)}$
8	$t e^{-t/\tau}$	$\dfrac{\tau^2}{(1 + s\tau)^2}$
9	$\dfrac{\omega_0{}^2}{\omega_n} e^{-\alpha t} \sin \omega_n t$	$\dfrac{1}{1 + 2\zeta(s/\omega_0) + (s/\omega_0)^2}$ $\alpha = \zeta\omega_0; \omega_n = \omega_0\sqrt{1 - \zeta^2}$

A3-5. Transformation of Operations

Equation 2-1 defines the Laplace transform:

$$\hat{f}(s) = \int_0^\infty f(t)e^{-st}\, dt \hspace{2cm} (5\text{-}1)$$

Knowing $f(t)$, we find $\hat{f}(s)$ by integration. Suppose $f(t)$ is multiplied by a constant, c. The result of the integration is then $c\hat{f}(s)$. That is, *if $f(t)$ transforms to $\hat{f}(s)$, $cf(t)$ transforms to $c\hat{f}(s)$.* This is our first transformation of an operation. It relates to *multiplication by a constant,* and it is illustrated by equations 4-1 and 4-2.

Suppose $f(t)$ in equation 5-1 can be written as the *sum* of two functions:

$$f(t) = f_1(t) + f_2(t) \tag{5-2}$$

We substitute this into equation 5-1 and, since the integral of the sum of two functions is the sum of the two integrals taken individually, we can write:

$$\hat{f}(s) = \int_0^\infty f_1(t)\, e^{-st}\, dt + \int_0^\infty f_2(t)\, e^{-st}\, dt \tag{5-3}$$

The first integral alone gives a function that we may call $\hat{f}_1(s)$, the transform of the time function $f_1(t)$; the second integral gives $\hat{f}_2(s)$, the transform of $f_2(t)$. Then $\hat{f}(s)$ is the sum of these two; that is, $\hat{f}(s) = \hat{f}_1(s) + \hat{f}_2(s)$. In words, *the transform of the sum of two functions is the sum of the transforms of those functions taken individually.* This is the second transformation of an operation, and it results in *summation.*

The third relation relates to multiplication. Suppose $f(t)$ in equation 5-1 can be written as the *product* of two functions:

$$f(t) = f_1(t) \cdot f_2(t) \tag{5-4}$$

This can be substituted into equation 5-1, but it does *not* lead to any simple result. We know from integral calculus that the integral of the product of two functions is *not* the product of their integrals. Hence our third theorem is a negative one: *the transform of the product of two functions is not the product of their transforms taken individually.*

Another useful transformation is of the integral of a function. The relation between $f(t)$ and $\hat{f}(s)$ is given in equation 5-1. Then if $f(t)$ is the integral of another function that may for convenience be called $g(t)$, so that

$$f(t) = \int_0^t g(t)\, dt \tag{5-5}$$

and this is substituted into equation 5-1, we find * that its transform

---

* The substitutions into equation 5-1 that lead to the transformations of operation listed as 5-6 and 5-8, not given here in detail, may be found in Reference A3-2 (Gardner and Barnes) or 145.

(A3-5)

$\hat{f}(s)$ is $(1/s)\hat{g}(s)$. That is, *the integral of a function transforms to 1/s times the transform of the function.* Of course the letter used, f or g or something else, makes no difference, and this transformation of integration can be written

$$\int_0^t f(t)\ dt \quad \text{transforms to} \quad \frac{1}{s}\hat{f}(s) \tag{5-6}$$

Finally, it is useful to know the transformation of differentiation. If $f(t)$ is the derivative of another function that may for convenience be called $h(t)$, so that

$$f(t) = \frac{d}{dt}h(t) \tag{5-7}$$

we find from equation 5-1 that its transform $\hat{f}(s)$ is $s\hat{h}(s) - h(t)\,|_{t=0}$. Writing, as is more usual, f for h, we have

$$\frac{d}{dt}f(t) \quad \text{transforms to} \quad s\,\hat{f}(s) - f(t)\,|_{t=0} \tag{5-8}$$

In words, *the derivative of a function transforms to s times the transform of the function* less the value of the function at zero time.

If the differentiation is repeated, this transformation is repeated, and for the second differentiation

$$\frac{d^2}{dt^2}f(t) \quad \text{transforms to} \quad s^2\,\hat{f}(s) - s f(t)\,|_{t=0} - \frac{d}{dt}f(t)\,|_{t=0} \tag{5-9}$$

A3-6. Transformation of Differential Equations

Four rules may now be given for the solution of differential equations by Laplace transformation.

1. Write the differential equation.
2. Transform the differential equation. Transform functions by the pairs of Table A3-4 and transform operations by the theorems of Section A3-5. In general, replace v, i, F, T, Ω, etc., by $\hat{v}$, $\hat{i}$, $\hat{F}$, $\hat{T}$, $\hat{\Omega}$, etc., and write $1/s$ in place of an integral and s in place of a derivative, taking initial values into account if necessary.
3. Solve the transformed equation. It will be algebraic. The transform of the desired time function is found.
4. Find the desired time function from its transform. Locate the transform in Table A3-4 and read out the corresponding time function.

A3-7. Examples

Let us use this method to find the current in the capacitive circuit of Figure 7a when a constant voltage is suddenly applied to the resistance and capacitance in series. The capacitance has no charge before the switch in the circuit is closed. By closing the switch at time $t = 0$, a step function of voltage is applied. The height of the step is V_1, so the applied voltage is equal to the unit step function of Figure 3a multiplied by V_1. There are four moves in the solution.

1. The differential equation is

$$v = Ri + \frac{1}{C} \int_0^t i \, dt \tag{7-1}$$

2. This equation is transformed. On the left, the transform of v is $\hat{v}$. On the right, i transforms to $\hat{i}$, R being a constant. The integral of i, transformed as an operation, becomes $(1/s)\hat{i}$. Thus

$$\hat{v} = R\hat{i} + \frac{1}{C}\frac{1}{s}\hat{i} \tag{7-2}$$

3. Solve for $\hat{i}$, the transform of the desired quantity:

$$\hat{i} = \frac{sC\hat{v}}{1 + sRC}$$

Now v, the applied voltage, is a step function, with value 0 until $t = 0$, and V_1 thereafter. From pair 1 of the table, the transform of the unit step function is $1/s$; the transform of the applied voltage is therefore V_1/s. That is, $\hat{v} = V_1/s$, and

$$\hat{i} = V_1 C \frac{1}{1 + sRC} \tag{7-3}$$

4. The time function of current, the actual current, is now found. If we let $RC = \tau$, the fraction in equation 7-3 is similar to the transform of pair 2, and it is identical with equation 4-2. The corresponding time function, from the table, or from the equation, is now used to give the current in the circuit:

$$i = V_1 C \frac{1}{\tau} e^{-t/\tau} = \frac{V_1}{R} e^{-t/RC} \tag{7-4}$$

This completes the solution. The current is plotted in Figure 7b.

(A3-7)

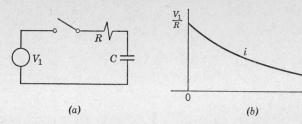

Figure 7. (a) A constant voltage is suddenly applied to a capacitive impedance; the current (b) is exponential.

Until $t = 0$ (that is, until the switch is closed) there is no current. When the switch is closed the current suddenly becomes V_1/R, for at that instant, the capacitor being uncharged, current is limited only by the resistance. Thereafter, as the capacitor becomes charged, the current dies away exponentially. The rate of dying away depends on τ, the time constant of the circuit.

As another example, consider the rotating armature of an electric motor (or any other flywheel) with a moment of inertia J and a rotational damping coefficient D (Figure 7c). This device was discussed in Section 140, and the differential equation of its motion was written as equation 140-1:

$$T = J\frac{d\Omega}{dt} + D\Omega \qquad (7\text{-}5)$$

Ω is the angular velocity of rotation, a function of time, initially zero, and T is applied torque.

To apply the four rules:

1. The differential equation has been written as equation 7-5.
2. Transformed, it becomes

$$\hat{T} = Js\hat{\Omega} + D\hat{\Omega} \qquad (7\text{-}6)$$

3. Solving for $\hat{\Omega}$, we obtain

$$\hat{\Omega} = \frac{\hat{T}}{Js + D} \qquad (7\text{-}7)$$

To find $\hat{\Omega}$ we have to know $\hat{T}$.

Let us suppose that this motor originally has no torque applied to start it turning. Then at the instant that will be called $t = 0$ there is suddenly applied a torque T_1, and this same torque is applied constantly thereafter. In other words, the applied torque is a step function

(A3-7)

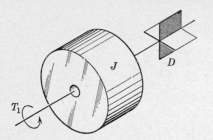

Figure 7c. A step function of torque is applied to a motor armature.

of magnitude T_1. Since the transform of a unit step function is $1/s$, the transform of our applied torque is T_1/s, and this we substitute for $\hat{T}$, giving

$$\hat{\Omega} = \frac{T_1/s}{Js + D} = \frac{T_1}{s(Js + D)} = \frac{T_1}{D}\frac{1}{s(1 + s\tau)} \tag{7-8}$$

where $\tau = J/D$.

4. Inverse transformation is now necessary. If we had available pair 3 of Table A3-4 the solution would be merely a matter of copying the tabulated time function. However, we have not yet derived pair 3. Let us therefore proceed to do so. The derivation will not only solve our particular problem, but it will also show how the method of partial fractions can be used to find new transform pairs.

A3-8. The Method of Partial Fractions

The method of partial fractions will be found in any good algebra textbook. The following is not a proof, but an illustrative example applied to our particular problem.

We write the function from equation 7-8 in the form in which we wish we had it:

$$\frac{1}{s} \cdot \frac{1}{1 + s\tau} = \frac{A}{s} + \frac{B}{1 + s\tau} \tag{8-1}$$

Is this permissible? The answer is yes, for the method of partial fractions provides a means by which values for A and B can be found that will make equation 8-1 valid.

To find A we multiply both sides of the equation 8-1 by the denominator of A, which is s. This gives *

---

* The rule illustrated here is inadequate if there is a linear factor repeated in the denominator. Any college algebra textbook gives a more complete discussion of partial fractions; or see Gardner and Barnes, Reference A3-2.

(A3-8)

$$\frac{1}{1 + s\tau} = A + \frac{Bs}{1 + s\tau} \tag{8-2}$$

Equation 8-1, and hence 8-2, are identities; that is, they must be true for *all* values of s. Hence equation 8-2 must be true when $s = 0$. (This is the denominator of A in equation 8-1.) We find A by letting $s = 0$ in equation 8-2:

$$A = 1 \tag{8-3}$$

Equation 8-1 is now used to find B. We multiply by the denominator of B, which is $1 + s\tau$, to get

$$\frac{1}{s} = \frac{A(1 + s\tau)}{s} + B \tag{8-4}$$

Now let $(1 + s\tau) = 0$ or $s = -1/\tau$. Equation 8-4 must be true for this value of s, with which it becomes

$$-\tau = B \tag{8-5}$$

so the required value of B is $-\tau$. We are now able to go back to equation 8-1 and write

$$\frac{1}{s} \cdot \frac{1}{1 + s\tau} = \frac{A}{s} + \frac{B}{1 + s\tau} = \frac{1}{s} - \frac{\tau}{1 + s\tau} \tag{8-6}$$

This is the end of the method of partial fractions. Using this result in equation 7-8, we have

$$\hat{\Omega} = \frac{T_1}{D}\left(\frac{1}{s} - \frac{\tau}{1 + s\tau}\right) \tag{8-7}$$

Now we have obtained $\hat{\Omega}$ as the *sum* of two recognizable functions. We know that $1/s$ transforms to 1, and $\tau/(1 + s\tau)$ transforms to $e^{-t/\tau}$ (pairs 1 and 2 in the table). Since these appear in the expression as a sum (not a product) they can be transformed individually, giving, finally, the expression for speed:

$$\Omega = \frac{T_1}{D}(1 - e^{-t/\tau}) \tag{8-8}$$

Note that the result is exactly analogous to that for current in an inductive circuit. (See Figure 11b.) The motor armature comes up to speed gradually, following an exponential curve. The time constant of the rotating system is J/D.

(A3-8)

A3-9. Example with Initial Response

If the device in the previous section had not initially been standing still, but had been turning with a speed Ω_0 at the instant $t = 0$, the solution would be but slightly different. The differential equation 7-5 would be unchanged. However, instead of transforming to equation 7-6 it would become

$$\hat{T} = J(s\hat{\Omega} - \Omega_0) + D\hat{\Omega} \qquad (9\text{-}1)$$

Solving, by rule 3, we have

$$\hat{\Omega} = \frac{\hat{T} + J\Omega_0}{Js + D} = \frac{T_1}{D}\frac{1}{s(1 + s\tau)} + \frac{\Omega_0\tau}{1 + s\tau} \qquad (9\text{-}2)$$

with $\tau = J/D$.

Pairs 3 and 2 give the inverse transformations to time functions:

$$\Omega = \frac{T_1}{D}\left(1 - e^{-t/\tau}\right) + \Omega_0 e^{-t/\tau}$$

$$= \frac{T_1}{D} + \left(\Omega_0 - \frac{T_1}{D}\right)e^{-t/\tau} \qquad (9\text{-}3)$$

This answer reduces to equation 8-8, of course, if there is no initial speed. Note that there is a particular value of initial speed that will eliminate the transient term, the natural response, entirely. It happens in this case to be the steady-state value.

A3-10. Transformed Impedance Equations

In solving problems of a thoroughly familiar type, it is often easier not to write the differential equation at all. The transformed equation can be written directly, often with the familiar steady-state equation as the starting point.

In electrical problems, the Laplace transform of impedance, $Z(s)$, can be obtained from the steady-state impedance, $Z(j\omega)$, by writing s in place of $j\omega$; this is valid because the steady-state impedance is itself a form of transform. $Z(s)$ is then combined with the transform of voltage, or that of current, as the problem may indicate. Thus the first two rules of Section A3-6 can be eliminated. An example will show the method.

(A3-10)

A3-11. A Circuit Example

For instance, in Figure 11a, let a constant voltage be suddenly applied to the inductive circuit shown. The applied voltage, being a step function, will have as its transform, $\vartheta = V_1/s$. The impedance is $Z(j\omega) = R + j\omega L$, or $Z(s) = R + sL$. To find current, then,

$$i = \frac{\vartheta}{Z(s)} = \frac{V_1/s}{R + sL} = \frac{V_1}{R} \frac{1}{s(1 + s\tau)} \tag{11-1}$$

where $L/R = \tau$. Thus the transformed equation has been written quite easily, without starting from the differential equation.

The final transformation to the time function i uses pair 3 of Table A3-4:

$$i = \frac{V_1}{R}(1 - e^{-t/\tau}) \tag{11-2}$$

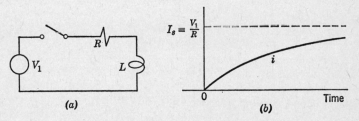

Figure 11. (a) A constant voltage is suddenly applied to an inductive circuit, and (b) current in the circuit.

The resulting current is shown in Figure 11b. This curve can also be a curve of speed with suddenly applied torque, for it is a graph of equation 8-8.

A3-12. Summary

Any function (of practical form), though discontinuous, can be analyzed into continuous exponential components. Analysis is done by the *Laplace* transformation. Each component is then operated upon separately, by steady-state methods. The desired response is found by summing the responses of the individual components. The summation is done by the inverse Laplace transformation. Thus *all (linear) problems become steady-state problems.*

(A3-12)

Both direct and inverse transformation of functions are aided by a *table* (such as A3-4) of transform pairs.

Solution of differential equations requires also the *transformation of operations*. Among the most useful are multiplication by a constant, addition, integration, and differentiation.

Linear differential equations are solved by the *four rules* of Section A3-6. The differential equation is transformed to an algebraic equation; solution of the algebraic equation yields the transform of the desired quantity; inverse transformation gives the result.

Initial values of the response function can be taken into account. The method of *partial fractions* is explained.

Electrical engineers are highly adept at writing $Z(j\omega)$, the steady-state *impedance* of a circuit or network. $Z(s)$ is then easily written. It is often possible to solve electrical problems by finding $Z(s)$ from $Z(j\omega)$ without writing the differential equations.

PROBLEMS

A3-1. Using the defining integral of equation 2-1, verify pair 6 of Table A3-4, the ramp function. **(Sec. A3-4)**

A3-2. Verify equation 4-2 by the defining equation 2-1, and compare with pair 2 of the table. This illustrates the first theorem of Section A3-5. Prove this theorem in general. **(Sec. A3-5)**

A3-3. Derive, both by integration in equation 2-1 and also by the method of partial fractions, pairs 4 and 7 of Table A3-4. **(Sec. A3-8)**

A3-4. Derive pair 9 from pair 7, letting τ_1 and τ_2 be complex. **(Sec. A3-8)**

A3-5. Verify pair 8 by any method you prefer. **(Sec. A3-8)**

A3-6. Derive pair 7 from pair 4 by differentiation. Considering equation 5-8, is this derivation valid? **(Sec. A3-5)**

A3-7. Given the differential equation

$$3\frac{d^2x}{dt^2} + 11\frac{dx}{dt} + 6x = y$$

find x as a function of tine by Laplace transformation. It is given that $y = 5$ for positive time, $y = 0$ for negative time. When $t = 0$, x and its first derivative are zero. Verify your solution by substitution into the given equation.   **(Sec. A3-9)**

A3-8. Given $2\dfrac{d^2x}{dt^2} + 7\dfrac{dx}{dt} + 6x = 6$, find x as a function of t: (a) When $t = 0$, $x = 0$, and $dx/dt = 0$. (b) Also when $t = 0$, $x = 0$, and $dx/dt = 2$. (c) Also when $t = 0$, $x = 1$, and $dx/dt = 2$. In each part, verify your solution by substitution in the given equation.

(Sec. A3-9)

A3-9. Given the differential equation: $\dfrac{dx}{dt} + x = t$ find x as a function of t by Laplace transformation. It is given that when $t = 0$, $x = 0$. Verify your solution by substitution into the given equation.

(Sec. A3-9)

UNITS AND DIMENSIONS
appendix 4

A4-1. Problem Solving

Three men were at lunch. Two were eminent research scientists, one of these a Nobel laureate. The talk turned to problem solving, and to those simple things that every student can profitably do as he works. These are the suggestions that were written down. You may well take note; they come from high authority.

In forming a problem, ask yourself:

1. Has all pertinent physical information been put into the mathematics?
2. Is the number of equations equal to the number of unknowns?

In planning the solution, ask:

3. Can any symmetry be found that will simplify the solution?
4. Do any conservation laws apply?

When you have an answer you can ask:

5. Is the answer reasonable? Does it change in a sensible manner with the input variables?
6. Does the answer reduce to something obvious in limiting cases?
7. Can you check by solving in another way, perhaps approximate?
8. Do the dimensions and units check?

Checking units and dimensions is more helpful in electromechanics than in many other branches of science, and at the same time more difficult, for there are electrical units, mechanical units, and magnetic units, all involved in the same equations.

If dimensions, units, and standards are treated comprehensively,

(A4-1)

the subject is an involved one.* But as long as we are working within the systematic and consistent meter-kilogram-second-coulomb system (mksc system) the situation is relatively simple, for equations can be checked by balancing units. Consideration of dimensions would be an unnecessary elaboration.

A4-2. Physical Equations

A mathematical equation relates numbers, as

$$3 \cdot 50 = 150 \tag{2-1}$$

A physical equation relates physical quantities that are measured in units, as

$$3 \text{ boxes} \cdot 50 \text{ apples/box} = 150 \text{ apples} \tag{2-2}$$

or

$$3 \text{ seconds} \cdot 50 \text{ meters/second} = 150 \text{ meters} \tag{2-3}$$

A physical equation is valid if the relation among units is correct—that is, in equation 2-3, if

$$1 \text{ second} \cdot 1 \text{ meter/second} = 1 \text{ meter} \tag{2-4}$$

and also the relation among numbers of the units is correct—that is, in the same equation, if $3 \cdot 50 = 150$. The relation among units is quite commonly written

$$(\text{seconds}) \cdot (\text{meters/second}) = \text{meters} \tag{2-5}$$

Physical relations are generalized with letter symbols. For instance, the equation relating time and distance can be written:

$$ts = w \tag{2-6}$$

where t is time (seconds)
  s is speed (meters/second)
  w is distance (meters)

In such a physical equation the symbol is understood to stand for both the unit and the number of units. Thus, t means the quantity of time. For the specific example given in equation 2-3, $t = 3$ seconds, and not just the number 3.

It has been shown (beginning, it seems, with Newton, and continuing with Fourier and others) that physical quantities can be measured

---

* See, for instance, *Physical Units and Standards,* by Ernst Weber, Reference A4-1.

in units that are related to each other. Thus the unit of speed in equation 2-6 is not some arbitrary measure of speed, but is 1 meter/second; the unit of speed is derived from the unit of distance and the unit of time. It is found that all the units of mechanics can be derived from three "fundamental" units, usually taken to be distance, mass, and time. All the units of electromechanics can be derived from four "fundamental" units, including the three of mechanics and adding one electrical unit. The electrical unit can be electric charge, and this is rather commonly although not universally accepted. The mksc system accepts as fundamental the meter, the kilogram, the second, and the coulomb.

A4-3. A System of Units

The unit of a physical quantity is established by the definition of the quantity. A system of units is built upon a basis of definitions. To establish the mksc system, let us start by assuming that distance w is measured in meters, mass m in kilograms, time t in seconds, and charge q in coulombs. Then speed is to be defined. Under specified circumstances speed is

$$s = \frac{w}{t} \tag{3-1}$$

The unit of speed is therefore 1 meter/second.

Next, acceleration is defined as being, under certain circumstances,

$$a = \frac{s}{t} \tag{3-2}$$

from which the unit of acceleration is the meter/second^2.

Newton defined force by writing

$$F = ma \tag{3-3}$$

so force is measured in kilogram·meters/second^2.

We find it convenient to give a particular name to this unit of force; we call it the *newton*. This is justified by the obvious fact that it is easier to say "newton" than to say "kilogram-meter-per-second-squared."

Turning to electrical quantities, current can be defined in terms of charge:

(A4-3)

$$I = \frac{q}{t} \qquad (3\text{-}4)$$

from which the unit of current is the coulomb/second.

Magnetic flux density is defined in terms of the force exerted on a conductor of length l carrying current I:

$$B = \frac{F}{lI} \qquad (3\text{-}5)$$

And by combining the unit of force from equation 3-3 and that of current from 3-4, and using the meter for the unit of length, we find the unit of magnetic flux density to be

$$\frac{(\text{kilogram} \cdot \text{meter/second}^2)}{(\text{meter}) \cdot (\text{coulomb/second})} = \frac{\text{kilogram}}{\text{coulomb} \cdot \text{second}} \qquad (3\text{-}6)$$

Magnetic flux is defined as the flux density multiplied by the normal area:

$$\Phi = BA \qquad (3\text{-}7)$$

and this gives the unit of flux as the kilogram $\cdot$ meter^2/coulomb $\cdot$ second. Here, again, a special name is adopted. The unit of flux is called the *weber*, which is surely easier to say.

From the weber, the unit of flux density B is ordinarily called the weber-per-square-meter, and this is both more convenient and more informative than its derived name of kilogram-per-coulomb-second.

A4-4. Checking Equations

By continuing this process, Table A4-4 is obtained. With its aid we can check units in any equations involving the tabulated quantities.

Table A4-4

Quantity	Symbol	Name of Unit	Relation to Fundamental Units
Fundamental			
Distance	w	meter	m
Mass	m	kilogram	kg
Time	t	second	sec
Charge, electric	q	coulomb	cmb
Mechanical			
Force	F	newton	$kg \cdot m/sec^2$
Torque	T	newton·meter	$kg \cdot m^2/sec^2$
Velocity (speed)	S	meter/sec	m/sec
Angular velocity	Ω	radian/sec	sec^{-1}
Acceleration	a	meter/sec²	m/sec^2
Angular acceleration	α	radian/sec²	sec^{-2}
Moment of inertia	J	kilogram·meter²	$kg \cdot m^2$
Energy	W	joule (= watt·sec)	$kg \cdot m^2/sec^2$
Power	P	watt	$kg \cdot m^2/sec^3$
Mechan. resistance	r	mechanical ohm	kg/sec
Rotational damping coefficient	D	newton·meter/radian/sec	$kg \cdot m^2/sec$
Compliance	c	meter/newton	sec^2/kg
Electrical			
Current	I	ampere	cmb/sec
Elect. potential	V	volt	$m^2 kg/cmb \cdot sec^2$
Resistance (elect.)	R	ohm	$kg \cdot m^2/cmb^2 sec$
Electric intensity	E	volt/meter	$m \cdot kg/cmb \cdot sec^2$
Electric flux density	D	coulomb/meter²	cmb/m^2
Dielectric constant	ε	farad/meter	$cmb^2 sec^2/kg \cdot m^3$
Capacitance	C	farad	$cmb^2 sec^2/kg \cdot m^2$
Magnetic			
Magnetomotive force	$\mathfrak{F}$	ampere (turn)	cmb/sec
Magnetic intensity	H	ampere(turn)/meter	$cmb/m \cdot sec$
Magnetic flux density	B	weber/meter²	$kg/cmb \cdot sec$
Magnetic flux	Φ	weber	$kg \cdot m^2/cmb \cdot sec$
Permeability	μ	henry/meter	$kg \cdot m/cmb^2$
Inductance	L	henry	$kg \cdot m^2/cmb^2$
Reluctance	$\mathfrak{R}$	ampere(turn)/weber	$cmb^2/kg \cdot m^2$

As an example, let us check equation 39-1, writing it

$$F = \frac{B^2 A}{2\mu_0} \tag{4-1}$$

This equation can be correct only if

$$(\text{kg} \cdot \text{m}/\text{sec}^2) = \frac{(\text{kg}/\text{cmb} \cdot \text{sec})^2(\text{m}^2)}{\text{kg} \cdot \text{m}/\text{cmb}^2} \tag{4-2}$$

Appropriate cancellation shows that the units agree, and that the equation can indeed be correct. This check of units does not show that the equation *is* correct, but if the check fails the equation is surely wrong.

A4-5. Numbers

Note that the number 2 in the denominator of equation 4-1 is merely a number, and not a physical quantity. (It results, in this case, from integration, and is comparable to the 2 by which we divide the sum of two quantities to get their average.) Mere numbers are not physical quantities; they have no units and are dimensionless. The ratio of two physical quantities of the same kind is a number, and is always dimensionless: 6 meters divided by 2 meters equals 3, a number without unit or dimension.

Similarly π is a number. It is the ratio of distances, the circumference of a circle divided by the diameter. Any number of radians is dimensionless, for it is the ratio of a circumferential distance to a radius. Trigonometric functions are likewise ratios and hence dimensionless numbers. Thus $\cos x$ is dimensionless. Note that x, the argument of the function, must also be dimensionless. There is something wrong about any equation that requires finding the cosine of a physical quantity.

A4-6. Mixed Units

Proportionality factors such as 12 inches/foot, or 16 ounces/ pound, although dimensionless, are essential in equations relating mixed units. They are unfortunately common in practical applications of electromechanical equations. Since the science of electromechanics requires the use of electrical, mechanical, and magnetic units, such a list as we have in Table A4-4 is necessarily rather long at best. It seems too bad to add unnecessary confusion with inches and ounces.

A4-7. Other Sciences

When equations go beyond the realm of electromechanics, the four assumed "fundamental" units may prove inadequate. When energy conversion includes heat, another unit is needed. This might be a unit quantity of heat, but it is customarily a degree of temperature.

In still other realms, other units are required. Thus in economic considerations the dollar would doubtless be a useful fundamental unit. And equation 2-2 employs units suitable to the fruit business. Engineering equations may often go beyond the limits of electromechanics, and it is never wise to call a physical quantity dimensionless, or to neglect its units. The only result is to reduce the value of your opportunity to check your equations.

A4-8. Standard Units

After units are chosen the standards of mass, distance, time, and charge must be defined; that is, how much mass is 1 kilogram? The answer is by international agreement. The standard *kilogram* is the mass of a cylinder of platinum-iridium alloy kept in a vault in Sèvres, near Paris.

Originally the standard meter was the distance between two marks on a platinum bar in Sèvres. The *meter* was redefined in 1960 as 1,650,763.73 wavelengths of the orange-red line of krypton-86, a definition in terms of the wavelength of light. The General Conference on Weights and Measures thus broke away from the idea that a standard should be something that could be put in a vault for safekeeping.

For the standard *second*, there are now 31,556,925.9747 seconds in the tropical year 1900. (Until 1960 there were 86,400 seconds in the mean solar day, a standard that was nearly equivalent, but a trifle less constant.)

"The electrical units are based upon the ampere, which is defined by assigning the value $4\pi \cdot 10^{-7}$ to the magnetic constant in the equation for the interaction force between two current elements [μ in equations 10-1 and 2 solved simultaneously], with the meter, kilogram, and second as the units of length, mass, and time." (Courtesy Dr. C. H. Page, National Bureau of Standards.) The *coulomb* can then be defined in terms of this standard ampere. Neither an ampere nor a coulomb can be preserved on a shelf, so a set of stable resistors and a set of saturated standard cells are used in disseminating the electrical units.

It seems probable that the standards of the future will be such natural quantities as the mass of the neutron, the wavelength of krypton light, the speed of light, and the charge of the electron. Four quantities like these would make an invariant system that would remain the same not only from century to century but even from planet to planet.

PROBLEMS

A4-1. Check units in the following equations: 14-2, 34-1, 157-1, 205-7, 205-10, 122-4, 56-2.

A4-2. Check units in the following equations: 38-7, 43-1, 50-3, 56-2, 120-1, 195-1, 221-6.

REFERENCES

appendix 5

(The number is that of the section in which the reference is first cited.)

7A. Skilling, H. H., *Electrical Engineering Circuits*, John Wiley and Sons, New York, 1957.

7B. Skilling, H. H., *Fundamentals of Electric Waves*, 2nd ed., John Wiley and Sons, New York, 1948.

9A. Skilling, H. H., *Exploring Electricity*, Ronald Press Co., New York, 1948.

9B. Bleaney, B. I., and B. Bleaney, *Electricity and Magnetism*, Oxford University Press, London, 1957.

24. Maxwell, J. C., *Electricity and Magnetism*, 3rd ed., Oxford University Press, Oxford, 1904.

25A. Page, L., and N. I. Adams, *Principles of Electricity*, D. Van Nostrand Co., New York, 1931.

25B. Webster, D. L., "Relativity of Moving Circuits and Magnets," *American Journal of Physics*, Vol. 29, p. 262, April 1961.

40. Harris, F. K., *Electrical Measurements*, John Wiley and Sons, New York, 1952.

78A. Brown, G. S., A. Kusko, and D. C. White, "A New Educational Program in Energy Conversion," *Electrical Engineering*, pp. 180–185, February 1956.

78B. White, D. C., and A. Kusko, "A Unified Approach to the Teaching of Electromechanical Energy Conversion," *Electrical Engineering*, pp. 1028–1033, November 1956.

78C. White, D. C., and H. H. Woodson, "A New Electromechanical Energy Conversion Laboratory," *Transactions AIEE*, Paper 57-603, 1957.

78D. White, D. C., and H. H. Woodson, *Electromechanical Energy Conversion*, John Wiley and Sons, New York, 1959.

78E. Adkins, B., *The General Theory of Electrical Machines*, Chapman and Hall, London, 1957.

78F. Fitzgerald, A. E., and C. Kingsley, Jr., *Electric Machinery*, McGraw-Hill Book Co., New York, 1952.

78G. Ku, Y. H., *Electric Energy Conversion*, Ronald Press Co., New York, 1959.

78H. Robertson, B. L., and L. T. Black, *Electric Circuits and Machines*, D. Van Nostrand Co., New York, 1949.

78I. Carr, C. C., *Electric Machinery*, John Wiley and Sons, New York, 1958.

78J. Fitzgerald, A. E., and D. E. Higgenbotham, *Basic Electrical Engineering*, McGraw-Hill Book Co., New York, 1957.

83. Gibson, J. E., and F. B. Tutcur, *Control System Components*, McGraw-Hill Book Co., New York, 1958.

89. McFarland, T. C., *Alternating Current Machines*, D. Van Nostrand Co., New York, 1948.

109. Terman, F. E., *Electronic and Radio Engineering*, McGraw-Hill Book Co., 4th ed., New York, 1955.

117. Alger, P. L., *The Nature of Polyphase Induction Machines*, John Wiley and Sons, New York, 1951. (Out of print.)

145. Skilling, H. H., *Transient Electric Currents*, McGraw-Hill Book Co., 2nd ed., New York, 1952.

146. Olson, H. F., *Elements of Acoustical Engineering*, D. Van Nostrand Co., New York, 1947.

148. "IRE Standards on Circuits," *Proceedings IRE*, Vol. 48m, pp. 1608–1610, September 1960.

173. Bruns, R. A., and R. M. Saunders, *Analysis of Feedback Control Systems*, McGraw-Hill Book Co., New York, 1955.

187A. Bower, J. L., and P. M. Schultheiss, *Introduction to the Design of Servomechanisms*, John Wiley and Sons, New York, 1958.

187B. Chestnut, H., and R. W. Mayer, *Servomechanisms and Regulating System Design*, John Wiley and Sons, New York, Vol. 1, 2nd ed. 1959; Vol. 2, 1955.

187C. Savant, C. J., Jr., *Basic Feedback Control System Design*, McGraw-Hill Book Co., New York, 1958.

187D. Brown, G. S., and D. P. Campbell, *Principles of Servomechanisms*, John Wiley and Sons, New York, 1948.

215. Pestarini, J. M., *Metadyne Statics*, John Wiley and Sons, New York, 1952.

222A. Hopkin, A. M., "Transient Response of Small Two-Phase Induction Motors," *Transactions AIEE*, Vol. 70, Part I, p. 881, 1951.

222B. Brown, L. O., Jr., "Transfer Function for a Two-Phase Induction Servo Motor," *Transactions AIEE*, Vol. 70, Part II, p. 1890, 1951.

225. Koopman, R. J. W., "Operating Characteristics of Two-Phase Servomotors," *Transactions AIEE*, Vol. 68, Part I, p. 319, 1949.

229. Frazier, R. H., "Analysis of the Drag-Cup A-C Tachometer by Means of Two-Phase Symmetrical Components," *Transactions AIEE*, Vol. 70, Part II, p. 1894, 1951.

232. Linvill, W. K., "System Theory as an Extension of Circuit Theory," *IRE Transactions on Circuit Theory*, p. 217, December 1956.

238A. Truxal, J. G., *Automatic Feedback Control System Synthesis*, McGraw-Hill Book Co., New York, 1955.

238B. D'Azzo, J. J., and C. H. Houpis, *Control System Analysis and Synthesis*, McGraw-Hill Book Co., New York, 1960.

238C. Thaler, G. J., and R. G. Brown, *Servomechanism Analysis*, McGraw-Hill Book Co., New York, 1953.

242A. Bush, V., *Journal of the Franklin Institute*, Vol. 212, p. 447, 1931.

242B. Skilling, H. H., and M. H. Yamakawa, "A Graphical Solution of Transient Stability," *Electrical Engineering*, Vol. 59, p. 462, 1940.

242C. Skilling, H. H., "An Electric Analog of Friction," *Transactions AIEE,* Vol. 50, p. 1155, September 1931.

244A. Vautrey, M. L., "L'emploi des pompes électromagnétiques," *Bulletin de la Société Française des Electriciens,* p. 399, June 1960.

244B. Schwab, M. B., "Différents types de pompes électromagnétique," *Bulletin de la Société Française des Electriciens,* p. 404, June 1960.

245A. Hermant, C., "Amélioration des caractéristiques de la pompe électromagnétique a induction, du type linéare," *Bulletin de la Société Française des Electriciens,* p. 161, March 1960.

245B. Cambillard, E., and B. Schwab, "Pompes électromagnétique annulaires d'induction polyphasées calcul et réalisation," *Bulletin de la Société Française des Electriciens,* p. 417, June 1960.

246A. Kolin, Alexander, "Electromagnetic Blood Flow Meters," *Science,* Vol. 130, October 23, 1959.

246B. Shirer, H. W., R. B. Shackleford, and K. E. Jochim, "A Magnetic Flowmeter for Recording Cardiac Output," *Proceedings IRE,* Vol. 47, November 1959.

247A. Porter, R. W., "Adventures in Energy Conversion," *Electrical Engineering,* p. 801, October 1960.

247B. *Electrical Engineering,* p. 4, January 1961.

247C. *The Wall Street Journal,* March 14, 1961.

247D. Mills, R. G., "The Quest for Thermonuclear Power," *Electrical Engineering,* p. 176, March 1961.

247E. Harris, D. J., "Electric Power from a High-velocity Gas Jet," *Electrical Engineering,* p. 974, December 1961.

248. Sohn, R. L., and Howard W. Wheater, *Environmental Problems Associated with the Design and Operation of Space Vehicle Power Systems,* Publication of Space Technology Laboratories, Inc., Los Angeles, Calif., April 1960.

249A. Flagg, J. F., "Small-Scale Unconventional Power Sources Now Assume New Significance," General Electric Review, p. 30, July 1958.

249B. Acker, Roy M., et al., "Solar-Cell Power Supplies for Satellites, *Electronics,* March 11, 1960.

A1-2. Attwood, S. S., *Electric and Magnetic Fields,* 3rd ed., John Wiley and Sons, New York, 1949.

A3-2. Gardner, M. F., and J. L. Barnes, *Transients in Linear Systems,* John Wiley and Sons, New York, 1942.

A4-1. Weber, Ernst, *"Physical Units and Standards,"* Section 3 of *Handbook of Engineering Fundamentals,* edited by O. W. Eshbach, 2nd ed., John Wiley and Sons, New York, 1952.

Truxal, J. G., "Electrical Machinery in an Electronics-Oriented Curriculum," *IRE Transactions on Education,* p. 66, September 1958.

Blackwell, W. A., and H. E. Koenig, "A Combined Machinery and Control Systems Laboratory," *IRE Transactions on Education,* Vol. E-2, No. 4, September 1959.

Hammond, P., "Forces in Electric and Magnetic Fields," *Bulletin of Electrical Engineering Education,* No. 25, December 1960.

Adkins, Bernard, "The Rotating Electric Machine in an Electrical Engineering Degree Course," *Electrical Engineering,* p. 347, May 1961.

INDEX